Sustainable Urban Mining of Precious Metals

Sustainable Urban Mining of Precious Metals

Edited by
Sadia Ilyas, Hyunjung Kim, and Rajiv
Ranjan Srivastava

CRC Press
Taylor & Francis Group
Boca Raton London New York

CRC Press is an imprint of the
Taylor & Francis Group, an **informa** business

First edition published 2021
by CRC Press
6000 Broken Sound Parkway NW, Suite 300, Boca Raton, FL 33487-2742

and by CRC Press
2 Park Square, Milton Park, Abingdon, Oxon, OX14 4RN

CRC Press is an imprint of Taylor & Francis Group, LLC

ISBN: 978-0-367-51750-2 (hbk)
ISBN: 978-1-003-05506-8 (ebk)

Typeset in Times
by SPi Global, India

This book is dedicated to our beloved parents whose footprints of grace have kept us going in life and granted us continuous enlightenment.

Sadia Ilyas, Hyunjung Kim, and Rajiv Ranjan Srivastava

Contents

Chapter 9   Integrated Recovery Processes for Precious Metals from Urban
Mine Sources and Case Studies...213

Sadia Ilyas, Hyunjung Kim, and Rajiv Ranjan Srivastava

List of Figures and Tables

Tables

Preface

Metals are essential commodities in modern society. They are divided into various groups, depending upon their physico-chemical properties, molecular weight, and place in the periodic table. The group of precious metals, comprising gold (Au), silver (Ag), platinum (Pt), palladium (Pd), rhodium (Rh), osmium (Os), iridium (Ir), and ruthenium (Ru), are regarded as the most critical metals and are of higher economic value than common industrial metals. Their monetary values are driven not only by their practical uses but also by their associated role as investments and a capital value store. Chemically, precious group metals tend to be less reactive than most of the other elements, and are usually ductile with a high lustre. For these reasons they are in continuous rapidly increasing demand for modern high-tech equipment, advanced electronic gadgets, low-energy consumption, and clean energy production devices. It is estimated that the global demand for precious metals will continue to rise, fuelled both by consumer sectors and by their global trade value.

The primary supplies of precious metals are naturally occurring ore deposits, and new reserves are regularly needed to meet the growing requirement for precious metals. The finite deposits of minerals in the Earth's crust will be exhausted if consumption continues without the discovery of new reserves. It is also the case that every gadget and item of equipment has a fixed life-span, after which the exhausted materials need replacing with new ones, generating a mass of waste which has traditionally gone for landfill disposal or sometimes directly to smelters. However, the increasing complexity of materials/equipment containing a mixture of metallic and non-metallic substances (sometimes even more than 20 elements alloyed in one material) presents a serious challenge to simple disposal via smelting and converting to new material. Such practices always compromise the value of minute amounts of precious metals present in any material more than that of the other alloy elements. Hence, neither landfill disposal nor improper treatment of materials can be regarded as a sustainable process under the goals of the United Nations' Sustainable Development Plan.

If we consider the economic value of the precious metals locked within the waste/exhausted materials, effective recycling to produce new metals/compounds for the manufacturing of virgin materials can be part of a circular economy. This practice not only eliminates the environmental risks by reducing the volume of waste, but also mitigates the supply risks of precious metals, bringing economic benefits due to the associated monetary values of the metals. Exploiting naturally occurring mineral resources by utilizing the waste for 'urban mining' provides great potential for a new business economy in parallel with the conventional mainstream business economy. However, the increasing complexity of materials in contrast to the increasing demand for high-purity virgin material presents a plethora of challenges and issues.

This book aims to provide comprehensive coverage of the exploitation of precious metals through the recycling of urban mine resources. The continuously increasing mass of electronic (e)-waste and spent catalysts (including three-way catalytic converters, diesel oxidative catalysts, and petroleum catalysts) in particular is addressed in terms of a circular economy and the idea of urban mining. More specifically, sustainable recycling techniques and the extensive possible uses of the precious metals gold, silver, platinum, palladium, and rhodium, along with the techno-economic aspects, are covered in detail. To build up understanding of this topic, there is a balanced discussion of the relevant legislation dealing with urban mining. The fundamentals of extractive metallurgy of precious metals, and the downstream processing of separation are covered, including material liberation, urban mining with halide-, cyanide-, thiosulfate-, and thiourea-based lixiviants, purification, precipitation, adsorption, supercritical fluid extraction, bio-mediated approaches, solvent extraction, and chromatographic techniques. Throughout the book, practical applications of recycling techniques and their industrial implications are explored.

We believe that this book will be beneficial to professionals, researchers, and students involved in resource recovery from urban mines, and in particular, will contribute to establishing the circular economy of precious metals.

SADIA ILYAS (*Jeonju, South Korea*)
HYUNJUNG KIM (*Jeonju, South Korea*)
RAJIV R. SRIVASTAVA (*Da Nang, Vietnam*)

Editors

Sadia Ilyas is currently working as Brainpool Scientist (NRF)/research professor at the Department of Mineral Resources and Energy Engineering at Jeonbuk National University, Jeonju, Republic of Korea. After receiving her M.Phil. and Ph.D. in inorganic chemistry from Bahauddin Zakariya University, Multan and University of Agriculture, Faisalabad, Pakistan, respectively, she worked in China as senior researcher at the School of Chemical Engineering and Pharmacy (Wuhan), in Korea as a postdoctoral fellow at Korea Institute of Geoscience and Mineral Resources, and in Pakistan as an assistant professor at GC University, Faisalabad. In addition to academic lecturing in inorganic chemistry, she is involved in research dealing with hydrometallurgical exploitation of energy-critical elements and urban mining of value-added metals. She has published more than 50 research articles in peer-reviewed international journals and authored 25 books/contributed book chapters/textbooks/laboratory manuals.

Hyunjung ("Nick") Kim is professor in the Department of Mineral Resources and Energy Engineering at Jeonbuk National University, Jeonju, Korea. Dr. Kim received his B.S. and M.S. degrees from Hanyang University in Seoul, Korea and his Ph.D. in chemical and environmental engineering from the University of California, Riverside. He has over ten years' academic research experience and specializes in colloidal chemistry, froth flotation, bio-hydrometallurgy, and microplastics. Prof. Kim currently serves as editorial member/associate editor of several reputed journals. Prof. Kim has authored more than 100 refereed journal publications and several book chapters. He was awarded the Young Scientist Award by the Industrial Minerals and Aggregates Division of the Society for Mining, Metallurgy, and Exploration (SME) in 2016. Professor Kim has served as lead director of Brain Korea 21+ that is among Korea's most prestigious projects.

 **Dr. Rajiv Ranjan Srivastava** is a senior lecturer at the Faculty of Natural Sciences and senior researcher at the Institute of Research and Development, Duy Tan University (DTU), Da Nang, Vietnam. Dr. Srivastava holds a Ph.D. in resources recycling (under the discipline of engineering) from the Korea University of Science and Technology (UST). Before joining DTU, he worked at TAE-HYUNG Recycling R&D Centre, Korea, Rubamin Limited (Rubamin Technology Centre), India, and CSIR-National Metallurgical Laboratory, India. His inter-disciplinary research interests include waste management, urban mining, sustainable management of environmental resources, and hydrometallurgical exploitation of energy-critical elements for clean and alternative energy production. He is a member of several scientific societies and has published several papers in top-ranking SCI journals, as well as a number of book chapters, and has edited several books.

1 Sustainable Urban Mining of Precious Metals
An Introduction

Sadia Ilyas
Mineral Resources and Energy Engineering, Jeonbuk National University, Jeonju, Jeonbuk 54896, Republic of Korea

Hyunjung Kim
Mineral Resources and Energy Engineering, Jeonbuk National University, Jeonju, Jeonbuk 54896, Republic of Korea

Department of Environment and Energy, Jeonbuk National University, Jeonju, Jeonbuk 54896, Republic of Korea

Rajiv Ranjan Srivastava
Center for Advanced Chemistry, Institute of Research and Development, Duy Tan University, Da Nang 550000, Vietnam

CONTENTS

1.1   URBAN MINING AND THE CIRCULAR ECONOMY APPROACH

The finite deposits of minerals in the Earth's crust will be exhausted if consumption continues for long without the discovery of new natural reserves. At the same time, the demand for mineral commodities is likely to continue to increase due to new technologies that have become essential to our daily life. Under the traditional linear flow approach, many end-of-life (EoL) items are simply disposed of as waste (see Figure 1.1). There is no choice but to use and then discard the raw materials. Most waste materials are currently sent for landfill disposal, putting additional strain on the environment. The slow leaching of metals due to weathering is a phenomenon known to contaminate soil and water bodies, altering their nature and causing a severe threat to human health and environmental ecology.

In the light of these challenges, the transition from a linear approach to a circular strategy for advanced waste management has been developed over recent decades (see Figure 1.2). The circular approach arises principally from the soaring demand for raw materials. Attention is therefore shifting from the limited stocks of raw materials to the increasing anthropogenic stockpile of (waste) materials. This is the basis for the development of the 'urban mining' concept (Stallone, 2011; Cossu, 2013). In this context, urban mining comprises the activities/technologies designed for recovery of resources (including materials and energy) from products of urban catabolism

FIGURE 1.1   Conventional approach to material flow.

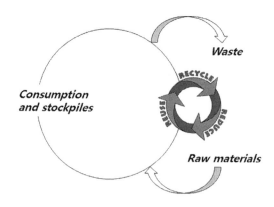

FIGURE 1.2   Transition circular material flow strategy.

(Baccini and Brunner, 2012). It provides systematic management of anthropogenic stockpiles of waste/EoL materials, with a view to long-term resource conservation, environmental protection, and economic benefits (Cossu, 2012, 2013). Not only for its technological aspects, but also in terms of economy, urban mining is an intriguing and pragmatically based concept that is strongly structured within a circular economy strategy. The concept of a circular economy has emerged in the search for the redesign of production systems to meet sustainable business models. The circular economy, which proposes a restorative and regenerative model, can be performed by different instruments, such as reverse logistics and urban mining. It is regarded as a potential solution for waste management, while enabling the recovery of valuable waste/EoL materials and their reinsertion into production processes as secondary raw materials.

1.2 SUSTAINABILITY THROUGH URBAN MINING

Sustainable urban mining provides systematic management of stockpiles of anthropogenic resources and waste materials, providing resource harvesting and conservation, environmental protection, economic and societal benefits. It is a concept that can increase the conservation and efficiency of primary resources worldwide. By conserving metals in high-value products, or reverting waste to the mainstream economy as secondary raw material, the practice of circular economy will significantly reduce the demand for primary raw materials. Consequently, it helps to reduce the import dependence of any country, with effective supply-chain management to control price volatility and supply crunches in the commodity market caused by scarcity and/or geopolitical factors. The conventional linear economy approach (Figure 1.1) reduces competitiveness and opportunities for cost saving in various industries. The cost of recycling urban mined resources is much lower than that of the same quantity of metals harvested from primary minerals. For example, the cost of recycled gold ingots from urban mined materials has been estimated to be $1591/kg against $33,404.626/kg of gold ingots produced by primary mining of gold ore (average values compared in 2015), mainly due to energy savings. The energy saved via urban mining of common metals and materials is summarized in Figure 1.3. It is a well-known fact that energy/

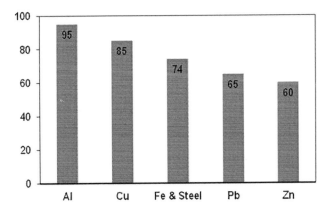

FIGURE 1.3 A summary of energy savings by recycling common metals and materials.

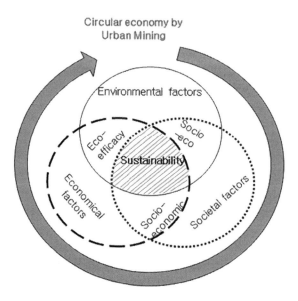

FIGURE 1.4 A sustainable pathway using the circular economy concept for the recycling of urban mined resources.

electricity generation through fossil fuels is the major source of greenhouse gas (GHG) emissions globally, contributing one-third of CO_2 accumulation in the environment.

The social transformation associated with reuse, recycling, eco-design, and other developments should result in more sustainable consumer behavior, which in turn contributes to safety and human health. The circular economy with urban mining is also expected to create job opportunities. A legislative proposal impact assessment on waste by the European Commission emphasizes that increased recycling targets for handling municipal, solid, and packaging waste, simplified legislation, and the diffusion of result-oriented practices can potentially create up to 178,000 new direct jobs by 2030 (**European Commission**, 2015). In this way, urban mining will significantly contribute to all three pillars of sustainability: environment, society, and economy (Figure 1.4).

1.2.1 URBAN MINING AND SUSTAINABLE DEVELOPMENT GOALS

In September 2015, under the umbrella of the United Nations, the Agenda for Sustainable Development with its 17 Sustainable Development Goals (SDGs) and 169 targets for ending poverty was adopted by all member states (Forti et al., 2020). Increasing volumes of waste/EoL materials and their improper or unsafe disposal by either incineration or landfill have been identified as posing significant stress to the environment, public health, and ultimately to the achievement of the SGDs. Progress towards the SDGs is measured by indicators and official statistics. Urban mining is closely related to many SDGs: Goal 8 on decent work and economic growth; Goal 3 on good health and well-being; Goal 8.4.1on high raw-material demand for the production of virgin materials; Goal 12.1.1on material footprint indicators; and Goals 8.4.2 and 12.1.2 on domestic material consumption. Relatively general indicators are being used to measure progress towards these SDGs. Some waste streams, in particular

TABLE 1.1

United Nations Sustainable Development Goals that involve urban mining

Target no.	Description
Goal 12	Ensure sustainable consumption and production patterns
Goal 12.4	Environmentally sound management of chemicals and all waste throughout the life cycle, and significantly reduce their release into soil, water, and air to minimize the adverse impacts on human health and the environment.
Goal 12.4.2	Treatment of waste, generation of hazardous waste, and hazardous waste management, by type of treatment.
Goal 12.5	By 2030, substantially reduce waste generation through prevention, reduction, repair, recycling, and reuse.
Goal 12.5.1	Increase the recycling rate of EoL/waste materials.

Source: Summarized from Forti et al. (2020).

electronic (e-)waste and spent catalysts, come under the heading of hazardous waste, sustainable management of which is included under SDG Goal 12.4.2. Some of the important SDGs which deal directly with urban mining are given in Table 1.1.

1.2.2 Urban Mining of Precious Metals for a Circular Economy

Precious metals (PMs) are rare metallic elements of high economic value, naturally occurring in the Earth's crust. Historically, PMs have been an important currency; currently they are regarded as an investment and a critical raw material for advanced and clean technologies. Traditionally, PMs included the coinage metals (gold and silver) as well as platinum group metals (PGMs), platinum, palladium, rhodium, osmium, ruthenium, and iridium, the latter being widely used in jewellery and being as noble as gold. The elements commonly termed PMs are shown in Figure 1.5. Osmium, ruthenium, and iridium (shown in the dark boxes of Fig. 5) are not so widely used as industrial metals and to date have not been widely recycled; hence, they are excluded from the scope of this book.

The most important aspect of the urban mining of PMs is their concentration in the waste/EoL materials. This is usually several thousand times higher than in naturally occurring primary ores. For example, the average concentration of gold in the Earth's

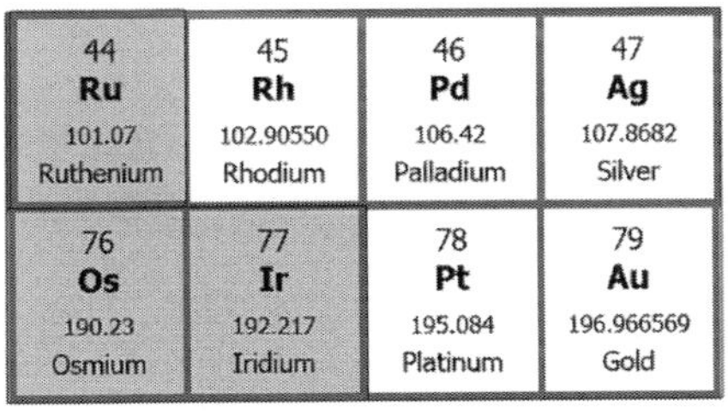

44 **Ru** 101.07 Ruthenium	45 **Rh** 102.90550 Rhodium	46 **Pd** 106.42 Palladium	47 **Ag** 107.8682 Silver
76 **Os** 190.23 Osmium	77 **Ir** 192.217 Iridium	78 **Pt** 195.084 Platinum	79 **Au** 196.966569 Gold

FIGURE 1.5 Representation of precious metals (elements in darker boxes are not the prime focus of this book).

TABLE 1.2

Values of precious metals as primary resource and for urban mining

Precious metal	Primary mineral resources			Anthropogenic urban mine resources		
	Contents in the crust	Grade in ores	Enrichment factor	Contents in waste/EoL materials	Possible enrichment factor	Difference from primary minerals
Gold; Au	1.5 ppb	6 ppm	×4000	400 ppm (in smart phone PCBs)	×1000 (plastic removal)	×66666
Silver; Ag	850 ppm	17500 ppm	×21	317 ppm (in computer PCBs)	×1000 (plastic removal)	×18.1
Platinum; Pt	5 ppb	5 ppm	×1000	650 ppm (in autocatalyst)	×10 (collection by smelting)	×1300
Palladium; Pd	5 ppb	5 ppm	×1000	500 ppm (in autocatalyst)	×10 (collection by smelting)	×1000
Rhodium; Rh	1 ppb	1 ppm	×1000	100 ppm (in autocatalyst)	×10 (collection by smelting)	×1000

Source: Arndt et al., 2017; Bizzo et al., 2014; MP-BGS, 2009; https://www.britannica.com/technology/silver-processing.

crust is estimated to be 0.5 parts per billions (ppb); however, the printed circuit boards (PCBs) of a smartphone may contain on average > 350 parts per millions (ppm) of gold (see Table 1.2). Similarly, the concentration of PMs in spent auto-catalysts is more than 1000 times higher than in an enriched ore. Although the individual weight fractions of PMs in urban mine resources remain very low compared to other metals (usually base metals, iron, and silicates), the accumulated market value of PMs is significantly high that it always several hundred or thousands higher than all other constituents of the materials treated. This makes urban mining attractive to recyclers as a small quantity of PMs can give a return of millions of dollars. The estimated relative values (relative price) of metals for processed/recycled materials (Figure 1.6) show that gold is the second most valuable non-ferrous metal. Approximately 2% to overall PMs' and 2% to silver mine value are estimated. The recyclability of these metals and their direct impact on the sustainable life-cycle of materials and contribution to the circular economy is clear.

The consumption habits established by linear economical models are a barrier to changing the status quo in the consumption of goods containing PMs. The move towards a circular economy will therefore need the power of both rational (economic) and non-rational (moral) motives to be leveraged if consumer behavior is to change (Planing, 2015). Mainstreaming alternative (circular) models involves taking EoL products back from consumers and creating a demand for remanufactured/refurbished goods (Bittar, 2018; van Weelden et al., 2016). In particular, remanufacturing is not common for consumer products, and this issue cannot be resolved without reference to purchasing behavior (Vogtlander et al., 2017). In addition, new product

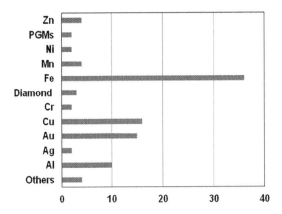

FIGURE 1.6 Relative values of metals production for processed materials.
Source: Modified from Arndt et al., 2017.

designs and circular models need to expand beyond the physical characteristics that encompass the human aspects of consumption (Wastling et al., 2018).

1.3 SPENT AUTO-CATALYSTS: URBAN MINING AND STRATEGIES FOR ITS MANAGEMENT

Over time, the urban mining of e-waste and spent catalysts has been regulated by a number of agencies worldwide due to illegal dumping by developed countries of (hazardous) waste materials in under-developed/developing countries. Not only technological and economic considerations, but also environmental issues must be taken into account in selection of an optimal recycling process for a specific waste material. It is necessary to determine the environmental, health and safety (EHS) risks of a particular recycling process, the risks that the spent generator is exposed to, and the reliability of its technical, commercial and environmental performance. It is essential to balance the ecological and economic costs of recovering metals from spent materials. The interdependencies of recycling costs, and the efficacy and environmental soundness of the recovery process must be considered. Under the umbrella of the United Nation Environment Programme (UNEP) and the Basel Convention for controlling transboundary movements of hazardous wastes and their disposal[1], [2] the commercial transfer of e-waste and spent catalysts from one region/country to another is restricted. The following provisions were adopted on 22 March 1989 at the Conference of Plenipotentiaries in Basel, Switzerland:

- the reduction of hazardous waste generation and the promotion of environmentally sound management of hazardous waste, wherever the place of disposal;
- the restriction of transboundary movements of hazardous wastes except where it is perceived to be in accordance with the principles of environmentally sound management; and
- a regulatory system applying to cases where transboundary movements are permissible.

In the event of illegal transboundary movement of hazardous waste in contravention of the provisions of articles 6 and 7, or if such movement cannot be completed as anticipated, one or more of the states involved is responsible for ensuring safe disposal, either by re-import into the state generating it or otherwise (articles 8 and 9).

1.3.1   REGULATORY GUIDELINES ON RECYCLING OF SPENT AUTO-CATALYSTS

The following guidelines relate to the recycling of spent auto-catalysts (Hagelüken, 2008):

- to make EHS and resource conservation critical for all new/existing products and processes;
- to provide information on public health and environmental risks to pursue protective measures and operation facilities for the key stakeholders;
- to work with carriers, customers, distributors, and suppliers to foster the safe use, transport, and disposal of chemicals.

The movement of spent catalysts across borders falls under the Basel Convention transfrontier movement of waste (TFMW) regulations. Council Regulation 259/93 describes TFMW within, into and out of the European Community[3] and is similar to the OECD regulations as per the revision of decision C(92)39/final on the control of transboundary movements of waste destined for recovery operations[4]. In principle, spent auto-catalysts that contain any of the precious metals (gold, silver, ruthenium, rhodium, palladium, osmium, iridium, and platinum) are classified under entry GC 060 as green waste. However, material on the green list may be amber list or red list controlled if contamination by other materials is sufficient to render it hazardous waste and to prevent environmentally sound recovery of the metals (Hagelüken, 2008). Some of the many hazardous characteristics are listed in Annexure III of Council Directive 91/689/EEC[5].

If a spent auto-catalyst is classed as amber-listed waste, it must be classified under entry AB 080 in two possible EURAL codes (European Waste List) as (i) 16 08 01: spent catalysts containing gold, silver, rhenium, rhodium, palladium, iridium, or platinum; or (ii) 16 08 07: spent catalysts contaminated with dangerous substances. When green- and amber-list entries are combined, the following two categories emerge (Hagelüken and Kegels, 2004):

- **16 08 01:** GC 020 green-list procedure. Transportation does not require notification of the competent authorities of the country of despatch, transit and destination, but documents signed by the holder and containing detailed information are required to accompany the shipment.
- **16 08 07:** AB 080 amber-list procedure. This implies notification of the intended shipment to the competent authorities in the countries of despatch, transit and destination. Consent must be obtained before shipping commences, and must be accompanied by a movement-tracking form. The procedure here is therefore more complex. The decisive factors are the source, composition, and quantity of the waste for recovery, a description of the treatment process, and the amount of recycled material as compared to the residual waste.

1.3.2 Structural Components of Spent Auto-catalysts

Depending on the component material and substrate structure, auto-catalysts are usually classified into two types: (i) beads-type (old-generation) catalyst, and (ii) honeycomb-type (new-generation) catalyst. At present, the auto-catalyst market is dominated by new-generation honeycomb catalysts made of ceramic cordierite substrate. The advantages of honeycomb-type catalysts over beads-type catalysts are the low-cost substrate with highly porous surface, stability, and improved washcoat adhesion (Kašpar et al., 2003).

The structural morphology of a honeycomb-type catalyst is shown in Figure 1.7. The scanning electron micrograph (SEM) and its components clearly show that the honeycomb structure of the auto-catalyst contains numerous rectangular channels. These channels help to increase the contact area between the catalytic surface (containing precious metals Pt, Pd, and Rh on the washcoat surface of γ-alumina) and the exhaust gases (Pardiwala et al., 2011), and further assist the free flow of gases through the substrate (Heck and Farrauto, 2001). The cell wall is of variable thickness and its primary purpose is to provide a large density of about 900 cells/inch^2 (Kašpar et al., 2003). Notably, the washcoat layer of γ-alumina (thickness 10–30 lm on the wall and 60–150 lm at the cell corners) increases the effective surface area for PGM dispersion onto the substrate cordierite (Pardiwala et al., 2011; Lox, 2008; Aberasturi et al., 2011). In this case, the auto-catalysts containing Pt, Pd, and Rh are classified as green-listed materials under entry GC 060.

In contrast, when their lifespan is exhausted, spent auto-catalysts cannot be considered green-listed materials, as they become poisoned after long-term exposure to hazardous gaseous emissions by fuel burning (see Figure 1.8). Highly toxic metals like lead, cadmium, and mercury are deposited onto the pore-sites of the catalyst's

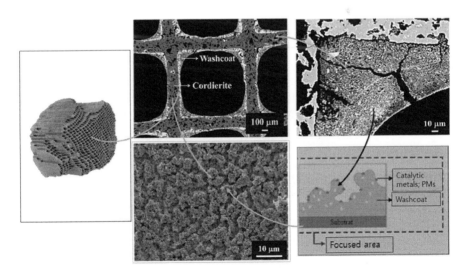

FIGURE 1.7 Structural components of a honeycomb-type auto-catalyst.

Source: Modified from Aberasturi et al., 2011; Leman al., 2017.

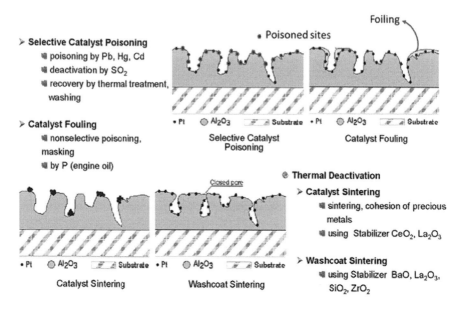

FIGURE 1.8   The poisoning and foiling effect of catalysts, causing them to move from green to amber list.

surface along with sulphur compounds like SO_2[6]. It is notable that lead, mercury, and cadmium are restricted under the Basel Convention, while SO_2 is considered a hazardous substance, as in the case of spent petro-refinery catalysts. Spent auto-catalysts are therefore no longer green listed, coming instead under amber-listed waste material, which requires notification and consent prior to shipping.

1.4   ELECTRONIC WASTE: URBAN MINING AND STRATEGIES FOR ITS MANAGEMENT

E-waste commonly refers to EoL/discarded white goods, electrical and electronic equipment, and information and communication technology (ICT) hardware. Some specific definitions are as follows:

- any electrically powered appliance reaching its EoL (Sinha-Khetriwal, 2002);
- a broader range of discarded/EoL electronic devices ranging from large household items to personal computers (Puckett et al., 2002);
- multifarious combinations of metallic, ceramic and plastic materials (APME, 1995).

More specifically, e-waste covers six categories of waste (Balde et al., 2015):

(i) Heat- and temperature-exchange equipment. including refrigerators, air conditioners, and heat pumps;
(ii) Display screens and monitors, including computers, laptops, televisions, notebooks, and tablets.

  (iii) Electric bulbs, including fluorescent, high-intensity discharge and LEDs.
  (iv) Large items, including electric stoves, washing machines, photocopiers, and photovoltaic panels.
   (v) Small items, mostly household items such as microwaves, toasters, vacuum cleaners, electric kettles, calculators, video cameras, electrical toys, and small medical devices.
  (vi) Small ICT equipment including telephones and mobiles, routers, printers, global positioning systems, and personal computers.

Rapid advances in technology are leading to continuing consumption of a large number of these electrical and electronic items, which are then discarded, increasing the volume of waste. Global e-waste generation has been estimated at 5% of total solid waste generated worldwide (Kiddee et al., 2013). A recent study by the United Nations University states that global e-waste generation amounted to 44.7 million metric tons (MMT) in 2016 (Balde et al., 2017) and will exceed 50 MMT in 2018, fuelling concerns over its effective management.

The United States and the leading countries of the European Union have traditionally been the main producers of e-waste (Robinson, 2009), although the scenario has been changing rapidly in recent decades. Currently, China is the top contributor among e-waste producer countries, generating 7.2 MMT/year, and pushing the US into second place. Figure 1.9 shows the top 10 e-waste producer countries globally by 2016 (based on total e-waste generation and per-capita consumption). As a region, Asia is obviously producing the highest at 18.2 MMT e-waste (~41%) followed by the US (~29%) and Europe (~27%) (E-waste, 2014). The gap in e-waste generation between the developed and developing countries is very wide. The richest country is generating 19.6 kg/inhabitant against the poorest country with only 0.6 kg/inhabitant.

The ~44.7 MMT of e-waste generated in 2016 can be divided into the six categories defined above: (i) temperature-exchange equipment, 7.6 MMT; (ii) screens and

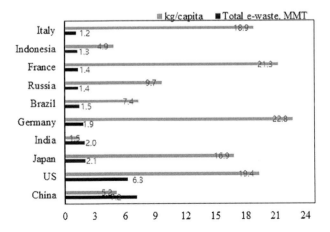

FIGURE 1.9   E-waste generation by top 10 countries worldwide, 2016.

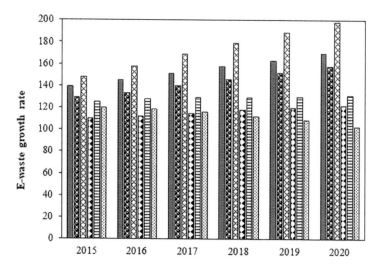

Small equip **Large equip** **Temp. exchanger** **Small ICT** **Lamp** **Screen**

FIGURE 1.10 Growth rate of each category of e-waste.

monitors, 6.6 MMT; (iii) bulbs, 0.7 MMT; (iv) large equipment, 9.1 MMT; (v) small equipment, 16.8 MMT; and (vi) small ICT, 3.9 MMT (E-waste Recycling Facts and Figures, 2018). While the growth rates vary between categories, total generation is expected to grow continuously (Figure 1.10).

1.4.1 E-waste Hazards and Environmental Impact

E-waste is known to contain a mixture of numerous metals listed under the heavy and hazardous categories. Studies of e-waste air, water, and soil contamination have been carried out by numerous researchers (Borthakur and Singh, 2017; Williams, 2011). Copper, iron, nickel, cobalt, lead, cadmium, and chromium are principally responsible for the toxicity of e-waste, along with the lucrative presence of precious metals, albeit in a relatively lower concentration. The composition of plastics and ceramics changes according to the manufacturing company and application area (Robinson, 2009). Table 1.3 summarizes e-waste hazards with respect to the major components (except the precious metals). The residual cadmium in one mobile phone alone can pollute 600 m³ water. PCBs and other plastic components are highly flammable and release acutely toxic dioxins and furans on burning, causing severe threats to vital components of the ecosystem (Awasthi et al., 2016; Wang et al., 2005). A significant proportion of heavy metals can be leached by weathering at landfill sites and gets adsorbed on nearby soil, contaminating the groundwater. Suspended particulates released into the environment during the dismantling and shredding process produce atmospheric pollution and an increase of particulate matter (PM 2.5 and 10) in the ambient air, causing breathing difficulties, eye and respiratory irritation, coughing, choking, pneumonitis, tremors, and neuropsychiatric problems in humans. The

TABLE 1.3
E-waste hazards to public health and the environment

E-waste components	Toxic metals	Limit, ppm	Disease caused by the exposure above permissible limit
Gallium arsenide used in light emitting	As**	5.0	Chronic effect causing skin disease, lung cancer and impaired nerve signalling
Electron tubes, lubricants, fluorescent bulbs, CRT guns	Ba**	<100	Causes brain swelling, muscle weakness, damage to the heart
Power supply boxes, motherboards	Be**	0.75	Causes lung cancer, skin disease, carcinogens
PCBs, casing, PVC cables	Br**	0.1	Damage to thyroid gland, hormonal issues, skin disorders, DNA damage, hearing loss
PCBs, batteries, CRTs, semiconductors, infrared detectors, printer ink, toners	Cd**	1.0	Risk of irreversible impacts on human health, particularly the kidney
Printed circuit boards (PCBs)	CN**	<0.5	Cyanide poisoning > 2.5 ppm may lead to coma and death
Plastic computer housing, cabling, hard discs, as a colorant in pigments	Cr(VI)**	5.0	Toxic in the environment, causing DNA damage and permanent visual impairment
Batteries, LCD, switches, backlight bulbs or lamps	Hg**	0.2	Damages brain, kidneys and foetus
Mobile phones, batteries	Li*	<10#	Diarrhoea, vomiting, drowsiness, muscular weakness
Batteries, semiconductors, CRTs, PCBs	Ni*	20.0	Allergic reactions, bronchitis, reduced lung function, lung cancer
Transistors, LED lead-acid batteries, solder, CRTs, PCBs, florescent tubes	Pb***	5.0	Damages brain, nervous system, kidneys, and reproductive system, acute and chronic effects on human health
CRT glass, plastic computer housing and a solder alloy	Sb**	<0.5	Carcinogen, causing stomach pain, vomiting, diarrhoea and stomach ulcers
Fax machines, photoelectric cells	Se**	1.0	High concentration causes selenosis
CRT, batteries	Sr***	1.5	Somatic as well as genetic changes due to this cancer in bones, nose, lungs, skin
Batteries, luminous substances	Zn**	250.0	Nausea, vomiting, pain, cramps and diarrhoea
Cooling units and insulation foam	CFCs**	<1.0 for 8 h/ day	Impacts on the ozone layer which can lead to greater incidence of skin cancer
Transformers, capacitors, condensers	PCBs**	5.0	PCB causes cancer in animals and can lead to liver damage in humans
Monitors, keyboards, cabling and plastic computer housing	PVC**	0.03	Hazardous and toxic air contaminants, release of HCl causes respiratory problems

*Critical; **Hazardous and toxic; ***Radioactive waste; #limit in serum/blood

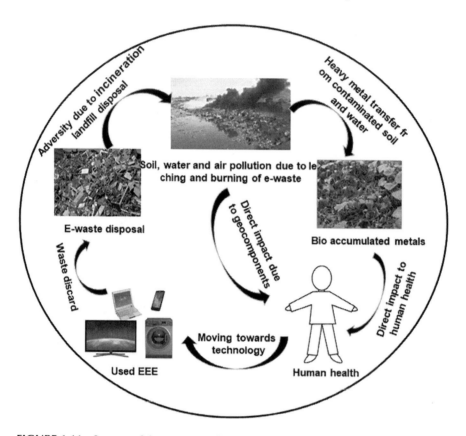

FIGURE 1.11   Impacts of the e-waste cycle on public health and the environment.

unsafe incineration of e-waste releases several toxic and hazardous substances (organic and inorganic components) responsible for air pollution, through which it reaches our food chain and directly affects human health (Tue et al., 2014, 2016; Luo et al. 2011). These impacts are summarized in Figure 1.11.

1.4.2   REGULATORY GUIDELINES ON URBAN MINING OF E-WASTE

Proper handling of the fastest-growing waste stream worldwide can mitigate the severe environmental issues associated with e-waste management and its legal framework. About 66% of the global population is presently covered by legislation under legal regulatory bodies (Balde et al., 2017). Although e-waste comes under the Restriction of Hazardous Substances (RoHS) list and its transboundary movement is restricted, out of 50 million metric tons of global e-waste only 20% is estimated to contribute to formal recycling practices under legal norms. The volume of waste being handled illegally by the informal sector is difficult to trace and treat in a sustainable manner. Developing and under-developed countries are still struggling to establish proper guidelines and require effective legislation for coordination of formal collection and recycling practices. The key components of an effective

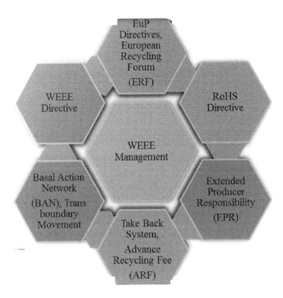

FIGURE 1.12 Components required for e-waste management legislative framework.

legislative framework are summarized in Figure 1.12. Prominent regulatory frameworks developed by leading countries are summarized in Table 1.4 (Pathak and Srivastava, 2017). The transboundary movement of e-waste is a major issue for both exporter and receiver countries. A large portion of e-waste described as EEE (electrical and electronic equipment) and UEEE (used EEE) is shipped from the northern hemisphere to developing countries for informal disposal. It is therefore difficult to monitor the exact volume of the e-waste flow and very few statistics based on hard data are available on waste, UEEE, and e-waste flows. Under Article 13 of the Basel Convention, the signatory countries provide some analytical information on transboundary flows of e-waste, but it is incomplete and contains discrepancies in reporting, ambiguous definitions, incorrect categorization of items, and data inaccuracies (Forti, Balde, and Kuehr 2018). As the present international trade data cannot differentiate between new and UEEE, informal trade flows across countries are cumbersome to identify due to the illegal nature of the activity. The Harmonised System Committee (RSC) has provisionally adopted amendments to the HS codes that identify e-waste under heading 8549, and these are likely to enter into force on 1 January 2022 (Basel Convention 2019).

A few initiatives to quantify the transboundary flows of UEEE and e-waste have been taken under the umbrella of "Solving the e-waste problem" (STEP) (Duan et al., 2013). The study undertook a quantitative analysis of the transboundary flows of UEEE between and from North American countries, which concluded that about 8.5% and 7% of UEEE products generated in 2010 and 2011, respectively, were exported (Lasaridi et al. 2016; USITC 2013). The transboundary flows of e-waste from developed to developing countries is problematic as it causes an additional environmental burden in the destination countries which is likely to be handled inappropriately by the informal sector. As the e-waste collection system makes progress

TABLE 1.4

Important initiatives in developing the legal framework for management and urban mining of e-waste

Nation/ territory	Regulations	Description
Belgium	Directive 2002/96/EC on WEEE, 2002	The Public Waste Agency of Flanders controls waste management and producer responsibility
China	Catalogue of restricted imports of solid wastes, 2008	Restriction on junk electrochemical products and electrical wires mainly for copper recycling
Finland	Government Decree on WEEE, 2004	Export prohibited out of the EU unless exporter proves that reuse and/or, recycling will be practised as directed in the Decree
France, Germany and the Netherland	Under EU directives in 2005	Limited use of toxic materials by producers; collection and processing of used electronics by distributors and municipalities; France introduced an 'eco-cost' for treating WEEE
Hong Kong	Advice on movement of UEEE, 2011	Legislative control on UEEE
India	E-waste (Management and Handling) Rules, 2010 and 2011; E-waste (Management) Rules, 2016	Commencement of e-waste legislation with EPR guidelines incorporated all suggestions made in 2010; responsibility of refurbishers and manufacturers established
Japan	Law for the Control of export, import and others of specified hazardous and other wastes	Export prohibited without consent of the import country
Nigeria	Guide for importers of UEEE into Nigeria, 2011	Import of WEEE banned with compulsory registration of importers
Norway	Revised EU directives, 2006	WEEE register established with mandatory membership for every producer and importer of an approved take-back company
Pakistan	Import policy order, 2009	Import of refrigerators and air conditioners banned; CRTs can be imported only with used computers
Republic of Korea	Act on the control of trans-boundary movement of hazardous wastes and their disposal, 1994	Restriction on export without consent of the importing country
Singapore	Import and export of e-waste and used electronic equipment, 2008	Movement of hazardous e-waste approved on case-by-case basis
Thailand	Criterion for import of used EEE (UEEE), 2007	Control of the classified UEEE
United Kingdom	Under EU directives in 2007	Adopted the EU directives
United States	HR 2284: Responsible Electronics Recycling Act, 2011	Banned the export of WEEE items: PCs, TVs, printers, xerox, phones, CRTs, batteries containing Pb, Cd, Hg, Cr, Be, and organic solvents
Vietnam	Law on environmental protection, 2005	Prohibits the movement of hazardous waste from abroad; stipulates responsibilities for waste generator

in developing counties, however, there is evidence that valuable components such as PCBs are being shipped for recycling. Additionally, there are growing indications that historically well-regarded import countries worldwide (such as China) are also increasingly exporting e-waste to other South-east Asian, African, and other countries (Lepawsky, 2015). The transboundary movement also appears to be dynamic in nature, reacting to social, economic, and regulatory changes, and this can be seen in the rapid shift of processing operations from China to other nearby South-east Asian countries like Pakistan, Bangladesh, Malaysia, Thailand, and Vietnam as a consequence of the 2018 import ban on waste.

According to a study conducted by BIO Intelligence Service (2013) for the European Commission, ~15% of UEEE is exported from the European Union, mainly for reuse. It is important to note that part of this UEEE either becomes WEEE (waste EEE) during transportation (e.g., if there is no appropriate protection of the product during transport) or shortly after arriving in the destination country. This is confirmed by the Countering WEEE Illegal Trade (CWIT) project, which found that ~15.8% of the e-waste generated in the European Union was exported. Although the main economic driver behind these shipments is reuse and repair, about 30% of this volume is e-waste (Huisman 2003). Zoeteman, Krikke and Venselaar (2010) discovered that free riders are responsible for 10–20% of the e-waste that is illegally exported to non-OECD countries, and that part is exported legally for reuse in developing countries. A more recent study by Balde et al. (2020) reports that ~8% of the total e-waste generated in the Netherlands is exported for reuse, which is in line with an earlier study by Geeraerts, Mutafoglu, and Illés (2015) that states up to 10% of e-waste is exported from the EU both legally and illegally in the name of UEEE. Hence, on average the transboundary movement of UEEE/e-waste is found to be between 7% and 20 % of total e-waste.

1.4.3 Stakeholders in the Management and Urban Mining of E-waste

Life-cycle assessment (LCA) is an important tool in determining the entire flow of EEE and clearly defining the role of each stakeholder involved in the management and urban mining of e-waste. A closed-loop value chain (Figure 1.13) reveals more about the LCA, under which e-waste can be refurbished, reused, or sent back to the manufacturers. Many components/metals can be either treated or sent for landfill/incineration. The prominent use of eco-friendly substances to produce new EEE can avoid the emission of hazardous and toxic substances into the environment, mitigating the public health risks. Further, reduced consumption of EEE, together with an increase in product life, would be the best forward-logistics step. The reverse flow of EEE is the primary problem in most of the developing countries. Extended producer responsibility (EPR) and the polluter pays principle (PPP) are influential actors discussed below[7].

1.4.3.1 Producers

Comprehensive e-waste management including effective disposal is one of the prime responsibilities of EEE producers. Other roles of producers are defined as: obeying legal EEE guidelines to avoid informal handling of e-waste; itemizing the product's composition and treatment of e-waste; and driving awareness programmes for users about improper disposal of e-waste with municipal waste. The introduction of new eco-design standards to improve efficacy and product life, refurbishing and recycling used EEE are also defined as producers' responsibility. If these tasks are to be properly performed, producers must open accessible e-waste collection centers and establish appropriate management from collection to resource recovery.

1.4.3.2 Consumers

Consumer are usually unaware that switching to a new product generates e-waste. This puts the responsibility onto consumers not only to select the correct product for use throughout its life but also to realize that after the end of life the e-waste generated could be recycled/reused as shown in Figure 1.13. Scavenging is a major issue in environmentally friendly processing of e-waste in developing countries; however, consumers can opt for collection centres established by producers or a governing body that can contribute to solving the scavenging problem.

1.4.3.3 Recyclers

The role of recyclers is crucial for the recycling of e-waste either through formal or informal practices at each stage of the process (including collection, sorting, dismantling, treatment, recovery, and final disposal). The rising price of precious metals is lucrative for the illegal e-waste business, and informal recyclers are not interested in factors like environment friendliness and public health. Recycling must therefore be formalized to meet current environmental regulations. Meanwhile, LCA can be a key aspect of assessing e-waste recycling, providing information from collection to recovery. Although integrated e-waste management combining formal and informal sectors yields maximum recycling rates and mitigation of environmental concerns, the lack of sound technologies has led to weak performance in both resource recycling and environmental improvement.

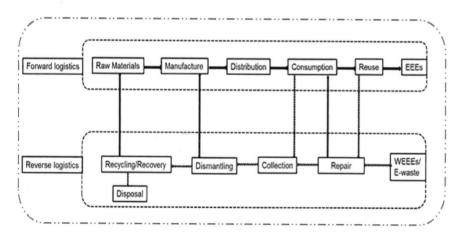

FIGURE 1.13 Life-cycle assessment of EEE and WEEE (e-waste) flow in forward and backward logistics.

1.4.3.4   Regulatory Bodies

Legally constituted regulatory bodies can act to bind all stakeholders together by fixing their engagement in e-waste management. They can play a vital role in imposing the rules and regulations, and the practice of EPR, and determining obligations of e-waste volume management, including encouraging consumers to reuse products or extend their use, promoting awareness of prohibition on discarding e-waste as household waste, and providing information about health and environmental hazards. Key aspects for consideration by regulators designing policies include: a regulatory framework based on EPR in compliance with the obligations and rights of each stakeholder; action and awareness programmes on EHS in public participation; promoting collection, refurbishment, and recycling practices by the formal sector and preventing illegal trade in e-waste; and promoting R&D policies to reduce the volume of metals recycling and waste. The role of stakeholders in the urban mining of e-waste and its management system (as defined by the Swiss e-waste management system) is summarized in Table 1.5.

1.4.4   GLOBAL E-WASTE MANAGEMENT PRACTICES

In the global framework, the collection, handling, and processing (to include resource recovery and recycling processes), followed by the final disposal of e-waste are regarded as the main factors affecting overall e-waste management strategies. The threat posed by the improper handling of a greater amount of e-waste through the informal sector, along with either weak or non-existent legislation specific to e-waste, are the major problems faced by developing countries (Heeks et al., 2015). Nevertheless, the contribution of these problems to the economy of lower- and middle-income countries cannot be neglected (Pathak and Srivastava, 2017). Current e-waste management practices are summarized in Figure 1.14.

Despite the slow technological advancement of developing countries, they are currently consuming electronic goods at a faster rate than developed countries previously did. Thus their contribution to e-waste generation has significantly increased (Garlapati, 2016). It is estimated that developing countries will discard 400–700

TABLE 1.5

Stakeholders and their defined roles in the Swiss e-waste management system

Stakeholders	Roles and responsibilities
Federal government	Supervision of entire system and initiation of basic guidelines
Producers/importers	Management of day-to-day operations
Distributers/retailers	Support for day-to-day affairs of producers/importers
Consumers	Return of e-waste to collection centres/retailers
Collectors	Collections, safe storage, and preventing illegal e-waste trading
Recyclers	Ensuring environmentally friendly recycling with minimum emissions and EHS concerns

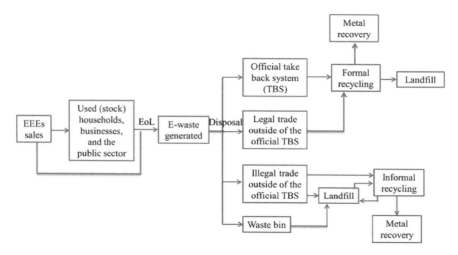

FIGURE 1.14 A representation of the overall e-waste management system.
Source: Modified from Balde et al., 2015; Pathak and Srivastava, (2017).

million obsolete computers by 2030, against 200–300 million by developed countries (Sthiannopkao and Wong, 2013). However, the lack of rules and regulations poses an even greater challenge to their proper handling of e-waste than the issues faced by the developed countries. A policy comparison between developed and developing countries is summarized in Table 1.6. Several developing countries have slowly started to prepare and some have enacted specific e-waste policies, but developed countries still have the advantage over developing countries, mainly in terms of the implementation of legislation. The national registry system including a proper collection and logistics system is very strong in developed countries (Sthiannopkao and Wong, 2013). Germany's Avoidance of Packaging Waste is the first EPR-mandated programme that places a financial obligation on manufacturers for the collection and reduction of packaging waste (Ongondo et al., 2011; Van et al., 2006), and this has been adopted and extended to EEE manufacturers by countries including Sweden, Norway, Taiwan, and Switzerland. EU legislation restricting the use of hazardous substances in EEE and WEEE/e-waste (Directive 2002/95/EC, the RoHS Directive), and promoting their collection and recycling (Directive 2002/96/EC), was enacted in 2003. China and India, which are among the fastest-growing e-waste countries, have implemented EPR systems, although monitoring e-waste generation is difficult due to the lack of a national registry and a greater availability of grey markets for second-hand UEEE (Pathak and Srivastava, 2017). Among the major destination countries in Asia (India, China, Pakistan, and Vietnam), the significant influence of the informal and private sectors represents a major bottleneck to inventoried e-waste (Abbas, 2010; Jain, 2010; Kurian, 2007). Despite lower labour costs, the larger volume of e-waste generation (including a significant amount of UEEE imports), transport costs, and the high costs of advanced technology for eco-friendly disposal present barriers to effective management, which is why informal players processing the majority of e-waste volume in developing countries continue to grow.

TABLE 1.6

Legislation in developed and developing countries compared

Developed countries	Developing countries
United States: Responsible Electronics Recycling Act came into force in 2011. Banned the export of WEEE items: PCs, TVs, printers, xerox, phones, CRTs, batteries containing Pb, Cd, Hg, Cr, Be, and organic solvents.	China: Restriction on junk electrochemical products and electrical items mainly for copper recycling. Catalogue of restricted imports of solid wastes, 2008.
United Kingdom: Under EU directives in 2007. Adopted the EU directives.	India: Import policy under 2005. Transboundary movement and EPR introduced in e-waste rule, 2011, providing strategy and method for treatment of e-waste.
Belgium: Directive 2002/96/EC on WEEE, 2002. The Public Waste Agency of Flanders controls waste management and producer responsibility	Pakistan: Import policy order, 2009. Banned the import of refrigerators and air conditioners; CRTs can be imported only with used computers.
France, Germany and the Netherland: Under EU directives in 2005. Limited use of toxic materials by the producers; collection and processing of used electronics by distributors and municipalities; France introduced an 'eco-cost' for treating WEEE.	Thailand: Criterion for import of used EEE (UEEE), 2007. Control of classified UEEE.
Japan: Law for the control of export, import and others of specified hazardous and other wastes. Export prohibited without consent of the import country.	Vietnam: Law on environmental protection, 2005. Prohibits the movement of hazardous waste from abroad and stipulates responsibilities for waste generator.
Norway: Revised EU directives, 2006. A WEEE register established with mandatory membership for every producer and importer of an approved take-back company.	Nigeria: Guide for importers of UEEE into Nigeria, 2011. Import of WEEE banned with compulsory registration of importers.
South Korea: Restrictions on export without consent of the importing country. Trans-boundary movement act on hazardous wastes and their disposal.	Hong Kong: Advice on movement of used EEE, 2011. Legislative control on used EEE.

Source: Modified from Pathak and Srivastava (2017).

1.4.4.1 Argentina

E-waste is a major concern in Argentina, which generates 2.5 kg/inhabitant e-waste annually. About a quarter of the total e-waste is obsolete telecommunications equipment and computers, but recycling accounts for only 2% of the volume of e-waste. Governmental organizations' share is as low as < 5% of the total e-waste processed. The scenario changes drastically when white goods and other consumer electronics are included, giving e-waste generation of ~7.8 kg/inhabitant in 2018[8]. Due to the lack of e-waste regulation, informal recycling mainly controlled by marginalized and unemployed groups has a strong presence[9]. Hence, most of the e-waste in Argentina ends up as municipal waste. In the absence of EPR legislation, Argentina's point of reference for the e-waste problem is the Basel Convention framework and the Mercosur environmental management policy agreement on universally generated special waste and post-consumption responsibility. A national plan on integrated e-waste management presented in 2005 has lost its parliamentary status (Silva et al., 2008) [10, 11.]

1.4.4.2   Brazil

Brazil is the second-highest producer of (1.5 Mt) e-waste in the Americas, after the United States, which currently produces 6.3 Mt, largely in the form of mobile phones, radios, televisions, computers, washing machines, and refrigerators. Estimates put average per-capita e-waste generation at >3.4 kg during 2001–30, which will require the disposal of a total of about 25 Mt of e-waste by 2030. This increases concern over appropriate management, and a national 'Garbage Law' has been introduced making everyone responsible for e-waste generation, from manufacturers to end users. Federal Law no. 12.305 under the National Solid Waste Policy ensures proper treatment of e-waste. State law no. 13.576, enacted in July 2010, makes producers responsible for formally treating collected e-waste, including the recycling of resources. However, strong opposition from producers has been reported (Silva et al., 2008) because e-waste is considered an asset with societal value due to its job creation potential. Under the umbrellas of federal and state laws, Brazil has specialized e-waste management companies that contribute to the urban mining of e-waste. The major players in Brazil are: CEDIR (sends e-waste to recycling companies); Coopermiti (offers management, processing, and recycling of e-waste in co-operation with the Prefeitura Municipal de Sao Paulo); Descarte Certo (offers collection and recycling services on a large scale); Ecobraz (specializes in collection and recycling of obsolete electronics); Estre (recycles all kind of e-waste); Lorene (operates in all parts of e-waste treatment); RecicloMetais (provides e-waste treatment at all stages); Reciclagem Brasil (specializes in providing a proper destination for e-waste recycling); and Recicladora Urbana (offers reverse logistics and waste management services)[12]. Once collected, the e-waste goes through a dismantling process for individual classification of each component. Thereafter, the recycling companies carry out processing to recover raw materials like plastics, metals, wires, and cables, while neutralizing the hazardous substances through specific chemical processing.

1.4.4.3   China

Over the last decade, the Asia-Pacific region has recorded a 63% hike in e-waste production i.e., ~16 Mt[13]. China's domestic e-waste generation more than doubled (~6.7 Mt) within the same period[14], establishing China as the largest e-waste producer, contributing alone about 15% of global generation[15,16]. However, the 2018 import ban is expected to make a noticeable change, as domestic e-waste volume is significantly smaller than the amount imported by China from developed countries to China (estimated to be ~35 Mt) (Ongondo et al. 2011).

Owing to the inherent problems of e-waste, imported items end up in primitive processes. The informal sector does not use a scientific approach that safeguards public health and the environment (Green Peace-BAN, 2004). Rather, dismantling of e-waste and metal stripping is done using an open acid bath or burning wires/PCBs in a family-run home workshop (Leung et al., 2006). These activities cause serious environmental pollution near the recycling sites. For example, an accumulation of heavy metals and hydrocarbons has been found in the air, water, and soil of the Guiyu area (Yu et al., 2010; Bridgen et al., 2005; Zhang and Min, 2009), where more than 150,000 people work in about 5,500 shops (Driscoll and Shiheng, 2010). China needs to develop an efficient system, and the Chinese government is continuing to work on it, the import ban being one step in this direction. Specific efforts are summarized in Table 1.7. The Management of Prevention and Control of Pollution from

TABLE 1.7
Laws and regulations related to e-waste management in China

Regulations	Status/date	Major contents
Notification on Importation of Seventh Category Waste.	1 February 2000	Ban on the import of the seventh category of waste.
Circular on strengthening environmental management of waste electrical and electronic equipment (WEEE).	26 August 2003	Prohibits the environmentally harmful processing of WEEE; encourages electronic product manufacturers to promote cleaner production and eco-design.
Ordinance on Management of Prevention and Control of Pollution from Electronic Information Products (Ministry of Industry and Information Technology (MIIT), 2006).	6 November 2006	Aims to reduce the use of hazardous and toxic substances in electronic appliances as well as pollution generated by manufacture, recycling, and disposal of these products. Counterpart of the EU RoHS directive, including requirements for eco-design and restrictions on the use of six hazardous substances.
The Technical Policy on Pollution Prevention and Control of WEEE (MEP).	27 April 2006	Sets out the guiding principles of "3R" and the "polluter pays principle"; stipulates the general provisions of eco-design, product information disclosure; makes provision for environmentally sound collection, reuse, recycling, and disposal of WEEE.
Ordinance on Management of prevention and Control of Pollution from Electronic and Information Products (MIIT).	1 March 2007	Requirements for eco-design; restrictions on the use of hazardous substances; requirements for producers to provide information about their products.
Administrative measure on pollution prevention of waste electrical and electronic equipments (MEP).	1 February 2008	Aims to prevent pollution caused during disassembly, recycling, and disposal of e-waste; specifies responsibilities of relevant parties and the license scheme for e-waste recycling companies.
Circular economy law (NPC, 2009).	1 January 2009	Specifies provisions on Reduce, Reuse and Recycle (3R) of electronic products during production, consumption, and other processes.
Regulation on management of the recycling and disposal of waste electrical and electronic equipment	1 January 2011	Mandatory recycling of WEEE; implementation of Extended Producer Responsibility; establishes special fund to assist e-waste recycling; certification for second-hand appliances and recycling enterprises.

Electronic Information Products (EIPs), a waste disposal law dealing with total e-waste management including metal recovery, is usually referred to as China's RoSH.

1.4.4.4 India

A compound annual growth rate of 25% generating 1.85 Mt of e-waste has placed India fifth in the global list of e-waste producer countries (ASSOCHEM India report, 2016). The volume imported from OECD countries contributes up to 60% of the total e-waste in India, making it difficult to quantify precisely how much waste is being generated (Borthakur and Sinha, 2013; Pathak and Srivastava, 2017). Mumbai (1.2 Mt) tops the list, while Delhi-NCR (98,000 t), Bangalore (92,000 t), Chennai (67,000 t), Kolkata (50,000 t), Ahmedabad (36,000 t), Hyderabad (32,000 t) and Pune (25,000 t) are the major metropolitan cities on the list (The digital dump, 2013). The amount of e-waste generated in India by category is shown in Table 1.8. Good levels of economic growth enhancing the purchasing power of middle-income groups generates significant demand for e-goods, and thus an exponential rise in e-waste generation has been observed. Pathak and Srivastava (2017) estimate that e-waste generation for the two most saleable products (mobile phones and computers) will continue to increase until 2022. Computer waste will slowly reach saturation point by 2028, but no saturation point appears likely for the waste generated by mobile phones. Recently, India has introduced a legislative framework specific to e-waste, the E-waste Management Rule 2016. The EPR introduced in 2010 is incorporated in the 2016 framework and extends to manufacturers and refurbishers (Pathak and Srivastava, 2017; Pathak and Srivastava, 2019). The advent of specific legislation has increased awareness of its management, so collection centres, recycling companies, local

TABLE 1.8
E-waste categories and generation in India

E-waste type		Consumer electronics	Communications & IT equipment	Households	Total e-waste generation
Description of items included		DVDs and players, video games, iPods, remote control cars, etc.	Monitors, printers, keyboards, central processing units, typewriters, mobile phones, chargers, remotes, compact discs, headphones, batteries, semiconductors, etc.	LCD/plasma TVs, air conditioners, refrigerators, washing machines, microwave ovens, food processors, etc.	
E-waste (Mt/year)	2012	0.07	0.35	0.02	0.44
	2014	0.20	1.04	0.07	1.30
	2016	0.28	1.48	0.09	1.85
	2018	0.39	2.09	0.13	2.61
	2020	0.50	2.65	0.17	3.31

bodies and societies are emerging, albeit only making a minor contribution. Volume reduction through e-waste processing and metals recovery are the benefits identified by emerging private-sector recyclers like E-Parisaraa, Attero, E-waste Recycling India, Evergreen Recycling, and Green India E-waste & Recycling Opc Pvt. Ltd. It is a slow but a positive start, but the fact is that 90% of e-waste generated in India is still going to the unorganized sector[17].

1.4.4.5   Pakistan

Pakistan has emerged as a major dumping ground for the large volume of e-waste coming from the United States, the EU, Japan, the UK, Australia, and Gulf countries. E-waste enters the country in the form of donations by charities or second-hand used items for resale and reuse purposes. However, only 2% of the total amount of goods imported as second-hand used items is actually going for reuse. The rest is sent directly for dismantling to informal recycling works (Ilyas, 2018 a, b; Sthiannopkao and Wong, 2013). Locally generated e-waste data is not quantified, but was thought to be 317,000 tons in 2015. According to a recent report, 72% of the total population of the country have mobile phones, of which there will be over 140 million by the year 2017[18]. Purchase of televisions is forecast to increase at a rate of 12% per annum, mainly because of the rapid change in technologies. Sales of personal computers are also increasing at a rate of 5.8% per annum due to increasing demand from individuals, companies, and the public sector (International, 2015). Rapid urbanization and the increasing population of the country are the major factors driving EEE consumption, as newer technologies attract people to buy the products. The local grey market for second-hand goods also contributes, making it difficult to quantify e-waste generation in the country. The large lower middle-income population is a big consumer of this grey market, which sees refurbished items used more than twice, leading eventually to a higher volume of domestic e-waste. The lack of proper disposal or collection facilities also plays a part, as people throw e-waste away once the UEEE no longer works. The journey towards environmental conservation in the country started with the formation of Pakistan's Environmental Protection Council in 1984, following the Pakistan Environmental Protection Ordinance enacted in 1983 (GISW, 2010). Thereafter, the National Conservation Strategy was adopted in 1992, presented at the Rio Earth Summit, and later endorsed by the United Nations with grants through the International Union for Conservation of Nature for the Sustainable Development Networking Programme. A milestone for environmental safeguarding policy in the country was the Pakistan Environmental Protection Act (PEPA), enacted in December 1997. Section 11 prohibits the discharge/emission of any hazardous chemical into the environment; Section 13 prohibits the import of any hazardous substance; and Section 14 does not allow the hazardous elements to be handled in the territory of Pakistan (PEPA, 1997; Abbas, 2010). The National Environment Policy 2005 defines hazardous materials, and restrictions on their import, including those mentioned in the Basel Convention, were introduced by the Import Policy Order 2007–08. The recent (2016) edition of the Import Policy Order clearly states that air conditioners, refrigerators, monitors, CCTVs, and other home appliances in UEEE or second-hand condition are not allowed to be imported (IPO, 2007, 2016). While these laws and regulations set out basic constraints on e-waste, the generalized form of elements involved and principles restrict their implementation, so the flow of e-waste in other forms is set to continue and increase. The e-waste volume can only be regulated by framing specific legislation on e-waste, its management, and informal recycling. EPR is currently the foremost policy worldwide designed to provide incentives for EEE manufacturers to integrate environmental considerations during product design as well as assuming responsibility for the environmental impact throughout product life-cycle, including recycling, reuse, and disposal of e-waste (Ongondo et al., 2011).

1.4.4.6 Nigeria

Nigeria has become a favorite destination for e-waste dumping for developed countries due to stringent regulation and awareness in big Asian import countries like China, India, and Pakistan. Reports suggest that Nigeria received 66,000 tons of old computers, televisions, and monitors as UEEE during the year 2015–16, of which 16,900 tons had already reached EoL in non-working condition[19]. More interestingly, despite stringent EU laws on e-waste shipments, about 70% of the total e-waste arrives in Nigeria from Europe, mostly smuggled in in old vehicles [20,21]. Particularly at the Lagos seaport, brokers/importers provide illegal entry for the e-waste through the Computer and Allied Product Dealer Association of Nigeria (CAPDAN, which coordinates IT industry matters)[22]. The importers purchase containers based on weight, working items are shorted and sold either in the Ikeja Computer Village or the Alaba international market. Non-working goods are sent directly to landfill (Babatunde, 2016; Ideho, 2012). These informal practices are causing environmental and health damage and creating disputes between individual groups of scavengers. Nigeria's domestic e-waste generation rate is also high, largely consisting of EoL-UEEE. The life of repaired/refurbished mobile phones in Nigeria extends up to seven years, but at the cost of twice-yearly replacement of batteries and chargers, generating additional e-waste estimated to amount to more than 1 Mt (Nnorom and Osibanjo, 2008). In view of this vulnerable situation, Nigeria has approved the opening of its first organized e-waste recycling plant[23]. In the absence of strong enforcement of e-waste management, this move is widely welcomed (Nnorom and Osibanjo, 2008). The recently implemented National Environmental Regulations for the electronics sector only explicitly prohibits trade in unusable e-goods.

1.4.5 Proposed Management of E-waste and Urban Mining for the Circular Economy

The active implementation of reverse logistics will provide stainability in e-waste management. The three main steps are (Tsydenova and Bengtsson, 2011):

(i) Disassembly: Selective disassembly targets hazardous or valuable components for special treatment.
(ii) Upgrading: Mechanical processing and/or metallurgical processing increases the content of desirable materials.
(iii) Refining: purifying the recovered materials using chemical (metallurgical) processing makes them acceptable for the original use.

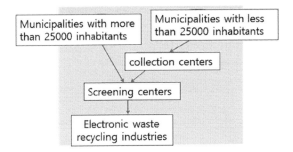

FIGURE 1.15 Proposed model for government guidelines, collection and screening centres. *Source*: Developed from guidelines proposed by Azevedo et al., 2017.

On the other hand, covering all recommended steps (including recycling and disposal) is challenging for developing countries due to their limited availability, technological access, and investments. Implementing a 'best-of-2-worlds' (Bo2W) principle that provides a network and pragmatic solution for e-waste treatment (via urban mining) could boost emerging economies (Nnorom and Osibanjo, 2008). Figure 1.15 illustrates the installation of collection and screening centres by local bodies on the basis of population density, which seeks to integrate the best logistical and technical pre-processing practices for manual dismantling of e-waste and the best end-processing practices for treating hazardous and complex components in international state-of-the-art end-processing facilities. In addition, cleaner production design, EPR, standards and labelling, product stewardship, recycling and remanufacturing through urban mining are practices being adopted by various countries to deal with the problem of e-waste generation and raise their overall sustainability (Azevedo et al., 2017). These practices are inspiring government/non-governmental organizations, researchers, and academics to propose sustainable models for e-waste management. Most developing countries have the potential to utilize and manage EEE/UEEE and e-waste.

Numerous mathematical models have been proposed in this direction (Azevedo et al., 2017; Pathak and Srivastava, 2017). 3-R is the Reduce–Reuse–Recycle model for e-waste management (Habib et al., 2015; Parajuly et al., 2017), while a flow model specifying the need for and importance of urban mining is proposed by Pathak and Srivastava, (2017) (Figure 1.16). The schematic flow indicates the potential for e-waste collection and recycling (urban mining) to mitigate environmental impacts worldwide. In this context, a quick shift from informal to organized sectors is not easy; the formal sector cannot achieve the desired result alone, hence the need for an integrative approach.

The circular economy concept which enables the slowing down of the rate of EEE consumption by keeping it in circulation for the longest possible time and minimizing waste generation through smarter product design and business models (Parajule et al., 2017) involves a multi-R system (reduce, reuse, refuse, recycle, recovery, rethink, redesign, etc.) that emphasizes social, environmental and economic aspects[24]. Barriers identified by researchers include access to advanced technology, goods collection systems, the need for finance and the involvement of the private sector,

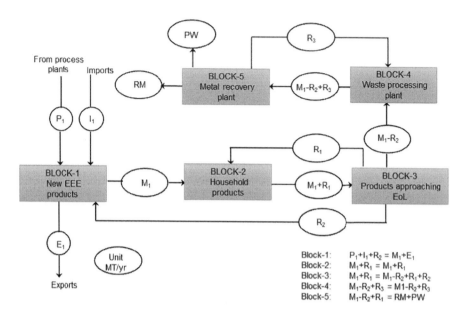

FIGURE 1.16   A sustainable model: EEE flow and urban mining of e-waste. *Note*: **Block 1** New EEE product comes to the market; **Block 2** Household used product; **Block 3** Products approaching EoL; **Block 4** Waste processing plant; **Block 5** Metal recovery plant; E_1 Exported EEE; I_1 Imported EEE; M_1 New EEE; M_2 EoL completed EEE; R_1 EEE with uncompleted EoL to be reused; R_2 Consumer sending the unused EEE to second-hand market; R_3 Metal recycling (formal and informal) of WEEE; **RM** Recovered metals; **PW** Potential waste. *Source*: Modified from Pathak and Srivastava, (2017).

training needs in the informal sector, and availability of a volatile recycled materials market through urban mining of e-waste (Balde et al., 2017). Decentralized e-waste repair/refurbishing initiatives can be a panacea for building a sustainable e-waste model.

ACKNOWLEDGEMENTS

This work was supported by the Brain Pool Programme through the National Research Foundation of Korea (NRF), funded by the Ministry of Science and ICT (Grant No. 2019H1D3A2A02101993), and the Basic Science Research Programme through the National Research Foundation of Korea (NRF), funded by the Ministry of Education (Project no. 2020R1I1A1A01074249).

NOTES

1   http://www.basel.int/TheConvention/Overview/tabid/1271/Default.aspx
2   https://www.rohsguide.com/
3   http://www.basel.int
4   http://www.oecd.org
5   http://www.basel.int

6 https://en.ppt-online.org/605816

7 https://www.uncclearn.org/sites/default/files/inventory/integrated_weee_management_
and_disposal-395429-normal-e.pdf

8 https://www.statista.com/statistics/727725/ewaste-generation-argentina/

9 https://www.giswatch.org/country-report/2010-icts-and-environmental-sustainability/
argentina

10 www.rezagos.com/descargas/Proyecto-Ley-RAEE.pdf

11 www.rezagos.com/descargas/ProyectoLeyRAEE-UTN.pdf

12 https://techinbrazil.com/e-waste-management-in-brazil

13 https://www.theguardian.com/environment/2017/jan/16/chinas-booming-middle-class-
drives-asias-toxic-e-waste-mountains

14 https://www.recycling-magazine.com/2017/10/19/electronics-recycling-china/

15 (https://i.unu.edu/media/unu.edu/news/52624/UNU-1stGlobal-E-Waste-Monitor-2014-
small.pdf

16 https://www.chinadialogue.net/article/show/single/en/9841-China-to-release-plan-
for-tackling-e-waste-by-end-of-year-

17 http://assocham.org/newsdetail.php?id=4633Assocham%20/

18 http://pas.org.pk/digital-in-2017-global-overview/

19 https://www.ehn.org/how-much-e-waste-is-shipped-to-nigeria-2561214315.html

20 http://collections.unu.edu/eserv/UNU:6349/PiP_Report.pdf

21 https://motherboard.vice.com/en_us/article/59jew8/e-waste-smuggling-nigeria

22 https://ejatlas.org/conflict/e-waste

23 https://www.dailytrust.com.ng/nigeria-gets-first-e-waste-recycling-facility.html

24 https://www.unido.org/sites/default/files/2017-07/Circular_Economy_UNIDO_0.pdf)

REFERENCES

Abbas, Z. (2010) In: *E-waste management in Pakistan*. Regional Workshop on E-Waste/
WEEE Management, Osaka, Japan, pp. 6–9.

de Aberasturi, D. J., Pinedo, R., de Larramendi, I. R., de Larramendi, J. R. and Rojo, T. (2011)
Recovery by hydrometallurgical extraction of the platinum-group metals from car catalytic converters. *Minerals Engineering*, 24(6), 505–513.

APME (Association of Plastics Manufacturers in Europe) (1995) *Plastics–a material of choice
for the electrical and electronic industry–plastics consumption and recovery in Western
Europe*. Brussels: APME.

Arndt, N. T., Fontboté, L., Hedenquist, J. W., Kesler, S. E., Thompson, J. F. and Wood, D. G.
(2017) Future global mineral resources. *Geochemical Perspectives*, 6(1), 1–171.

ASSOCHAM India Report (2016) India to sit on e-waste pile of 30 lakhs MT with Mumbai on
top of heap: ASSOCHAM-Frost & Sullivan study, Available at: http://www.assocham.
org/newsdetail.php?id=5642/; 2016 [accessed 10.06.2020].

Awasthi, A. K., Zeng, X. and Li, J. (2016) Environmental pollution of electronic waste recycling in India: A critical review. *Environmental Pollution*, 211, 259–270.

Azevedo, L. P., da Silva Araújo, F. G., Lagarinhos, C. A. F., Tenório, J. A. S. and Espinosa, D.
C. R. (2017) E-waste management and sustainability: A case study in Brazil.
Environmental Science and Pollution Research, 24(32), 25221–25232.

Babatunde, B.I. (2016) *Assessment of e-waste in Ikeja local government area of Lagos state,
Dissertation submitted to the department of urban and regional planning, Faculty of
environmental science, Ladoke Akintola University of technology*, Ogbomoso, Oyo State.

Baccini, P. and Brunner, P. H. (2012) *Metabolism of the anthroposphere: analysis, evaluation,
design*. Cambridge: MIT Press.

Balde, C. P., Kuehr, R., Blumenthal, K., Fondeur Gill, S., Kern, M., Micheli, P. and Huisman,
J. (2015) *E-waste statistics-Guidelines on classification, reporting and indicators*.
United Nations University, IAS-SCYCLE, Bonn, Germany.

Balde C. P., Forti V., Gray V., Kuehr R., Stegmann P. (2017). The global e-waste monitor –2017, United Nations University (UNU), *International Telecommunication Union (ITU) & International Solid Waste Association (ISWA)*, Bonn/Germany/Vienna.

Basel Convention. (2019). *The National Reporting Database*. Retrieved from http://basel.int/Countries/NationalReporting/ReportingDatabase(old)/tabid/1494/Default.aspx

BIO Intelligence Service (2013). Equivalent conditions for waste electrical and electronic equipment (WEEE) recycling operations taking place outside the European Union, Final Report prepared for European Commission – DG Environment.

Bizzo, W. A., Figueiredo, R. A. and De Andrade, V. F. (2014) Characterization of printed circuit boards for metal and energy recovery after milling and mechanical separation. *Materials*, 7(6), 4555–4566.

Boeni, H., Silva, U. and Ott, D. (2008) E-waste recycling in Latin America:Overview, challenges and potential. In *Proceedings of the 2008 Global Symposium on Recycling, Waste Treatment and Clean Technology, REWAS*, pp. 665–673.

Borthakur, A. and Singh, P. (2017) Researches on informal E-waste recycling sector: It's time for a 'Lab to Land' approach. *Journal of hazardous materials*, (323), 730–732.

Borthakur, A. and Sinha, K. (2013) Generation of electronic waste in India: Current scenario, dilemmas and stakeholders. *African Journal of Environmental Science and Technology*, 7(9), 899–910.

Bridgen, K., Labunska, I., Santillo, D., Allsopp, M. (2005) *Recycling of electronic waste in China and India: workplace and environmental contamination.* Amsterdam: Greenpeace International.

Cossu, R. (2012) The environmentally sustainable geological repository: The modern role of landfilling. *Waste Management*, (2), 243–244.

Cossu, R. (2013) The urban mining concept. *Waste management*, 33(3), 497.

de Vicente Bittar, A. (2018) Selling remanufactured products: Does consumer environmental consciousness matter? *Journal of Cleaner Production*, 181, 527–536.

Driscoll, A., Shiheng, W. (2010) *Poverty or poison: China's dire choice in an electronic world.* Available at: http://www.vermontlaw.edu/Documents/Driscoll%20WU,%20Poverty%20or%20Poison.pdf. [accessed 28.06.2020].

Duan, H., Miller, T. R., Gregory, J., Kirchain, R. (2013). Quantitative characterization of Transboundary Flows of Used Electronics: Analysis of Generation, Collection, and Export in the United States. Materials Systems Laboratory, MIT. http://www.step-initiative.org/tl_files/step/_documents/MITNCER%20US%20Used%20Electronics%20Flows%20Report% 20-%20December%202013.pdf.

European Commission (2015) Communication COM (2015) 614/2: Closing the Loop–An EU Action Plan for the Circular Economy.

E-waste. (2014) The escalation of a global crisis report. Available at: http://tcocertified.com/news/global-ewaste-reaches-record-high-says-new-un-report/. [accessed 25.03.2020].

E-waste Recycling Facts and Figures. (2018) Available at: https://www.thebalance.com/e-waste-recycling-facts-and-figures-2878189. [accessed 25.03.2020].

Forti, V., Balde, C. P., Kuehr, R. and Bel, G. (2020) The Global E-waste Monitor 2020: Quantities, flows and the circular economy potential. *United Nations University (UNU)/United Nations Institute for Training and Research (UNITAR) – co-hosted SCYCLE Programme, International Telecommunication Union (ITU) & International Solid Waste Association (ISWA)*, Bonn/Geneva/Rotterdam.

Garlapati, V. K. (2016) E-waste in India and developed countries: Management, recycling, business and biotechnological initiatives. *Renewable and Sustainable Energy Reviews*, 54, 874–881.

Geeraerts, K., Mutafoglu, K. and Illés, A. (2015). *Illegal e-waste shipments from the Eu to China. Quantitative and monetary analysis of illegal shipments and its environmental, social and economic impacts. A study compiled as part of the EFFACE project.* London: Institute for European Environmental Policy.

GISW-Pakistan. (2010) Global Information Society Watch 2010 Report Focus on ICTs and Environmental Sustainability. In Finlay, Alan (Ed.), *APC and Hivos*, p. 187190.

Green Peace-Basel Action Network. (2004). *Key finds from Taizhou field investigation.* Available at: http://www.ban.org/Library/TaizhouE-wasteResearch Report.pdf. [accessed 28.04.2020].

Habib, K., Parajuly, K. and Wenzel, H. (2015) Tracking the flow of resources in electronic waste – the case of end-of-life computer hard disk drives. *Environmental Science & Technology*, 49(20), 12441–12449.

Hagelüken, C. (2008) Recycling of Spent Catalysts Containing Precious Metals. *Handbook of Heterogeneous Catalysis: Online, 1846–1863.*

Hagelüken, C. and Kegels, J. (2004) Responsible care, precious results. *Hydrocarbon engineering*, 9(3), 31–36.

Heck, R. M. and Farrauto, R. J. (2001) Automobile exhaust catalysts. *Applied Catalysis A: General*, 221(1-2), 443–457.

Heeks, R., Subramanian, L. and Jones, C. (2015) Understanding e-waste management in developing countries: Strategies, determinants, and policy implications in the Indian ICT sector. *Information Technology for Development*, 21(4), 653–667.

Huisman J (2003) The QWERTY/EE concept, quantifying recyclability and eco-efficiency for end-of-life treatment of consumer electronic products, PhD thesis, Technical University Delft, Netherlands.

Ideho, B.A. (2012) *E-Waste Management: A Case Study of Lagos State, Nigeria, Social and Public Policy Master's Programme in Development and International Cooperation.* Department of Social Sciences and Philosophy University of Jyväskylä, Finland.

Ilyas, S. (2018a) *Metal recycling*. Available at: https://www.dawn.com/news/1444937.

Ilyas, S. (2018b) *Waste management and circular economy*. Available at: https://nation.com. pk/16-Nov2018/waste-management-and-circular-economy.

International, B. M. (2015) Pakistan Consumer Electronics Report, p. 64.

IPO, (2007) *In: Import Policy Order, Ministry of Commerce, Government of Pakistan.* Islamabad, Pakistan.

IPO. (2016) *In: Import Policy Order, Ministry of Commerce, Government of Pakistan.* Islamabad, Pakistan.

Jain, A. (2010). E-waste business model, policies and regulations in India. *Paper presented at the 2010-IEEE International symposium on sustainable systems and sechnology*, ISSST 2010, article 5507703.

Joseph, K. (2007) Electronic waste management in India–issues and strategies. In *Eleventh international waste management and landfill symposium, Sardinia.*

Jun-Hui, Z. and Hang, M. I. N. (2009) Eco-toxicity and metal contamination of paddy soil in an e-wastes recycling area. *Journal of Hazardous Materials*, 165(1-3), 744–750.

Kašpar, J., Fornasiero, P. and Hickey, N. (2003) Automotive catalytic converters: current status and some perspectives. *Catalysis today*, 77(4), 419–449.

Kiddee, P., Naidu, R. and Wong, M. H. (2013) Electronic waste management approaches: An overview. *Waste management*, 33(5), 1237–1250.

Kurian, J. (2007). Electronic waste management in India—issues and strategies. *Eleventh International waste management and landfill symposium.* Calgary, Italy, pp. 1–5.

Lasaridi, K., Terzis, E., Chroni, C., Kostas, A. (2016). Bir Global Facts & Figures World Statistics on E-Scrap Arising and the Movement of E-Scrap Between Countries 2016-2025.

Leman, A. M., Jajuli, A., Feriyanto, D., Rahman, F. and Zakaria, S. (2017) Advanced Catalytic Converter in Gasoline Engine Emission Control: A Review. In *MATEC Web of Conferences EDP Sciences*, 87, 02020.

Lepawsky, J (2015) The changing geography of global trade in electronic discards: Time to rethink the E-waste problem. *Geographical Journal*, 181(2): 147–159.

Leung, A., Cai, Z. W. and Wong, M. H. (2006) Environmental contamination from electronic waste recycling at Guiyu, southeast China. *Journal of Material Cycles and Waste Management*, 8(1), 21–33.

Lox, E. S. (2008) Automotive exhaust treatment. *Handbook of Heterogeneous Catalysis: Online, 2274–2345.*

Luo, C., Liu, C., Wang, Y., Liu, X., Li, F., Zhang, G. and Li, X. (2011) Heavy metal contamination in soils and vegetables near an e-waste processing site, south China. *Journal of hazardous materials*, 186(1), 481–490.

MP-BGS. (2009) Mineral profile – British Geological Survey. Available at: www.bgs.ac.uk

Nnorom, I. C. and Osibanjo, O. (2008) Overview of electronic waste (e-waste) management practices and legislations, and their poor applications in the developing countries. *Resources, conservation and recycling*, 52(6), 843–858.

Ongondo, F. O., Williams, I. D. and Cherrett, T. J. (2011) How are WEEE doing? A global review of the management of electrical and electronic wastes. *Waste management*, 31(4), 714–730.

Parajuly, K., Habib, K. and Liu, G. (2017) Waste electrical and electronic equipment (WEEE) in Denmark: Flows, quantities and management. *Resources, Conservation and Recycling*, 123, 85–92.

Pardiwala, J. M., Patel, F. and Patel, S. (2011) Review paper on catalytic converter for automotive exhaust emission. In *International Conference On Current Trends In Technology, NUiCONE*, pp. 382–481.

Pathak, P. and Srivastava, R. R. (2017) Assessment of legislation and practices for the sustainable management of waste electrical and electronic equipment in India. *Renewable and Sustainable Energy Reviews*, 78, 220–232.

Pathak, P. and Srivastava, R. R. (2019) Environmental Management of E-waste. In *Electronic waste management and treatment technology* (pp. 103–132). Amsterdam: Butterworth-Heinemann.

PEPA. (1997) In: Pakistan Environmental Protection Act, Government of Pakistan (Ed.), p. 29. Pakistan.

Planing, P. (2015) Business model innovation in a circular economy reasons for non acceptance of circular business models. *Open journal of business model innovation*, 1(11), 1–11.

Puckett, J., Byster, L., Westervelt, S., Gutierrez, R., Davis, S., Hussain, A. and Dutta, M. (2002) Exporting Harm: The high-tech trashing of Asia, the Basel action network (BAN) and Silicon Valley Toxics Coalition (SVTC).

Robinson, B. H. (2009) E-waste: An assessment of global production and environmental impacts. *Science of the total environment*, 408(2), 183–191.

Rudnick, R. L. and Gao, S. (2003) Composition of the continental crust. *The crust*, 3, 1–64.

Silva, U., Ott, D., Boeni, H. (2008). E-waste recycling in Latin America: Overview, challenges and potential. In: *Global symposium on recycling, waste treatment and clean technology*, Cancun, Mexico.

Sinha, D. (2004) *The management of electronic waste: A comparative study on India and Switzerland. MS thesis.* St. Gallen: University of St. Gallen.

Stallone, R. (2011) *What is Urban Mining?* Available at: http://jessestallone.com/2011/04/20/what-is-urban-mining. [accessed April 2012].

Sthiannopkao, S. and Wong, M. H. (2013) Handling e-waste in developed and developing countries: Initiatives, practices, and consequences. *Science of the Total Environment*, 463, 1147–1153.

Tsydenova, O. and Bengtsson, M. (2011) Chemical hazards associated with treatment of waste electrical and electronic equipment. *Waste management*, 31(1), 45–58.

Tue, N. M., Katsura, K., Suzuki, G., Takasuga, T., Takahashi, S., Viet, P. H. and Tanabe, S. (2014) Dioxin-related compounds in breast milk of women from Vietnamese e-waste recycling sites: Levels, toxic equivalents and relevance of non-dietary exposure. *Ecotoxicology and Environmental Safety*, 106, 220–225.

U.S. International Trade Commission (USITC). (2013). Digital Trade in the U.S. and Global Economies, Part 1 (Digital Trade 1). USITC Publication No. 4415. Washington DC, USA. http://www.usitc.gov/publications/332/pub4415.pdf.

Van Rossem, C., Tojo, N. and Lindhqvist, T. (2006) *Extended producer responsibility: an examination of its impact on innovation and greening products.* Available at: http://www.greenpeace.org/raw/content/international/press/reports/epr.pdf/.   [accessed 26.09.2020].

Van Weelden, E., Mugge, R. and Bakker, C. (2016) Paving the way towards circular consumption: exploring consumer acceptance of refurbished mobile phones in the Dutch market. *Journal of Cleaner Production,* 113, 743–754.

Vogtlander, J. G., Scheepens, A. E., Bocken, N. M. and Peck, D. (2017) Combined analyses of costs, market value and eco-costs in circular business models: eco-efficient value creation in remanufacturing. *Journal of Remanufacturing,* 7(1), 1–17.

Wang, D., Cai, Z., Jiang, G., Leung, A., Wong, M. H. and Wong, W. K. (2005) Determination of polybrominated diphenyl ethers in soil and sediment from an electronic waste recycling facility. *Chemosphere,* 60(6), 810–816.

Wastling, T., Charnley, F. and Moreno, M. (2018) Design for circular behaviour: considering users in a circular economy. *Sustainability,* 10(6), 1743.

Williams, E. (2011) Environmental effects of information and communications technologies. *Nature,* 479(7373), 354–358.

Yu, J., Williams, E., Ju, M. and Shao, C. (2010) Managing e-waste in China: Policies, pilot projects and alternative approaches. *Resources, Conservation and Recycling,* 54(11), 991–999.

Zhang, J. H., Min, H. (2009). Eco-toxicity and metal contamination of paddy soil in an e-waste recycling area. *J. Hazard. Materials,* 165: 744–750.

Zoeteman, B. C., Krikke, H.R., Venselaar, J. (2010). Handling WEEE waste flows: on the effectiveness of producer responsibility in a globalizing world. *The International Journal of Advanced Manufacturing Technology,* 47(5): 415–436.

2 Pre-treatment, Concentration, and Enrichment of Precious Metals from Urban Mine Resources

Pre-treatment, Concentration, and Enrichment of Precious Metals

Hyunjung Kim
Mineral Resources and Energy Engineering, Jeonbuk National
University, Jeonju, Jeonbuk 54896, Republic of Korea

Department of Environment and Energy, Jeonbuk National
University, Jeonju, Jeonbuk 54896, Republic of Korea

Sadia Ilyas
Mineral Resources and Energy Engineering, Jeonbuk National
University, Jeonju, Jeonbuk 54896, Republic of Korea

Rajiv Ranjan Srivastava
Center for Advanced Chemistry, Institute of Research and
Development, Duy Tan University, Da Nang 550000, Vietnam

CONTENTS

2.1 PRE-TREATMENT: DISMANTLING AND DE-SOLDERING PROCESS

Precious and base metals in spent printed circuit boards (SPCBs) are mostly mixed with or connected to other metals (connecters, solders), ceramics (capacitors and integrated circuits/chips), and resins (in layers of SPCBs). These complex combinations of metals and materials in SPCBs require appropriate pre-treatment for maximum metal liberation and recovery. First, SPCBs go through dismantling, de-soldering, and comminution prior to further leaching and recovery (Wang et al., 2013).

The conventional catalytic converter includes three main parts: the PGM-containing monolith, the outer steel shell which protects the monolith against external mechanical destruction, and the fibre blanket, which acts as a buffer between the steel shell and the monolith. Spent catalytic converters (SCCs) are also passed through dismantling and comminution prior to further leaching.

Although SPCBs are designed for 500,000 h durability, the average end of life (EoL) for electronic components is 20,000 h, or less than 5% of designed life span. Hence, many electronic components are still functioning and usable at the time of disposal. So a disassembling process is employed to segregate electronic components and/or materials that are reusable, identifiable, or hazardous in such a way as to maximize economic return, minimize the environmental burden and enable efficient subsequent processing by systematic removal of electronic components, parts, a group of parts, or a sub-assembly.

Electronic components are mounted on printed circuit board assemblies using various types of connections like a press-fit socket pedestal, solder wave-type holes, surface-mounted devices (solder by reflux), screw joints, and rivets. Operations including disassembling, fracturing, drilling, ungluing, heating, and lubricating can be used for electronic components.

In electronics, de-soldering is the removal of solder and electronic components from a circuit board for troubleshooting, replacement, repair, and recycle or reuse. De-soldering is necessary for dismantling electronic components from SPCB assemblies. Informal dismantling methods include the use of chisels, hammers, and cutting torches to open solder connections and separate various types of metals and components, while formal de-soldering is achieved by either thermal, chemical, or mechanical treatment (Chen et al., 2013).

2.1.1 THERMAL AND MECHANICAL DE-SOLDERING APPROACHES

Thermal treatment of SPCBs is performed in a tin melting stove, rotating drum dismantling machine, horizontal tunnel furnace, or infrared-heated rod/lamp (250 W) and brushes at around 225–265°C (above the melting temperature of the solder) (Duan et al., 2011). The disassembling rate (%) is calculated as follows:

$$\text{Disassembling rate} = \text{Number of electronic components released from SPCBs} / \text{Total number of components on SPCBs} \times 100$$

(2.1)

Electronic components are connected to SPCBs by solder, so solder is melted and removed first by heating with electricity in a tin melting stove. When the solder melts, electronic components are removed by hitting and shaking the board. Industrial MX-300 melting stoves have a capacity of 0.4–0.8 t/h/worker/table with an electric power supply of 4.0 KW, and a dimension of $720 \times 500 \times 390$ mm[1].

Infrared heat treatments use infrared (IR) lamps (commonly incandescent lamps) which emit invisible infrared radiation and transmit it to the object that is being heated. Depending on the temperature of the emitting object, the wavelength of the peak of the infrared radiation ranges from 700 nm to 1 mm (at frequencies between 430 THz and 300 GHz). No contact or medium between the two objects is needed for the energy transfer.

Bulk heating of SPCBs for de-soldering is achieved in water-soluble ionic liquids like 1-Butyl-3-methylimidazolium tetrafluoroborate (BMIM-BF4) and (Zeng et al., 2013) dielectric liquids (mineral oils, transformer oils, methyl phenyl silicone oil, and cryogenic liquids N_2, O_2, H_2, He, and Ar). Approximately 90% of electronic components are removed from SPCBs at 250°C with these ionic liquids, but most of them cannot be regenerated. Inert and stable molten salts (LiCl + KCl) and a NaOH-KOH eutectic composition (41% NaOH-59% KOH) (melting temperature: 170°C) can be used as a heat transfer fluid to dissolve glasses and oxides and to destroy plastics present in SPCBs without oxidizing most of the metals. At a range of 450–470°C, metal products in either liquid (solder, Zn, Sn, Pb, etc.) or solid (Cu, Au, Fe, Pd, etc.) form can be recovered (Riedewald and Sousa-Gallagher, 2015). A pulsating air jet (industrial waste heat) can also be used to melt solder and separate the electronic components from SPCBs (Chen et al., 2013).

Various dismantling machines are also in use to remove the solder and electronic components from mixed SPCB assemblies, including drum/barrel, tunnel-type, scanning and laser de-soldering automated component-dismantling systems.

In drum dismantling machines (Figure 2.1), the cylindrical drum/barrel is made of 6mm thickness steel to withstand abrasion and high temperature. The machine, with

FIGURE 2.1   Drum-type dismantling machine.

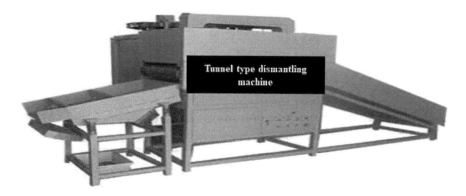

FIGURE 2.2   Tunnel-type dismantling machine.

a weight from 0.35 to 0.60 tons and power from 2.2 to 3.7 KW, works with a gas/dust cleaning system or under an exhaust hood. The machine's capacity ranges from 200 to 500 kg h^{-1} and has an electronic component dismantling rate of 99%. Activated carbon is used to avoid hazardous discharges to the environment in the off-gas.

Tunnel-type automated dismantling machines are equipped with a horizontal solder-melting furnace and infrared heaters, dust-catching systems, a conveyor and panel systems. SPCBs are passed along a conveyor through a tunnel furnace and heated. The electronic components are shaken from the SPCBs at the end of the conveyor. The machines have a capacity of 200 kg h^{-1} and external dimensions of 8135 × 1600 × 3260 mm, with vibrating screen dimensions of 0.8 × 1.2 × 0.7 m. The total power supply is 15.2 KW and the total weight is 1.37 tons. The dust-removing efficiency is more than 95%. The heating power requirement of the dismantling machine is 18kW and that of the feeder motor is $0.75kW^2$.

An automated component-dismantling system using scanning and laser de-soldering was developed by the Austrian Society for Systems Engineering and Automation.

In this system the machine first scans components, reading their identification data and storing them in a database before comparing them with the suggested price. It then checks whether the components identified are soldered or surface mounted: if mounted, they are disassembled by a robot in 3 to 5 seconds at a cost of €0.5; high-quality soldered components are disassembled via laser with minimum thermal input (18–20 s/component) and lower-quality components and/or those of the ball grid array type are disassembled via infrared heat input (Kaya, 2018).

2.2 SHREDDING, CRUSHING, AND GRINDING PROCESS

Some SPCBs and SCCs contain interlocking metallic and nonmetallic parts. Subsequent steps in the concentration/recycling process cannot proceed until the materials required are completely separated. The particle size of the material is progressively reduced to an optimum size for separation by a method suited to the physico-chemical properties of the metal of interest. A series of steps consisting of shredding/crushing, grinding, and pulverizing to reduce the size is an integral part of the process.

2.2.1 SHREDDING PROCESS: SINGLE-, DUAL-, AND QUAD-SHAFT SHREDDERS

Shredding is a process in which feed material is fragmented, then ground, ripped or torn into small pieces with the help of shredders. These uniquely designed machines feature low noise, high torque, and wide applications; their functions are shearing, tearing, fracturing, breaking, and auto-discharging. Shredders are size-reducing, crushing, and volume-reducing devices for various materials and are equipped with a cutting chamber, bearings and gears, a hexagonal shaft, feed hopper, guard, reducer, cushioned torque arm, drive belt, electric/hydraulic motor(s), electric panel with PLC (programmable logic control), and automatic reverse sensors. Various types of flexible and durable knives/blades are available for shredding different materials. The benefits of shredders are: robust cutting efficiency; high automation and production efficiency; low energy consumption; less dust and noise; less labour intensive; and ease of cleaning, maintenance, and service.

Single-shaft, dual-shaft, and quad-shaft shredders are the most commonly used in industry. Figure 2.3 shows a single-shaft shredder comprising a static knife and a

FIGURE 2.3   Sketch of single-shaft shredder.

knife disc for shredding various types of materials. The cutter consists of a base shaft and several quadrilateral knife blocks with three, four, or more replaceable blades. The knife block along the axis of the base has multiple V-type rows and finally a knife disc. These are attached with screws in the radial axis so that they rotate together with the base shaft. The two static knives are fixed onto the machine's frame. The material is sent to the cutter through the horizontal hydraulic cylinder. The speed and propulsive force of the machine are stable and adjustable. It is suitable for recovery of a variety of bulk solid materials, including wood, irregular plastic containers and plastic barrels, large-calibre pipes, tubes, films, fibres, paper, and die material. It has low noise and a spindle speed between 45 and 100 rpm[3]. Single-shaft shredders should be strong, durable, and energy saving. Single-shaft shredders crush material down to 20 mm. In single-shaft shredders, the number of rotary blades is between 24 and 57; the shaft diameter is between 220 and 350 mm; rotor length between 500 and 2000 mm; rotating shaft speed between 75 and 90 rpm; fixed knife between 1 and 2; pressure between 6 and 12 MPa; crushing capacity between 250–400 kg h[-1] and 600–1200 kg h[-1]; feeding calibre/hopper size between 550–650 mm and 1280–1300 mm; motor power outputs between 18.5 and 55 KW; mesh size between 20 and 40 mm; weight between 3.5 and 9.5 tons; and dimensions (L×W×H) between 3000×1600×2200 mm and 4500×2500×2800 mm.

Dual-shaft PCB shredders are mainly used for crushing packing belts, tyres, film, woven bags, fishing nets, and other plastic waste. The biaxial independent drive, the unique knife shaft structure, and a four-angle rotary knife produce high torque at low speed. In dual-shaft shredders, the number of rotary blades is between 60 and 150; rotating shaft speed between 65 and 87 rpm; fixed knife between 4 and 8; blade thickness between 30 and 75 mm; crushing capacity between 500 and 2000 kg h[-1]; feeding calibre between 700–800 mm and 1650–2000 mm; motor power between 18.5×2 and 45×2 KW; and weight between 4.0 and 9.5 tons. Size varies from 5 to 20 mm. Figure 2.4 shows a dual-shaft and a four-shaft shredder in an industrial application.

In quad-shaft shredders, the knife rotary diameter is between 150 and 400 mm; rotating speed between 25 and 43 rpm; feeding calibre between 1000–800 mm and 2000–1800 mm; and main power between 11×2 and 45×2 KW. Recently flat dual-shaft shredders/two-storey shredder and pulverizer on a single chassis have become available. A pre-crushing shredder is accumulated on the same monoblock body with a pulverizer in some industrial equipment[4].

FIGURE 2.4   Dual-shaft and quad-shaft shredders.

2.2.2 CRUSHING PROCESS: PRIMARY, SECONDARY, TERTIARY, AND IMPACT CRUSHERS

Crushing is achieved by compression of material against a rigid surface or impact against a surface in a rigidly constrained motion path. Crushing is usually a dry process and is carried out in succession by (1) primary, (2) secondary, and (3) tertiary crushers.

Primary crushers are heavy-duty rugged machines used to crush material up to 1.5 m in size. Large materials are reduced at the primary crushing stage to output of dimension 10–20 cm. The common primary crushers are of jaw and gyratory types. The jaw crusher reduces the size of large rocks by dropping them into a V-shaped mouth at the top of the crusher chamber consisting of one fixed rigid jaw and a pivoting swing jaw which are set at an acute angle to each other. Compression is created by forcing the rock against the stationary plate in the crushing chamber. The opening at the bottom of the jaw plates is adjustable to the desired aperture for the product size. The material remains between the jaws until small enough to be released through this opening for further size reduction by feeding to the secondary crusher. The type of jaw crusher depends on the input feed and output product size, rock/ore/material strength, volume of the operation, cost, and other related parameters. Heavy- and medium-duty crushers are installed on a commercial scale, depending on capacity of the plant, while small-scale jaw crushers are installed in laboratories for representative sample preparation.

The gyratory crusher consists of a long, conical, hard steel crushing element suspended from the top. It rotates and sweeps out in a conical path within the round, hard, fixed crushing chamber. The maximum crushing action is created by closing the gap between the hard crushing surface attached to the spindle and the concave fixed liners mounted on the main frame of the crusher. The gap is opened and closed through an eccentric drive on the bottom of the spindle which causes the central vertical spindle to gyrate. Figures 2.5 and 2.6 illustrate the jaw and gyratory crusher processes.

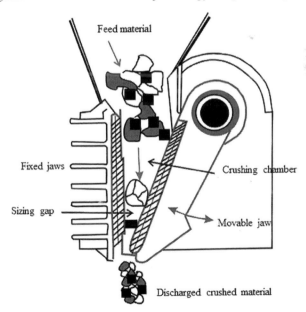

FIGURE 2.5 Jaw crusher process.

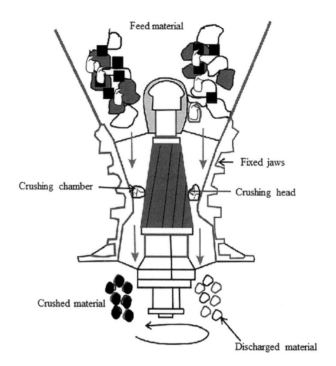

FIGURE 2.6   Gyratory crusher process.

The secondary crusher is mainly used to reclaim the primary crusher product, which measures around 15 cm in diameter. The secondary crusher product size is usually between 0.5 and 2 cm in diameter, making it suitable for grinding. Secondary crushers are comparatively lighter in weight and smaller in size. They generally operate with dry clean feed from which harmful elements like metal splinters, wood, clay, etc. have been removed during primary crushing. Common types of secondary crusher are cone, roll, and impact.

The cone crusher is very similar to the gyratory type, except that it has a much shorter spindle with the diameter of its crushing surface larger than its vertical dimension. The spindle is not suspended, as in the gyratory crusher. The eccentric motion of the inner crushing cone is similar to that of the gyratory crusher. A working cone crusher can act as a tertiary crusher when installed in a close circuit between secondary crusher and ball mill to crush any material overflowing from vibratory screening. Figure 2.7 shows how the cone crusher works for a variety of materials.

The roll crusher consists of a pair of horizontal cylindrical manganese steel spring rolls (Figure 2.8), which rotate in opposite directions. The falling feed material is squeezed and crushed between the rollers. The final product passes through the discharge point. This type of crusher is used in secondary or tertiary crushing applications. Advanced roll crushers are designed with one rotating cylinder that rotates toward a fixed plate or rollers with differing diameters and speeds. It improves the extraction of required material from the crushed product (Cui and Forssberg, 2003; Ogunniyi et al., 2009).

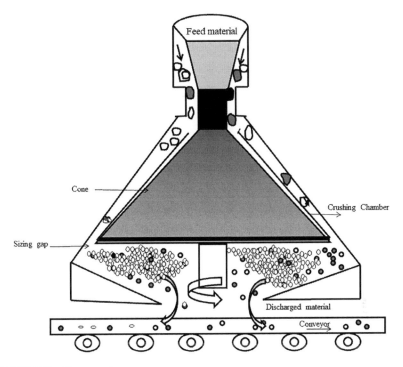

FIGURES 2.7 Cone crusher process.

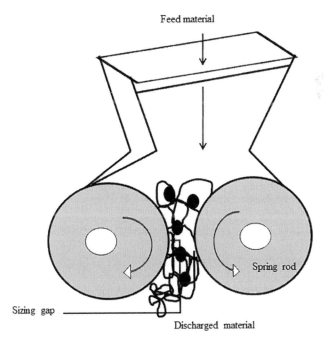

FIGURES 2.8 Roll crusher process.

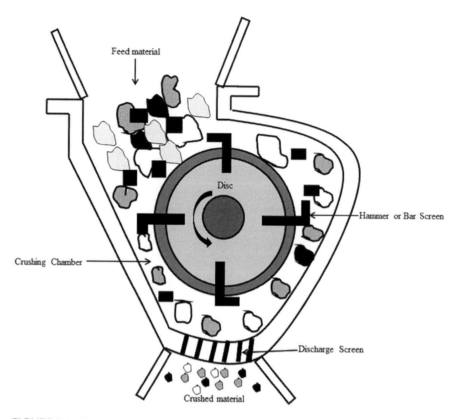

FIGURE 2.9 Impact crusher process.

If the desired size reduction is not completed with secondary crushing, tertiary re-crushing is recommended using secondary crushers in a close circuit. The screen overflow from the secondary crusher is collected in a bin and transferred to the tertiary crusher via a conveyor belt in close circuit.

The impact crusher uses high-speed impact or sharp blows to the free-falling feed rather than compression or abrasion. Hinged or fixed heavy metal hammers (hammer mill) or bars are attached to the edges of horizontal rotating discs. The hammers, bars, and discs are made of manganese steel or cast iron-containing chromium carbide. The hammers repeatedly strike the material to be crushed against the rugged solid surface of the crushing chamber, breaking the particles into uniform size. The final fine products drop down through the discharge grate, while oversized particles are swept around for another crushing cycle until they are fine enough to fall through the discharge gate. Impact crushers (Figure 2.9) are widely employed for secondary or tertiary crushing (Cui and Forssberg, 2003).

2.2.3 Grinding Process: Ball, Rod, Pebble, Autogenous and Semi-Autogenous Mills

Grinding takes place uses several mechanisms, such as a combination of impact or compression forces applied almost normally to the particle surface, chipping due to oblique forces, and abrasion due to forces acting parallel to the surfaces. Grinding as the final stage in the comminution process is usually carried out in rotating, cylindrical, heavy-duty steel vessels either dry or as a suspension in water.

The loose crusher products freely tumble inside the rotating mill in the presence of an agitated grinding medium. Grinding inside a mill is influenced by the size, quantity, type of motion, and space between individual pieces of medium within the mill. There are five types of grinding mill: ball mill, rod mill, pebble mill, autogenous mill, and semi-autogenous mill. The main differences between these mills are the ratio of the diameter to the length of the cylinder, and the type of grinding media employed. The grinding media can be steel balls, steel rods, hard rock pebbles, or the ore itself, and the mill is classified accordingly. The grinding mill reduces feed particles of 5–20 mm to optimum sizes of between 40 and 300 µm as required for further processing[5].

Ball mills are short cylindrical vessels with a shell-to-diameter ratio of 1.5 to 1 or less. When the length-to-diameter ratio varies between 3 and 5 it is called a tube mill. The grinding medium is high-carbon or cast-alloy steel balls which are moved up the side of the mill in such a way that they release and fall to the point where they impact the feed material particles in the trailing bottom region of the slurry. Ball mills are operated at higher speed so that the balls can be thrown up and strike the opposite wall with increased speed to hit the feed material particles. Ball mills are suitable for finer grinding of hard and coarse feeds.

Rod mills are long cylindrical vessels whose shell is 1.5 to 2.5 times longer than their diameter. The breaking medium is steel rods. The rotating drum causes friction and attrition between the steel rods and feed material particles. As the mill rotates, the rods cascade over each other in relatively parallel mode to prevent overgrinding of softer particles. Product discharge is either through central, end peripheral, or overflow types. Rod mills can take feed particles as coarse as 50 mm and turn them into material as fine as 300 µm. Rod mills are suitable for the preparation of feed to gravity and magnetic concentration.

Pebble mills are similar to ball mills except that the grinding media are closely sized, suitably selected rocks or pebbles. The rotating drum causes friction and attrition between rock pebbles (quartz or quartzite pebbles) and feed material particles. The pebble mill is inexpensive to operate with respect to grinding media, power consumption, and maintenance.

Self-grinding of the ore in autogenous mills removes the need for any additional breaking media. The drum is typically of larger diameter than its length, generally in the ratio of 2 or 2.5 to 1. The rotating drum throws larger feed material particles in a cascading motion, causing larger particle to break on impact and grinding finer ones through compression. Autogenous mills, which are cheaper to operate, are often integrated into large mineral-processing operations. However, where hardness and abrasiveness of the feed material vary widely, inconsistent grinding performance may result.

Semi-autogenous mills are essentially a variant of autogenous mills with the addition of steel balls along with the natural grinding media, which rectifies the problem of inconsistency in grinding. The total amount of balls in these mills ranges between 5% and 15% of volume. Many present-day plants install semi-autogenous mills as the primary or first-stage grinding system in combination with ball mills. Maintenance costs are generally low as they do not require media and replacement rods. Semi-autogenous mills are primarily used in the gold, copper, platinum, lead, zinc, silver, alumina, and nickel industries.

2.3 SCREENING AND CLASSIFICATION

Particle size plays a critical role in separation of metals/materials of interest during any particular downstream operation. Screening and classification are two distinct techniques for particle separation based on size. The relatively coarser particles are separated by screening. The screens are attached to all types of crushing units at the feed and discharge stages. Oversized materials are diverted to re-crush and re-grind devices. Undersized materials pass to the next finer stage for crushing or grinding. Particles that are too fine to be sorted efficiently by screening are separated by classification, with classifiers attached to the grinding units in close circuit[6].

2.3.1 SCREENING PROCESS: GRIZZLY, TROMMEL, VIBRATORY AND GYRATORY SCREEN SEPARATOR

The crushed particles are separated using a hard metallic screen with a perforated surface of fixed dimensions and uniform aperture. Crushed fragments of urban-mined material are dropped onto the screen surface. Particles finer than the openings pass through the screen, while oversized particles are conveyed to the discharge end for re-crushing. Factors affecting screen performance are particle size, shape, orientation, feed rate, angle of discharge, % open area, type of vibration, moisture content, and feed material, and its efficiency is measured by recovery of the desired size and the misplaced materials in each product. Different types of industrial screen are available, each suited to handling a particular type of material. The screen may be of non-vibrating (such as grizzly) or the more frequently used vibrating type (such as trommel screens, vibratory and gyratory types).

The grizzly is used for primary screening of very coarse materials and is most often found in crushing circuits. It is generally installed to size the feed to the primary crusher. It is formed of a parallel set of horizontal or inclined heavy wear-resistant manganese steel rails or bars set a fixed distance apart. Finer materials fall through the spacing of the bars. Oversized materials slide onto the surface of the bars and are reduced on site by manual hammering. Screens are static for very coarse materials. A grizzly can incorporate a mechanism for shaking or vibrating the screen to improve performance.

The trommel (derived from German word for a drum) is a horizontal or slightly inclined rotating cylindrical screen. The feed material enters at one end of the cylinder, undersized particles fall through the screening surface, and oversized particles move by a rotating motion to the discharge end. A trommel can separate several different-sized fractions by using a series of screens with apertures ranging from coarsest to finest. It can handle both dry and wet feed material. Although trommels are relatively cheap, they have lower capacities and are susceptible to rapid wear; hence they have been largely replaced by vibratory or shaking screens (Figure 2.10).

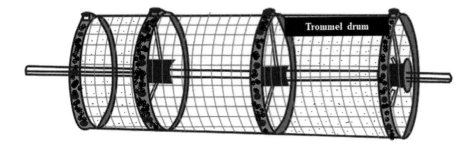

FIGURE 2.10 Sketch of trommel screen separator.

FIGURE 2.11 Sketch of vibratory screen separator.

The vibratory screen is the most common screening device found in mineral-processing applications for the various types of material and particle sizes encountered. The shaking motion of the surface impacts on the material being screened. It can be arranged as multiple decks so that different particle-size products can be obtained from a single feed (Figure 2.11).

Gyratory screen separators (Figure 2.12) consist of multiple, circular, removable and replaceable decks or trays for different-sized products. They work through both gyratory and slightly vertical motions operated by a specially designed motor mounted vertically at the centre of the baseplate of the screen. Gyratory separators are ideal for large and fine solid particles and solid/liquid applications.

2.3.2 CLASSIFICATION: HYDRAULIC, SPIRAL AND HYDROCYCLONE CLASSIFIER

Exceptionally fine materials composed of different metallic fractions cannot be effectively separated by screening. Sorting between two or more metallic or nonmetallic fractions of similar size is possible on the basis of the velocity at which the grains fall through a fluid medium. This method of separation and concentration by

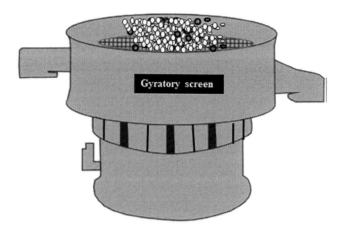

FIGURE 2.12   Sketch of gyratory screen separator.

difference in the settling rates due to variable particle size, shape, and density in a fluid medium is known as classification. The fluid medium in general is water under modified conditions, such as rising at a uniform rate, changing density, addition of suitable reagents, and passing air bubbles. The classifier consists of a sorting column in which a fluid rises at a uniform rate. Particles introduced into the sorting column sink and are classed as underflow if their terminal velocities are greater than the upward velocity of the fluid. On the other hand, if their terminal velocity is lower than the upward velocity of the fluid, they rise and are classed as overflow. Classification equipment includes hydraulic classifiers, horizontal current classifiers, spiral and rake classifiers, and hydrocyclones.

    The hydraulic classifier works on the differences in settling rates of particles of feed pulp against the rising water current. The unit consists of a series of conical sorting columns of successively larger size with relatively lower current velocity. The relative rate of settling against the up-flow of water current accumulates the coarsest particles in the first and the finest in the last conical vessel (Figure 2.13). Sediment is

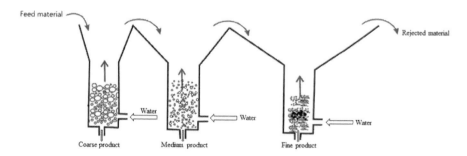

FIGURE 2.13   Hydraulic classifier processing.

removed from the bottom of the settling zone and treated accordingly. Very fine slime overflows in the last column.

Spiral classifiers are typically mechanically driven devices. The unit has a continuously revolving spiral that drags coarse sandy sediment from the settled feed pulp along the bottom of an inclined surface to a higher discharge point at one end of the settling tank. The fine sediment overflows at the other end. The rake classifier is a variation in the mechanism for shifting the coarser components. The rakes dip into the feed pulp, move in an eccentric motion along an inclined plane for a short distance, and then lift it up and go back to the starting point to repeat the operation. Backward sliding of material occurs when the rakes are lifted between strokes. Spiral classifiers are usually preferred to the rake type as the material does not slide backwards (Figure 2.14).

A hydrocyclone is a classifier that classifies, separates, and sorts particles. It consists of a cylindrical section at the top connected to a feed chamber for continuous inflow of pulp, which is then expelled through an overflow pipe. The unit continues downwards as a conical vessel and opens at its apex to the underflow of coarse material. The feed material is pumped under pressure through the tangential entry, imparting a spinning motion to the pulp. The separation mechanism works on this centrifugal force to accelerate the settling of particles. The velocity of the slurry increases as it follows in a downward centrifugal path from the inlet area to the narrow apex end. The larger and denser particles migrate nearest to the wall of the cone. The finer/lighter particles migrate toward the central axis of the cone, reverse their axial direction, and follow a smaller-diameter rotating path back towards the top. Oversized fractions are discharged to the mill for regrinding, while undersized fractions move to the conditioning tank for flotation, etc. (Figure 2.15). Hydrocyclones perform at higher capacities relative to their size and can separate at finer sizes than other screening and classification equipment (Dyakowski et al., 1999; Neesso and Donhauser, 2000; Colli et al., 2019; Brouwers et al., 2012).

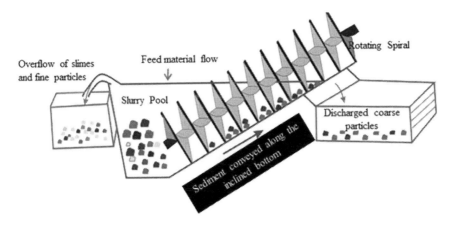

FIGURE 2.14 Spiral classifier processing.

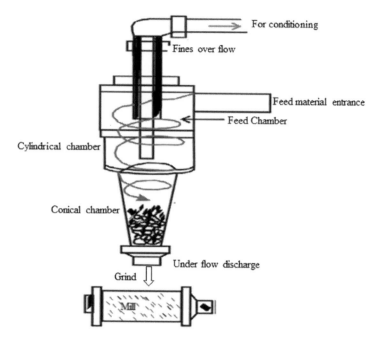

FIGURE 2.15   Hydrocyclone processing.

2.4 ENRICHMENT AND CONCENTRATION OF PRECIOUS METALS FROM URBAN MINE SOURCES

The process of upgrading materials of interest by exploiting various physico-chemical properties of the feed material is called concentration or enrichment. There are many concentration process, such as material sorting, gravity, magnetic, electrostatic, dense media separation, leaching/recovery, etc. (Wang et al., 2015; Kaya, 2018).

2.4.1 CONCENTRATION USING SORTING AND PANNING APPROACHES

Manual and automatic sensor-based sorting systems can be used for recycling of various material from urban-mined sources. Hand sorting is still a popular method in small-scale operations but mechanical sorting (using optical, electronic, and radioactive properties) is in common use for large-scale industrial applications. This is possibly due to the distinct contrast between the physical properties of valuable material and gangue material. The critical attributes are light reflectance, ultraviolet rays, magnetism, conductivity, and X-ray luminescence. The main objective of mechanical sorting is to reduce the bulk of the raw material by rejecting large volumes of waste material at an early stage. The process utilizes a two-stage separation process. The first stage involves primary crushing of feed to liberate pre-concentrate and barren rejects. In the second stage, re-crushing, grinding, and processing

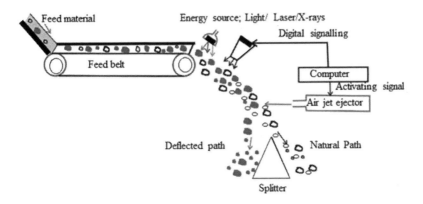

FIGURE 2.16 Automatic electronic sorter processing.

is performed to produce final concentrates and tailings. This two-stage operation substantially lowers the cost of large volumes of crushing and grinding, and the subsequent process of upgrading to produce marketable final concentrates. Fragments of desired size from urban-mined sources, preferably washed, move on a conveyor belt or vibrating feeders at uniform speed and are released, while the stream of feed material particles maintains a natural flow. Energy elements like light rays, laser beams, and X-rays converge from the source and reflect from the surface of the feed material passing through the sorting zone. The nature of the reflectance is sensed by the detector system, which sends signals to the computer. The amplified signal activates an air jet at the right instant and at the correct intensity to eject the particle from the stream. Accepted and rejected particles are dropped in separate stacks around a conical splitter. A fully automatic electronic sorting device comprises an integrated circuit of an energy source, a process computer, a detector, and an ejector (Fuerstenau and Han, 2003; Ammen, 1997; Wills and Finch, 2015; Kaya, 2018) (Figure 2.16).

Panning as a mineral/metal recovery technique was known to many ancient civilizations. Gold panning was popular and extensively practised in California, Argentina, Australia, Brazil, Canada, and South Africa during the nineteenth century. Panning is the manual shaking of a tray containing river-bed sand and gravel, and alluvial soil/dust of SPCBs or SCCs containing precious metals like gold, silver, tin, tungsten, and native platinum. The shaking tray separates sand, stones, and fine-grained metals into different layers by differential gravity concentrations. The undesired materials are removed. This is a primitive practice used by remote tribal people on a small scale and at low cost.

2.4.2 Gravity/Density Concentrator

Gravity concentration methods separate materials according to their relative movements in response to gravity along with one or two forces adding resistance to the motion. A concentration criterion (CC) can be used for gravity separation possibility as in following equation:

$CC = (\rho_h - \rho_{fluid})/(\rho_1 - \rho_{fluid})$ ρ_h is the density of heavy material, ρ_1 is the density of light material, and ρ_{fluid} is the density of fluid medium (water/air). If CC >±2.5, gravity separation is relatively easy. If $2.5 < CC < 1.25$, the efficiency of gravity separation decreases. If CC <1, gravity separation can be possible under careful density-controlled conditions.

For plastics and metals (here gravity separation is easy):

$$CC = \frac{7-1}{2-1} = 6.0 \tag{2.2}$$

For plastics and Al/glasses (here gravity separation is possible but not easy)

$$CC = \frac{2.65-1}{2-1} = 1.65 \tag{2.3}$$

For Al/glasses and metals (here gravity separation is easy)

$$CC = \frac{7-1}{2.65-1} = 3.64 \tag{2.4}$$

As well as gravity, the force exerted by the viscous liquids can serve as the separation medium.

Density-based separation uses differences in particle size and density to separate metallic and nonmetallic fractions. Equipment used for this type of separation includes water or airflow tables, rectangular riffled air tables, shaking tables/hydraulic shaking tables, jigs, rising-current separators, hydrocyclones, Falcon centrifugal separators and sink–float methods.

Based on these properties, several well-known separation methods—gravity separation, magnetic separation and electrostatic separation—can be selectively applied to metal recycling from SPCBs and SCCs.

The nonmetallic fraction of SPCBs has significantly lower densities than the metallic fractions. The density of plastic ranged from 0.9 to 2.0 g cm⁻³, epoxy resin ranged from 1.1–1.4 g cm⁻³, polyester resin ranged from 1.2–1.5g cm⁻³, fibreglass epoxy composite between 1.9–2.0 g cm⁻³; and glass fibre has a density of 2.5 g cm⁻³. The densities of Al, Mg, and Ti are between 1.7 and 4.5 g cm⁻³ while Cr, Sn, Fe, Zn, Ni, Cu, and Co have densities between 7 and 9 g cm⁻³, Pb, Ag, and Mo have a density between 10 and12 g cm⁻³, and Pd, W, Pt, Rh, and Au between 19.3 and 21.4 g cm⁻³ (Kaya, 2018).

2.4.3 SPIRAL CONCENTRATOR

The spiral concentrator is a modern device that works on a combination of solid particle density and its hydrodynamic dragging properties. The spirals consist of a single or double helical conduit or sluice wrapped around a central collection column. It is used for concentration of low-grade ores and industrial minerals in slurry form. The device has a wash water channel and a series of concentrate removal ports placed at regular intervals. Separation is achieved by stratification of material caused by a

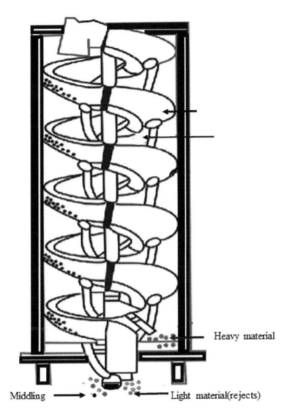

Heavy material

Middling ⟶ ⟵ Light material(rejects)

FIGURE 2.17 Spiral concentrator processing.

complex combined effect of centrifugal force, differential settling, and heavy particle migration through the bed to the inner part of the conduit. This technology is extensively applied to the treatment of heavy mineral beach sand consisting of monazite, ilmenite, rutile, zircon, garnet, and upgrade chromite concentrate. Two or more spirals are constructed around one central column to increase the amount of feed material that can be processed by a single integrated unit (Fuerstenau and Han, 2003; Ammen, 1997; Wills and Finch, 2015) (Figure 2.17).

2.4.4 JIG, SHAKING TABLE, AND MOZLEY CONCENTRATOR

Jigs are continuously pulsating gravity concentration devices. In urban-mined material, jigging is used to separate shredded metals and particularly plastics from metals. The method is also in common use for separating various types of plastics by making use of the fact that PVC has a specific weight of $>1 \mathrm{g\,cm^{-3}}$ (heavier than water) while those of PE, PUR, PP, and PS are usually $<1 \mathrm{g\ cm^{-3}}$.

Jigging for concentrating minerals is based exclusively on particle density differences. The elementary jig is an open tank filled with water. A thick bed of coarse heavy particles (ragging) is placed on a perforated horizontal jig screen. The feed material is poured from the top. Water is pulsated up and down (the jigging action) by a pneumatic or mechanical plunger. The feed moves across the jig bed. The heavier particles penetrate through the ragging and screen to settle down quickly as concentrate, which is removed from the bottom of the device. The jigging action causes the lighter particles to be carried away by the crossflow supplemented by a large amount of water continuously supplied to the concentrate chamber. Jig efficiency improves with the coarseness of feed material, which show wide variations in specific gravity. Jigs are widely used as efficient and economical processing devices. Sarvar et al. (2015) used a wet jig for +0.59 and 1.68 mm PCB particles with metal recovery between 85% and 97.5%.

Gravity concentration on inclined planes is carried out on shaking tables, which can be smoothed or grooved and which vibrate back and forth at right angles to the flow of water. As the pulp flows down the incline, the ground material is stratified into heavy and light layers in the water; in addition, under the influence of the vibration, the particles are separated in the direction of impact. Shaking tables use controlled vibration and particle density to separate materials. The flowing film effectively separates coarse light particles from small dense particles. The heavy fraction of the material goes to the concentrate launder on the left side, and light fraction goes to the tailing launder on the right side. Mixed particles go to the middle launder of the table. Holman Wilfley wet shaking tables can be used for recovery of PMs, Cu wire, synthetic diamonds, chromite, heavy mineral sands, and Au. The various models process feed streams of between 5 and 2500 kg h^{-1}.

Holman models are available for all fine mineral concentrations (e.g., mineral sands, Sn, W, Cr, Au). The Wilfley 7000 model is available for metal recycling and reprocessing of WEEE materials. 20–25% solid by weight can be used. Particle size can vary from 100–150µm to 5 mm at capacities from 0.5 to 12.5 t h^{-1}. Capacity can be increased using double- or triple-decker tables (Kaya, 2018). Figure 2.18 is a diagram of a typical shaking table for recovery of gold and platinum.

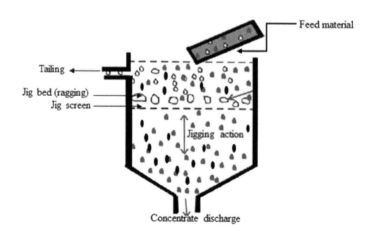

FIGURE 2.18 Shaking table.

2.4.5 Pinched Sluice and Cones Concentrator

Figure 2.19 shows processing by a pinched sluice and cone concentrator—an inclined trough made of wood, aluminium, steel, and fibreglass, 60–90 cm long. The channel tapers from about 25 cm wide at the feed end to 3cm at the discharge end. Feed consisting of 50%–65% solids enters the sluice and stratifies as the particles flow through it. The materials are squeezed into the narrow discharge area. The piling causes the bed to dilate and allows heavy particles to migrate and move along the bottom. The lighter particles are forced to the top. The resulting material strata are separated by a splitter at the discharge end. Pinched sluices are simple and inexpensive.

A large number of basic units and recirculation pumps are required for industrial applications. The system has been improved by the development and adoption of the Reichert cone. The complete device comprises several cones stacked vertically in integrated circular frames (Ammen, 1997).

2.4.6 Concentration by Multi-gravity Separator

The multi-gravity separator (MGS) is a new development in flowing film concentration expertise which makes use of the combined effects of centrifugal force and shaking. The centrifugal force enhances the gravitational force and obtains better metallurgical performance by recovering particles down to 1 μm in diameter, which would otherwise escape into the tailing stream if other conventional wet gravity separators (jigs, spirals, and table) are used. The principle of the system consists essentially in wrapping the horizontal concentrating surface of a conventional shaking table into a cylindrical drum, which then rotates. A force, many times greater than the

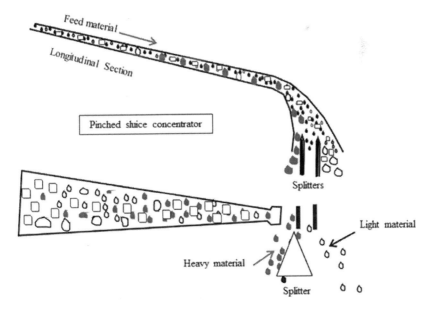

FIGURE 2.19 Pinched sluice concentrator processing.

normal gravitational pull, is exerted on particles in the film flowing across the surface. This enhances the separation process to a great extent. When treating graphitic schist-hosted lead sulphide ore, MGSs in close circuit with rougher cells improve the lead concentration from 20% to 40% +Pb. At the same time the graphitic carbon content is reduced from >10% to <3% (Wills and Finch, 2015).

2.4.7 CONCENTRATION BY AIR/PNEUMATIC GRAVITY SEPARATORS

The air-gravity separator (AGS) enables highly sensitive dry separation on the basis of one of three particle characteristics: density, size, or shape. When size and shape are controlled within certain limits, the gravity separator is unmatched in its ability to separate a complex mixture by density. Density separation is achieved by mechanical vibration and air fluidization.

Air tables are used for the separation of metallic and plastic components from a feed less than 7 mm in size after ferromagnetic separation. 76%, 83% and 91% recovery rates are achieved for Cu, Au, and Ag, respectively, from low-grade SPCB or general e-scrap. Air table techniques can be utilized for the separation of particulate fractions in the 5–10 mm, 2–5 mm, and <2 mm ranges, respectively. The Triple/S Dynamics, Inc. model T-20 air separator has a trapezoidal deck with surface area of 1.86 m^2 and separates Cu and Al granules from electric wire (i.e., PVC) and cable recycling systems. Metal particles can be separated from non-metal particles at an extraction rate between 60% and 80%. An exhaust hood for dust-free operations and for high temperature applications is available. Deck power is 1.5 HP, fan power is 10–20 HP, and total weight is 2.1 t. The closed-loop air supply recycles 85–90% of the air used.

Pneumatic tables use a throwing motion to move the feed along a riffled deck and blow air continuously up through a porous bed. Dry air tables use a shaking motion similar to that of wet shaking tables, but instead of water, air is used to separate heavy materials. On the air table, unlike wet tables, both particle size and density decrease from the top down. The table deck is covered with porous material, and air is blown up through the deck from a chamber underneath. The chamber equalizes the pressure from the compressor and thus ensures an even flow of air over the entire deck surface. Generally, SPCB recycling equipment of air-separation type is applicable to the recycling of various waste and bare PCBs. The mixture of metal and non-metal materials gained from crushing/pulverizing/classifying WPCB raw materials is fed into the material hopper of the air separator and then into the separating zone of the separator to separate metal, fibre, and resin mixtures. Since the separator is connected to a dust-removal system, a horizontal air current is formed which moves the materials horizontally. Meanwhile, the materials move downward due to gravity. Due to the different specific gravities of materials, non-metal materials, such as fine dust and grains with lower gravity, are taken away by the dust-removal system when the mixture passes the separating plate, leaving metal materials with larger gravity in the finished product recovery zone (Kaya, 2018).

2.4.8 CONCENTRATION BY MAGNETIC SEPARATION

Separation takes place on the basis of the difference in magnetic properties of various components of the feed material (either diamagnetic, paramagnetic, or ferromagnetic).

All materials are affected in some way when placed in a magnetic field.

$$F_m = V \times X \times H \times H_g \tag{2.5}$$

where
F_m = Magnetic attraction force
V: Particle volume (determined by process)
X: Magnetic susceptibility
H: Magnetic field (created by the magnet system design) in mT
H_g: Magnetic field gradient (created by the magnet system design) in mT (mT: milli Tesla, 1kGauss = 100 mT = 0.1 T)

Materials are classified into two broad groups according to whether they are attracted or repelled by a magnet. Non-/diamagnetics are repelled from and ferro-magnetics/paramagnetics are attracted to a magnet. Ferromagnetic substances are strongly magnetic and have a large and positive magnetism. The magnetic moments in ferromagnetic material are ordered and are of the same magnitude in the absence of an applied magnetic field. Paramagnetic substances are weakly magnetic and have a small and positive magnetism. The magnetic moments in a paramagnetic material are disordered in the absence of an applied magnetic field and ordered in the presence of an applied magnetic field. In diamagnetic materials, a magnetic field is opposite to the applied field. Magnetisms are small and negative. Nonmagnetic material has zero magnetism. These materials are not attracted to a magnet. Ferromagnetism is the basic mechanism by which certain materials (such as Fe) form permanent magnets or are attracted to magnets. Ferromagnetism (including ferrimagnetism) is the strongest type. Ferromagnetic materials can be separated by a low-intensity magnetic separa-tor at lower than 2T magnetic intensity. Paramagnetic materials can be separated by dry or wet high-intensity magnetic separators at 10–20 T magnetic intensities. Diamagnetic materials create an induced magnetic field in a direction opposite to an externally applied magnetic field and are repelled by the applied magnetic field. Nonmagnetic substances have little reaction to magnetic fields and show net zero magnetic moment due to random alignment of the magnetic field of individual atoms. Strongly magnetic materials can be recovered by a magnetic separator with the use of relatively weak magnetic induction, up to 0.15 T (1,500 Gauss). Weakly magnetic materials can be recovered by a high-intensity magnetic separator generating induc-tion up to 0.8T(8,000 Gauss) with modest values for the gradient of the magnetic field. Induced roll separators with field intensities up to 2.2 T and Perm roll separa-tors can be used for both coarse and dry materials (>75 μm). Fine materials reduce separation efficiency due to particle–rotor and particle–particle adhesion/ agglomer-ation. For wet high-intensity magnetic separators, Gill and Jones separators are used at a maximum field of 1.4 and 1.5 T, respectively, at -150 μm size (Bentli et al., 2017).

Commercial magnetic units follow a continuous separation process on a moving stream of dry or wet particles passing through a low or high magnetic field. The vari-ous magnetic separators are drum, cross-belt, roll, high-gradient magnetic separa-tion, high-intensity magnetic separation, and low-intensity magnetic separation.

The drum separator consists of a nonmagnetic drum fitted with 3–6% magnets composed of ceramic or rare earth magnetic alloys in the inner periphery. The drum rotates at uniform motion over a moving stream of preferably wet feed. The ferromagnetic and paramagnetic feeds are picked up by the rotating magnets and pinned to the outer surface of the drum. As the drum moves up, the concentrate is compressed, dewatered, and discharged leaving gangue/nonmetallic fractions in the tailing compartment. Drum rotation can be clockwise or counterclockwise and the collection of concentrate is designed accordingly. A drum separator produces extremely clean magnetic concentrate. It is suitable for the recovery of precious metals from various material like SPCBs, SCCs, beach sand etc.

The cross-belt separator consists of a suspended magnet fixed over a continuously moving belt carrying feed. The magnet attracts and lifts magnetic materials, strips off the captured trap metal and discharges it off the side or end of the conveyor, leaving gangue to tailing. It is widely used in the mineral beach sand industry for separation of ilmenite and rutile (Wills and Finch, 2015; Haldar, 2013).

The feasibility of using magnetic separation to recover PMs from the simulated auto-catalyst has been proposed recently (Taninouchi et al., 2017; Taninouchi and Okabe, 2018). PMs were converted to alloys with metals, such as Ni using the electro-less plating technique or Fe by $FeCl_2$ vapour treatment, which modified the PGMs from being nonmagnetic to ferromagnetic. PGMs, as ferromagnetic components in the alloy with Ni or Fe, can be separated from the ceramic substrate as the nonmagnetic component. The collected PMs–Ni/Fe alloy with proper ratios can either dissolve in acid solutions more effectively or be directly smelted to concentrate the PMs by pyrometallurgical processes without requiring the addition of other metal collectors.

2.4.9 Concentration by Electrostatic Separation: Corona, Triboelectric, and Eddy Current Separators

The electrostatic separation system is the most innovative technology in recycling for efficient final-stream granulometric separation. Electric field effects are used to separate the more conductive fraction (i.e., metallic) from the less conductive, dielectric, fraction (e.g., paper, plastic, rubber). The charged nonconductors are attracted to an oppositely charged electrode and collected. Electrostatic separation (e-sorting) adopts the high-voltage electrostatic processing principle, separating the conductive metal and nonconductive non-metal/nonferrous materials according to their different conductivities/resistivities. Conductors have valence electrons from a sea of electrons between positive ion cores, and insulators have valence electrons tightly bound to the nucleus.

There are three typical electrical conductivity-based separation techniques: (1) corona electrostatic separation, (2) triboelectric separation, and (3) eddy current separation.

The rotor-type corona electrostatic method is perhaps the most effective separation/concentration technology for the conductive (metallic fractions) and nonconductive (nonmetallic) fractions at present. The feed sample in the separator is bombarded by the high-voltage electrostatic field generated by a corona electrode and electrostatic electrode. Metallic fractions are neutralized quickly as they contact the earthed electrode and leave the rotating roller while the charged nonmetallic fractions are pinned by the electric image force to the rotating roller and move with it, finally falling into the holding tanks. In the corona electrostatic separator, electrode system, rotor speed, moisture content, and particle size have the greatest effect in determining the separation results. The corona electrostatic separator can be used for recovery of metals (Cu, Al) from chopped electrical wires and cables and the e-sorting, downstream of the SPCB system, separates metals and allows the finer fractions of PMs (Au, Pd, Ag) to be recovered. The SPCBs with their metallic components removed must be reduced to very small particles which can be achieved by accelerating them at high speed to impact on a hardened plate. Then, the small particles, typically less than 0.6 mm, are passed along a vibratory feeder to a rotating roll to which a high-voltage electrostatic field is applied using a corona and an electrostatic electrode. The nonmetallic particles become charged and attached to the drum, eventually falling off into storage bins, whereas the metallic particles discharge rapidly in the direction of an earthed electrode.

There are two types of corona electrostatic separator machines: double-roller and multi-roller electrostatic separators. The roller length varies from 1000 to 2000 mm, roller quantity 1–4, power 1.5–4 KW, speed 20–300 rpm, and outlet motor 0.75–2.2 KW at a production capacity between 300 and 500 kg h^{-1}. Separation efficiency is as high as 99%. Electrostatic separators feature high precision separation with easy operation and simple maintenance. They cover a small area and are easily movable. It has been found that particle sizes of 0.6–1.2 mm are the most suitable size for separation in industrial applications (Lu et al., 2008; Hadi et al., 2015).

The triboelectric effect (also known as triboelectric charging) is a type of contact electrification whereby certain materials become electrically charged after they are separated from a different material with which they were in contact. Static electricity is defined as an electrical charge caused by an imbalance of electrons on the surface of a material. Electrostatic charge is most commonly created by the contact and separation of two similar or dissimilar materials. Creating an electrostatic charge by contact and separation of materials is known as triboelectric charging. It involves the transfer of electrons between materials. The atoms of a material with no static charge have an equal number of positive (+) protons in their nucleus and negative (-) electrons orbiting the nucleus.

When the two materials are placed in contact and then separated, negatively charged electrons are transferred from the surface of one material to the surface of the other. Which material loses electrons and which gains them will depend on the nature of the two materials. The material that loses electrons becomes positively charged, while the material that gains electrons is negatively charged. This imbalance of electrons produces an electric field that can be measured and that can influence other objects at a distance. Electrostatic discharge is defined as the transfer of charge between bodies at different electrical potentials. When two materials contact and separate, the polarity and magnitude of the charge are indicated by the materials' positions in the triboelectric series. The triboelectric simply lists materials according to their relative triboelectric charging characteristics. When two materials contact and separate, the one nearer the top of the series takes on a positive charge and the other a negative charge. Materials further apart on the table typically generate a higher charge than ones closer together (Knoll et al., 1988; Bendimerad et al., 2009; Miloudi et al., 2011; Inculet et al., 1994; Higashiyama et al., 1997).

An eddy current separator uses a powerful magnetic field to separate nonferrous metals from waste after all ferrous metals have been removed previously by some arrangement of magnets. The device makes use of eddy currents to effect separation. Eddy current separators are not designed to sort ferrous metals, which become hot inside the eddy current field. This can cause damage to the eddy current separator unit belt. The eddy current separator is applied to a conveyor belt carrying a thin layer of e-waste. Nonferrous metals are thrown forward from the belt into a product bin, while nonmetals simply fall off the belt due to gravity. The eddy current separator uses a rotating drum with a permanent/electro- magnet. It produces high-frequency alternating magnetic fields on a magnetic roller; if conductive NMF goes through the magnetic field, it will produce induced current, and if this induced current produces a magnetic field opposite to the original magnetic field, then the NMF (i.e., Al, Cu, etc.) will fly ahead in the direction in which it is moving by repulsive force of the magnetic field; hence, nonferrous metals are separated from other nonmetallic fractions (plastics).

Not all nonmetallic fractions can be separated out by an eddy current separator because only material with a high σ/ρ can be separated out, where ρ is the density of the material and σ is its electrical conductivity. Eddy current separators are mainly used for recycling Cu, Al, and other nonferrous metals from industrial waste, and living garbage can be widely used in garbage disposal, recycling of SPCBs and SCCs, other environmental industries, and the nonferrous metal material processing industry. The main criterion to be distinguished is the ratio of material conductivity and density values; the higher ratio value is more likely to separate. Typical particulate sizes processed tend to be in the 3–150 mm size range. The high-frequency eddy current separator, where the magnetic field changes very rapidly, is needed for separation of smaller particles (Kaya, 2018).

2.4.10 Concentration by Froth Flotation

Historically, the flotation concept was the most flexible and adaptable mineral beneficiation technique of the twentieth century. Selective mineral separation by flotation works on the physical and chemical surface properties of valuable and unwanted gangue minerals. It is being continuously modified for low-grade complex sulphide ores like lead-zinc, lead-zinc-copper, nickel-platinum-gold, tin, fluorite, phosphate, iron ore, and recently for secondary materials like spent printed circuit boards (SPCBs) and spent catalytic converters (SCCs). Figure 2.20 shows a froth flotation cell.

The froth flotation process produces froth from selective mineral/material agglomerates and separates them from other associated metallic components and gangue minerals. The physical and chemical surface properties of minerals/materials make some specific materials hydrophobic. The particles become water repellent by coming into contact with moving air bubbles in the presence of certain reagents. The froth portion moves up, leaving the gangue (tailing) below, stabilizes for a while, and

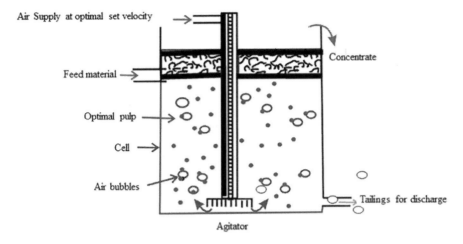

Air Supply at optimal set velocity

Concentrate

Feed material

Optimal pulp

Cell

Air bubbles

Tailings for discharge

Agitator

FIGURE 2.20   Froth flotation cell process.

collects as a concentrate for further cleaning. The three main groups of reagents used in flotation are collectors, frothers, and regulators. Each set of reagents plays a specific role in froth flotation.

Collectors are organic compounds that make the surface of selected material hydrophobic. Sodium isopropyl xanthate and potassium amyl xanthate are commonly used collectors.

Frothers are surface-active chemicals that concentrate at the air–water interface. They prevent air bubbles from coalescing or bursting by lowering the surface tension of slurry. Frothing properties can be persistent or non-persistent depending on the desired stability of the froth. Pine oil and alcohols such as methyl isobutyl carbinol are commonly used frothers, while regulators or modifiers are used to modify the action of the collector by intensifying or reducing the water-repellent effect of material surface conditions. Regulators assist in the selective flotation of the material of interest by acting as activators, depressants, or pH modifiers.

In the SPCB scenario, froth flotation is a promising technique for rejecting hydrophobic plastics from the comminution product to recover metallic fractions by reverse flotation without reagents. The contact angles of some hydrophobic plastics with water are: acrylonitrile butadiene styrene (ABS) 87.3°, polyethylene (PE) 96.8°, polypropylene (PP) 95°, polyvinylchloride (PVC) 86.4°, polystyrene (PS) 86.3°, and polyethylene terephthalate (PET) 76.5° (Kaya, 2018).

Liberation studies indicate that the liberation of metallic fractions from nonmetallic constituents at −1.0 mm size is promising, and the particulate system is significantly rich in metal value, containing around 23% metal. Single-stage flotation increases the metal content from 23% to over 37%, contributing a mass yield of around 75% with a recovery of nearly 95% metal values, suffering the nominal loss of only around 4% metal value while effectively rejecting 32% of the materials in the feed through float fraction (Vidyadhar and Das, 2013). Ogunniyi et al. (2009) recovered Au and Pd with 64% recovery at an enrichment ratio of 3:1. Gallegos-Acevedo et al. (2014) used a conventional laboratory flotation cell to separate metallic and nonmetallic fractions from SPCBs. 0.5 × 0.5 cm SPCBs fragments were subjected to chemical treatment to remove resin-holding metallic (30%) and nonmetallic fractions (70%). Dodecylamine was used as a cationic collector, methyl isobutyl carbinol (MIBC) as a synthetic frother (5–30 ppm), and NaOH as a pH regulator. Mixing speed was changed from 1200 to 1600 rpm and the solid content varied from 1% to 3% at 30°C, 20 min conditioning time, and 1 min flotation time. Nonmetallic glass-fibre material was floated (i.e., reverse flotation) and metallic material was sunk. At these optimum conditions, 99.49% metal and 99.5% non-metal recoveries were obtained. Estrada-Ruiz et al. (2016) efficiently separated the metallic and nonmetallic fractions from arcade PCBs at 1.25% solid content and -250 μm particle size in a continuous laboratory column flotation at pH: 7. The optimum superficial air velocity was 0.4 cm s^{-1}. Hydrophobic plastics (reinforced fibres) were floated and went to the concentrate, and hydrophilic metals (mainly Sn and Pb from solder) went to the tails. Oleksiak et al. (2013) obtained promising results while concentrating precious metals from end-of-life ceramic catalytic convertors by froth flotation in an acid-resistant steel flotation chamber equipped with an engine-propelled rotor with a height control device, air compressor, and mechanical rake. Rotor speed was 500rpm, the gas flow 2dm^3 min^{-1}, and at pH 8. Best results were obtained with corflot (poly(ethylene glycol) butyl ethers) as a frothing agent and sodium amyl xanthogenate as a collector. The final product was concentrated up to 0.38 % of precious-metal platinum which is close to its concentration in anode slime obtained in the process of copper electro-refining.

2.4.11 Enrichment/Concentration by Dissolving the Supported Material

Auto-catalysts consist of three major components: active metals (PMs), cordierite substrate (or support), and wash-coat (γ-alumina, γ-Al_2O_3), containing various additives. PM particles are dispersed in the wash-coat layer, which adheres to the surface of the cordierite substrate. Therefore, the selective separation of the wash-coat layer from the substrate can concentrate the PM particles, paving the way for easier PM extraction by a subsequent pyro- or hydro-metallurgical route. As previously stated, physical beneficiation is incapable of separating PMs from the substrate and efficiently enriching them.

The wash-coat layer dissolution method has been proposed to remove γ-alumina using an acid or alkaline solution, liberating PM particles from the wash-coat layer (Musco, 1985; Mishra, 1987; Hoffmann, 1988; Bolinski, 1993; Mishra, 1993). The acid solution can leach only a certain amount of PMs, which can be recovered through cementation using aluminium, which is a major component of the wash-coat layer. As the auto-catalyst substrate, mostly containing refractory cordierite, is significantly resistant to chemical leaching, it hardly dissolves in an acid and can be separated from fine PM particles by filtration. PM concentrates are collected from the acid dissolution, and the cemented PMs (residue) are combined and dissolved in an HCl solution and chlorine. The PMs can be subsequently separated and refined using a chemical process. Wash-coat layer dissolution does not require a large quantity of reagents to entirely dissolve wash-coat γ-alumina and also concentrates the PMs in the residue. However, it is not easy to separate fine PM particles and the substrate from an aqueous suspension of auto-catalyst slurry in acid solution, resulting in the loss of PM particles.

ACKNOWLEDGEMENTS

This work was supported by the Brain Pool Programme through the National Research Foundation of Korea (NRF) funded by the Ministry of Science and ICT (Grant No. 2019H1D3A2A02101993) and the Basic Science Research Programme through the National Research Foundation of Korea (NRF) funded by the Ministry of Education (Project no. 2020R1I1A1A01074249).

NOTES

1 http://en.jxmingxin.com/circuit-board/33.html
2 https://www.alibaba.com/product-detail/Energy-Saving-PCB-Dismantling-MachineElectronic_60474801054.html
3 http://www.stokkermill.com/en/recycling-plants/shredder-residues-refining-plant
4 http://mtmakina.com/en/shredder/double-storey-shredders.html
5 http://www.jordan-reductionsolutions.com/product-grinder.html
6 http://www.stokkermill.com/en/company

REFERENCES

Ammen, C. W. (1997). *Recovery and refining of precious metals*. New York: Chapman & Hall, pp. 244–247.

Bendimerad, S., Tilmatine, A., Ziane, M. and Dascalescu, L. (2009). Plastic wastes recovery using free-fall triboelectric separator. *International Journal of Environmental Studies*, 66(5): 529–538.

Bentli, İ., Erdoğan, N., Elmas, N., Kaya, M. (2017). Magnesite concentration technology and caustic-calcined product from Turkish magnesite middlings by calcination and magnetic separation. *Separation Science and Technology*, 52(6): 1129–1142.

Bolinski, L. (1993). Platinum and rhodium recovery from scrapped automotive catalyst by oxidative acid chloride leaching. Master dissertation, McGill University, Montreal, Canada.

Brouwers, J. J. H., Van Kemenade, H. P. and Kroes, J. P. (2012). Rotational particle separator: An efficient method to separate micron-sized droplets and particles from fluids. *Filtration*, 1: 49–60.

Chen, M., Wang, J., Chen, H., Ogunseitan, O. A., Zhang, M., Zang, H., Hu, J. (2013). Electronic waste disassembly with industrial waste heat. *Environmental Science & Technology*, 47(21): 12409–12416.

Colli, A. N., Fornés, J. P., Pérez, O. G. and Bisang, J. M. (2019). Evaluation of a modified hydrocyclone as electrochemical reactor for processing of two-phase (gas-liquid) systems. *Electrochimica Acta*, 309: 219–227.

Cui, J., Forssberg, E. (2003). Mechanical recycling of waste electric and electronic equipment: a review. *Journal of hazardous materials*, 99(3): 243–263.

Duan, H., Hou, K., Li, J., Zhu, X. (2011). Examining the technology acceptance for dismantling of waste printed circuit boards in light of recycling and environmental concerns. *Journal of Environmental Management*, 92(3): 392–399.

Dyakowski, T., Nowakowski, A. F., Kraipech, W. and Williams, R. A. (1999). A three dimensional simulation of hydrocyclone behaviour. In *Second international conference on CFD in the minerals and process industries*. CSIRO, Melbourne, Australia, pp. 205–210.

Estrada-Ruiz, R. H., Flores-Campos, R., Gámez-Altamirano, H. A. and Velarde-Sánchez, E. J. (2016). Separation of the metallic and non-metallic fraction from printed circuit boards employing green technology. *Journal of Hazardous Materials*, 311: 91–99.

Fuerstenau, M. C. and Han, K. N. (2003). Principles of mineral processing. Society for Mining, Metallurgy and Exploration, Inc. (SME), p. 573.

Gallegos-Acevedo, P. M., Espinoza-Cuadra, J. and Olivera-Ponce, J. M. (2014). Conventional flotation techniques to separate metallic and nonmetallic fractions from waste printed circuit boards with particles nonconventional size. *Journal of Mining Science*, 50(5): 974–981.

Hadi, P., Xu, M., Lin, C. S., Hui, C. W. and McKay, G. (2015). Waste printed circuit board recycling techniques and product utilization. *Journal of Hazardous Materials*, 283: 234–243.

Haldar, S. K. (2013). *Mineral exploration: Principles and applications*. Elsevier. eBook ISBN: 9780123914668.

Higashiyama, Y., Ujiie, Y. and Asano, K. (1997). Triboelectrification of plastic particles on a vibrating feeder laminated with a plastic film. *Journal of Electrostatics*, 42(1-2): 63–68.

Hoffmann, J. E. (1988). Recovery of platinum-group metals from gabbroic rocks metals from auto catalysts. *JOM*, 40(6): 40–44.

Inculet, I. I., Castle, G. S. P. and Brown, J. D. (1994). Tribo-electrification system for electrostatic separation of plastics. In *Proceedings of 1994 IEEE industry applications society annual meeting*, 2, 1397–1399.

Kaya, M. (2018). Current WEEE recycling solutions. In: Veglio, F., Birloaga, I. (eds) *Waste electrical and electronic equipment recycling, aqueous recovery methods.* pp. 33–93. Woodhead Publishing.

Knoll, F. S., Lawver, J. E. and Taylor, J. B. (1988). Electrostatic separation. In *Ullmann's encyclopedia of industrial chemistry*, VCH. 2, 20–21.

Lu, H., Li, J., Guo, J. and Xu, Z. (2008) Movement behavior in electrostatic separation: Recycling of metal materials from waste printed circuit board. *Journal of Materials Processing Technology*, 197(1-3): 101–108.

Miloudi, M., Medles, K., Tilmatine, A., Brahami, M. and Dascalescu, L. (2011). Modeling and optimization of a propeller-type tribocharger for granular materials. *Journal of Electrostatics*, 69(6): 631–637.

Mishra, R. K. (1987). PGM recoveries by atmospheric and autoclave leaching of alumina bead catalyst. *Precious Metals* 1987, 177–195.

Mishra, R. K. (1993) A Review of Platinum Group Metals Recovery from Automobile Catalytic Converters. *Precious Metals* 1993, 449–474.

Musco, S.P. (1985) PGM recovery from automotive catalyst. In: Zysk, E.D. (eds) *Proceedings of the Platinum Group Metals Seminar*, Washington, DC, USA.

Neesso, T. and Donhauser, F. (2000). Advances in the theory and practice of hydrocyclone technique. *Aufbereitungstechnik*, 41(9): 403–408.

Ogunniyi, I. O., Vermaak, M. K. G. and Groot, D. R. (2009). Chemical composition and liberation characterization of printed circuit board comminution fines for beneficiation investigations. *Waste Management*, 29(7): 2140–2146.

Oleksiak, B., Siwiec, G. and Blacha-Grzechnik, A. (2013). Recovery of precious metals from waste materials by the method of flotation process. *Metalurgija*, 52(1): 107–110.

Riedewald, F., Sousa-Gallagher, M. (2015). Novel waste printed circuit board recycling process with molten salt. *MethodsX*, 2: 100–106.

Sarvar, M., Salarirad, M.M., Shabani, M.A. (2015). Characterization and mechanical separation of metals from computer Printed Circuit Boards (PCBs) based on mineral processing methods. *Waste Management*, 45, 246–257.

Taninouchi, Y. K. and Okabe, T. H. (2018). Recovery of platinum group metals from spent catalysts using iron chloride vapor treatment. *Metallurgical and Materials Transactions B*, 49(4): 1781–1793.

Taninouchi, Y. K., Watanabe, T. and Okabe, T. H. (2017). Recovery of platinum group metals from spent catalysts using electroless nickel plating and magnetic separation. *Materials Transactions*, 58(3): 410–419.

Vidyadhar, A. and Das, A. (2013). Enrichment implication of froth flotation kinetics in the separation and recovery of metal values from printed circuit boards. *Separation and Purification Technology*, 118: 305–312.

Wang, Y. L., Wang, Q. Y., Gao, M., Chen, F. Q., Liu, G. F. (2013). A method for separation of components and solders from waste printed circuit boards. *Chinese patent: 2013101808637.*

Wang, F., Zhao, Y., Zhang, T., Duan, C., Wang, L. (2015). Mineralogical analysis of dust collected from typical recycling line of waste printed circuit boards. *Waste management*, 43, 434–441.

Wills, B. A. and Finch, J. (2015). *Wills' mineral processing technology: An introduction to the practical aspects of ore treatment and mineral recovery.* Butterworth-Heinemann. p. 512.

Zeng, X., Li, J., Xie, H., Liu, L. (2013). A novel dismantling process of waste printed circuit boards using water-soluble ionic liquid. *Chemosphere*, 93(7): 1288–1294.

3 Urban Mining of Precious Metals with Halide as Lixiviant

Sadia Ilyas

Mineral Resources and Energy Engineering, Jeonbuk National University, Jeonju, Jeonbuk 54896, Republic of Korea

Humma Akram Cheema

Mineral and Material Chemistry Lab, Department of Chemistry, University of Agriculture, Faisalabad 38040, Pakistan

Hyunjung Kim

Mineral Resources and Energy Engineering, Jeonbuk National University, Jeonju, Jeonbuk 54896, Republic of Korea

Department of Environment and Energy, Jeonbuk National University, Jeonju, Jeonbuk 54896, Republic of Korea

Rajiv Ranjan Srivastava

Center for Advanced Chemistry, Institute of Research and Development, Duy Tan University, Da Nang 550000, Vietnam

CONTENTS

3.1 URBAN MINING OF PRECIOUS METALS WITH HALIDE AS LIXIVIANT: AN OVERVIEW

Chlorine was firstly applied to the recovery of gold in the 1800s, long before the introduction of cyanidation. In 1846, bromine was introduced as a solvent for gold, as its leaching kinetics are greatly enhanced by the presence of a protonic cation and an oxidizing agent (Filmer et al., 1984; Kalocsai, 1984; von Michaelis, 1987). Although the cyanidation of gold diminished the potential of halogen in general, interest in halide(s) leaching emerged during the 1990s (Pesic et al., 1992; Tran et al., 2001).

The stability of gold-halide complexes is dependent on the Eh-pH of the solution, the composition (with respect to halide concentration), and the nature of the material to be processed (Sergent et al., 1992; Tran et al., 2001). A residual quantity of oxidant must maintain a high solution Eh, avoiding precipitation of metallic gold (Tran et al., 2001).

Gold ions in the +1 and +3 oxidation states are B-type metal ions, therefore their complexation stability decreases as the electronegativity of the donor ligand increases, forming the stability order $I^- > Br^- > Cl^- > F^-$. According to the hard and soft acid-base (HSAB) theory, in the complexation of Au^{3+} with halides, hard donors will be more stable. Complexes of the type AuL_4^{3+} with soft ligands will easily reduce to the +1 state.

All known AuL_4^{3+} complexes have the electronic configuration $4f^{14}5d^8$ and exhibit low-spin diamagnetic properties. Compounds like $AuCl_3$ form dimers to satisfy the coordination number of four required by Au^{3+}. Chlorine is mainly generated in two ways: (i) by reactions of sodium hypochlorite with HCl, and (ii) production of anodic chlorine via electro-dissociation of concentrated HCl at cathodic compartment. The reaction with sodium hypochlorite for chlorine takes place as:

$$NaOCl + NaCl + 2HCl \rightarrow 2NaCl + Cl_{2(g)} + H_2O \tag{3.1}$$

Chlorine generation in an electrolytic cell at anodic compartment can be obtained as the reactions below:

$$\text{At anode: } 2Cl^- \rightarrow Cl_{2(g)} + 2e^- \tag{3.2}$$

$$\text{At cathode: } 2H^+ + 2e^- \rightarrow H_{2(g)} \tag{3.3}$$

Gaseous chlorine has high solubility in acidic water as (Snoeyink and Jenkins, 1979; Lee and Srivastava, 2016):

$$Cl_{2(g)} \rightarrow Cl_{2(aq)} \tag{3.4}$$

At a pH above 2.5, aqueous chlorine predominantly forms HOCl as (Marsden and House, 2006):

$$Cl_{2(aq)} + H_2O \rightarrow HCl + HOCl \tag{3.5}$$

Both acids, HCl and HOCl, completely dissociate in aqueous solutions as:

$$HCl \rightarrow H^+ + Cl^- \tag{3.6}$$

$$HOCl \rightarrow H^+ + OCl^- \tag{3.7}$$

Further, soluble chlorine can react with chloride ions to form trichloride ions under high acidic conditions (< pH 3):

$$Cl_{2(aq)} + Cl^- \rightarrow Cl_3^- \tag{3.8}$$

Pt, Pd and Rh have great capacity to form halo-complexes with high acidity in halide solution. Pt is mainly present in the +2 and +4 oxidation states. In chloride solution, chloro-complexes of Pt are formed with coordination numbers 4 and 6 for +2 and +4 oxidation states, respectively. In the case of Pd, the oxidation states +2 and +4 are taken up in solid compounds. The chloro-complexes of Pd appear with the coordination numbers 4 and 6 for +2 and +4 oxidation states, respectively. The most stable oxidation state of Rh is +3. Rh has a strong tendency to form complex ions with coordination number 6 (Bard 1985). Chemical reactions involving Pt, Pd and Rh in $HCl-H_2O_2$ and $NaClO-HCl$ systems are described below (Harjanto et al., 2006; Bard, 1985; Pourbaix, 1974; Takeno, 2005).

3.2 MECHANISM FOR CHLORIDE LEACHING OF PRECIOUS METALS FROM URBAN MINE SOURCES

With chlorine species in aqueous solution, gold can form soluble chloride complexes as follows (Radulescu et al., 2008):

$$Au + Cl^- + \frac{3}{2}\left(Cl_2\right)_{aq} \rightarrow AuCl_4^- \tag{3.9}$$

$$Au + \frac{3}{2}HOCl + \frac{3}{2}H^+ + \frac{5}{2}Cl^- \rightarrow AuCl_4^- + \frac{3}{2}H_2O \tag{3.10}$$

The formation of soluble species (at < 6 pH) is also in line with the thermodynamic data plotted in Figure 3.1, for the Eh-pH diagram of the $Au-Cl_2-H_2O$ system.

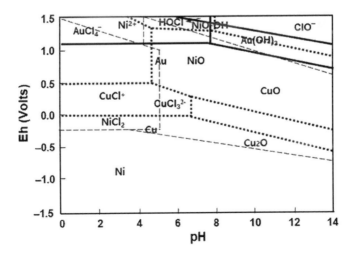

FIGURE 3.1 Eh-pH diagram of $Au-Cu-Ni-Cl-H_2O$ system at 25°C (conditions: 5×10^{-4} MAu; 0.5M Cu^{2+}; 0.35 M Ni^{2+}; 2 M Cl^-).

Interestingly, a direct formation of auric chloride ($AuCl_4^-$) with $Cl_{2(aq)}$ and HOCl differ with the reaction of Cl^- ions due to less oxidative power. In stepwise leaching of gold in the presence of Cl^- ions, an intermediate aurous complex forms on the surface as (Nicol, 1980; Nicol et al., 1987):

$$2Au + 2Cl^- \rightarrow 2AuCl^- \tag{3.11}$$

Again, by the HSAB principle, the high electronegative Cl^- ions (a hard donor atom) tend to form a secondary intermediate compound of high valance in a second step with the following reaction (Finkelstein and Hancock, 1974):

$$2AuCl^- \rightarrow AuCl_2^- + Au \tag{3.12}$$

In a subsequent step, $AuCl_2^-$ either oxidizes to form a stable auric complex (Nicol, 1980; Nicol et al., 1987) or diffuses into solution as in the reaction below, forming the $AuCl_2^-$:

$$AuCl_2^- + 2Cl^- \rightarrow AuCl_4^- \tag{3.13}$$

The copper and nickel often associated with gold sourced from electronic waste can also be leached in a chlorine environment:

$$Cu + Cl_{2(aq)} \rightarrow Cu^{2+} + 2Cl^- \tag{3.14}$$

$$Cu^{2+} + Cu + 2Cl^- \rightarrow 2CuCl \tag{3.15}$$

$$Ni + Cl_{2(aq)} \rightarrow Ni^{2+} + 2Cl^- \tag{3.16}$$

$$Ni^{2+} + Cl^- \rightarrow NiCl^+ \tag{3.17}$$

$$Ni^{2+} + 2Cl^- \rightarrow NiCl_2 \tag{3.18}$$

Based on the above reactions, the plausible electrochemical mechanism for the chloro-leaching of gold (along with Ni and Cu which remain present in MP-PCBs) is presented in Figure 3.2.

The dissolution of large amounts of base metals in chloro-leaching has been found to be problematic. The comparatively lower concentration of gold in the leach liquor can present difficulties for subsequent downstream processing. However, by taking into account the solution chemistry of gold at an ORP value <350mV, the maximum amount of base metals can be leached out in an acidic chloride solution from the electronic wastes (spent printed circuit boards) by leaving gold in the residues. The Eh-pH diagram for an Au-Cu-Ni-Cl-H_2O system (shown in Figure 3.1) also indicates plausible selectivity in leaching, as the copper and nickel form soluble species at lower potential than that required to form the chloro-complexes of gold. Kim et al.

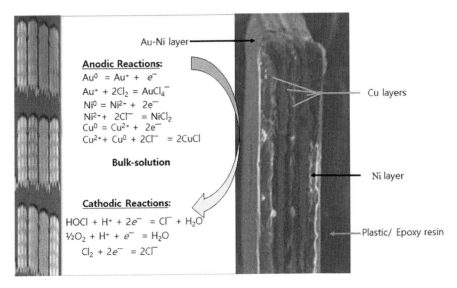

Au-Ni layer

Anodic Reactions:
$$Au^0 = Au^+ + e^-$$
$$Au^+ + 2Cl_2 = AuCl_4^-$$
$$Ni^0 = Ni^{2+} + 2e^-$$
$$Ni^{2+} + 2Cl^- = NiCl_2$$
$$Cu^0 = Cu^{2+} + 2e^-$$
$$Cu^{2+} + Cu^0 + 2Cl^- = 2CuCl$$

Bulk-solution

Cathodic Reactions:
$$HOCl + H^+ + 2e^- = Cl^- + H_2O$$
$$\tfrac{1}{2}O_2 + H^+ + e^- = H_2O$$
$$Cl_2 + 2e^- = 2Cl^-$$

Cu layers

Ni layer

Plastic/ Epoxy resin

FIGURE 3.2 Electrochemical mechanism of gold leaching in chlorine-based lixiviant. *Source*: Modified from Ilyas and Lee (2018).

(2016) investigated selectivity of gold from spent printed circuit boards under a controlled ORP system. In the first stage of leaching at 350mV ORP, the maximum amount of copper leaching (95%) could be obtained along with the minutely extracted gold (0.9 mg/L) in leach liquor. In the second stage of leaching performed at>1100mV ORP, the residues of the first stage of leaching yielded 93% gold with only 0.6 mg/L copper.

Studies conducted by various researchers indicate that palladium and platinum have a great capacity to form chloro-complexes in HCl solution, appearing to have coordination numbers 4 and 6 for +2 and +4 oxidation states, respectively (Bard, 1985). The most stable oxidation state of Rh is +3. Rh has a strong tendency to form complex ions with coordination number 6 (Ilyas et al., 2020: Harjanto et al., 2006).

The formation of metal chloro-complexes is shown in Figures 3.3–3.5. The Eh-pH diagrams for Pt-Cl-H$_2$O (Figure 3.3), Pd-Cl-H$_2$O (Figure 3.4) and Rh-Cl-H$_2$O (Figure 3.5) systems clearly illustrate the occurrence of metal species in two different oxidation states in the case of platinum and palladium and of one most stable oxidation state in the case of rhodium.

As these are noble metals, they are difficult to leach and their dissolution mainly depends upon lowering the redox potential in the presence of Cl$^-$ ions to form stable aqua chloro-complexes, which comes through HCl dissociation as:

$$HCl \leftrightarrow H^+ + Cl^- \qquad\qquad \Delta G_{298}^o = -29.6kcal\,/\,mol$$

Reactions forming the chloro-complexes of an anodic nature take place as below:

$$Pd + 4Cl^- \leftrightarrow PdCl_4^{2-} + 2e^- \qquad\qquad E^o = -0.59\ V \qquad (3.19)$$

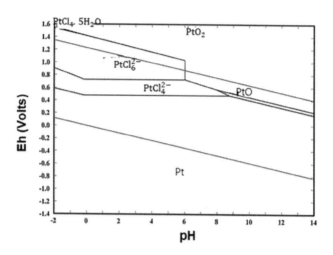

FIGURE 3.3 Eh-pH diagram of Pt-Cl-H$_2$O system at 25°C (0.01 mole/L metal concentration, 6 mole/L Cl⁻).

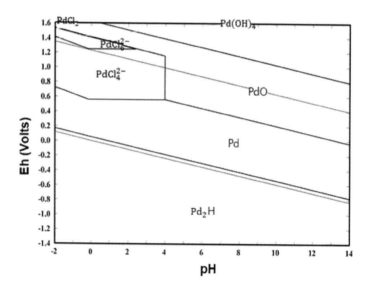

FIGURE 3.4 Eh-pH diagram of Pd-Cl-H$_2$O system at 25°C (0.01 mole/L metal concentration, 6 mole/L Cl⁻).

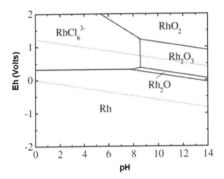

FIGURE 3.5 Eh-pH diagram of Rh-Cl-H$_2$O system at 25°C (0.02 mole/L metal concentration, 5 mole/L Cl$^-$).

$$PdCl_4^{2-} + 2Cl^- \leftrightarrow PdCl_6^{2-} + 2e^- \qquad E° = -1.26 \text{ V} \qquad (3.20)$$

$$Pt + 4Cl^- \leftrightarrow PtCl_4^{2-} + 2e^- \qquad E° = -0.75 \text{ V} \qquad (3.21)$$

$$PtCl_4^{2-} + 2Cl^- \leftrightarrow PdCl_6^{2-} + 2e^- \qquad E° = -0.77 \text{ V} \qquad (3.22)$$

$$Rh + 6Cl^- \leftrightarrow RhCl_6^{3-} + 3e^- \qquad E° = -0.45\text{V} \qquad (3.23)$$

The influence of Cl$^-$ ions on aqua chloro-complexation can be understood by comparing the above-mentioned oxidation potential (E^0) values with those in the absence of chloride ions (−0.98 V for Pd and −1.18 V for Pt) (Pourbaix, 1974). Thus, leaching can be promoted by decreasing the equilibrium potential and increasing the chloride concentration. On the other hand, in the presence of H$_2$O$_2$, the cathodic reaction can be more progressively driven due to a higher redox potential by following the equations below:

$$H_2O_2 + 2H^+ + 2e^- \leftrightarrow 2H_2O \qquad \Delta E = +1.76\text{V} \qquad (3.24)$$

$$H_2O_2 + 2HCl \leftrightarrow Cl_2 + 2H_2O \qquad \Delta E = +0.51\text{V} \qquad (3.25)$$

Then, the reactions in the presence of Cl$_2$ with an enhanced mass transfer reaction can be written as:

$$Pd + 2HCl + Cl_2 \leftrightarrow H_2PdCl_4 \qquad \Delta G_{298}^o = -40.1\text{kcal / mol} \qquad (3.26)$$

$$Pd + 2HCl + 2Cl_2 \leftrightarrow H_2PdCl_6 \qquad \Delta G_{298}^o = -45.8\text{kcal / mol} \qquad (3.27)$$

$$Pt + 2HCl + Cl_2 \leftrightarrow H_2PtCl_4 \qquad \Delta G_{298}^o = -27.2\text{kcal / mol} \qquad (3.28)$$

$$Pt + 2HCl + 2Cl_2 \leftrightarrow H_2PtCl_6 \qquad \Delta G_{298}^o = -57.9\text{kcal / mol} \qquad (3.29)$$

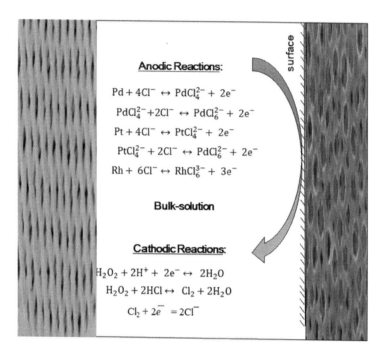

Anodic Reactions:

$$Pd + 4Cl^- \leftrightarrow PdCl_4^{2-} + 2e^-$$

$$PdCl_4^{2-} + 2Cl^- \leftrightarrow PdCl_6^{2-} + 2e^-$$

$$Pt + 4Cl^- \leftrightarrow PtCl_4^{2-} + 2e^-$$

$$PtCl_4^{2-} + 2Cl^- \leftrightarrow PdCl_6^{2-} + 2e^-$$

$$Rh + 6Cl^- \leftrightarrow RhCl_6^{3-} + 3e^-$$

Bulk-solution

Cathodic Reactions:

$$H_2O_2 + 2H^+ + 2e^- \leftrightarrow 2H_2O$$

$$H_2O_2 + 2HCl \leftrightarrow Cl_2 + 2H_2O$$

$$Cl_2 + 2\overline{e} = 2Cl^-$$

FIGURE 3.6   Electrochemical mechanism of Pt, Pd and Rh leaching in chlorine-based lixiviant.

The electrochemical mechanism of Pt, Pd and Rh leaching in chlorine-based lixiviant is depicted in Figure 3.6.

3.3 INFLUENCE OF VARIOUS PROCESS PARAMETERS

Various process parameters such as lixiviant concentration, oxidant ratio, temperature, contact time and pulp density affect the halide leaching of precious metals from urban mine sources.

3.3.1 EFFECT OF ACID CONCENTRATION

The basis of electrochemical kinetics for leaching gold in a chloride solution using dissolution chemistry have already been described (Finkelstein, 1972; Nicol, 1976; Avraamides 1982; Yen et al., 1990; Tran et al., 1992a ,b; Lee and Srivastava, 2016). More rapid weight loss of gold in various solutions of chloride-hypochlorite has been achieved than with the cyanidation process under similar parametric conditions (Tran et al., 2001). The formation of a stable species $AuCl_4^-$ strongly depends on the pH of the solution (< 3.0; as evident from the Eh-pH diagram in Figure 3.1) with high chloride/chlorine levels (> 100 g/L Cl^-), elevated temperature and various particle sizes. The dissolved gold complex can re-precipitate by contact with a reductant such as sulphidic material, therefore the application of the chloride–chlorine systems is limited. Notably, the solubility of chlorine increases with respect to increasing acid concentration and forming various soluble species, such as aqueous Cl_2 and Cl_3^- (Lee and Srivastava, 2016), creating a highly oxidative environment which can be helpful for processing material other than oxidized bodies. Additionally, the redox potential of the leaching system also needs to be maintained above 400 mV for faster kinetics and higher leaching yield of gold.

The leaching kinetics of gold in a chloride medium are proportional to the chlorine–chloride concentrations (Nicol, 1980). Leaching efficiency therefore increases with increased initial concentration of chloride and soluble chlorine in lixiviant solution with an enhanced temperature (preferably < 60°C). Gold leaching in chloride solution is much faster than the yield obtained in an alkaline cyanide solution. A rate of 0.008 $g/m^2/s$ gold leaching in cyanide solution was found to be much lower than the leaching rate of 0.3 $g/m^2/s$ obtained in chloride solution by Putnam (1944). The high solubility of chlorine in water compared with oxygen (used in cyanidation) is a plausible reason for this. The presence of 3% NaCl in a chlorine solution has shown a significant effect on gold leaching, which may be due to the retarding effect of Cl^- ions on chlorine dissolution (Chao, 1968). Additionally, the amount of initial chlorine in solution increases the kinetics of gold leaching by shifting the reaction mechanism from diffusion control to a chemically controlled reaction (Lee and Srivastava, 2016).

As well as the above parametric effects, the effect of roasting on chlorine leaching of a gold-bearing refractory concentrate has been studied (Birloaga et al., 2013). An increase in roasting temperature has been found advantageous in improving the removal efficiency of Hg (~94%). Sulphur removal by roasting could significantly reduce chlorine consumption and yielded a far better leaching of gold (~93%) than when using only cyanidation (27%).

Ilyas et al. (2020) studied the effect of acid concentration (from 2.0 mol/L to 10.0 mol/L) on precious metal leaching from spent catalysts. The other parameters, such as pulp density (5%, wt./vol.), temperature (55 ± 2°C), time (2 h), and agitation speed (400 rpm), were maintained at constant. The results (shown in Figure 3.7) showed that the leaching of palladium and platinum increased with increasing concentrations of HCl. This is explained by thermodynamic considerations, due to a higher dissociation of Cl^- ions at a higher acid concentration, which further allows a favourable dissolution of metals into HCl solution. Leaching of palladium and platinum was found to increase from 8.6% to 61.3% and 6.9% to 34.8%, respectively within the studied range of acid variation (2.0–10.0 mol/L). The higher leaching of palladium than platinum can be ascribed to the differences in redox potentials between the above equations. 8.0 mol/L HCl was found by these researchers to extract more than 50% of the palladium.

A similar study conducted by Harjanto et al. (2006) with 1% H_2O_2 and varied concentrations of HCl (1 mol/L up to 10 mol/L) indicated that Pt, Pd, and Rh leaching increases with an increase in the HCl concentration in the leaching solution with 1% H_2O_2. At any HCl concentration, the order of PM leaching, from the highest, is Pd, Pt, and Rh. The leaching of Pt, Pd, and Rh at 11.6 mol/L HCl was 95.5, 100, and 85.6%, respectively.

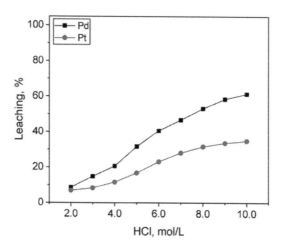

FIGURE 3.7 Leaching behavior of precious metals from exhausted DOC as a function of acid concentration (condition: pulp density, 5%; temperature, 55°C; time, 2 h; and agitation speed, 400 rpm).

Source: Adopted with permission from Ilyas et al. (2020).

3.3.2 Effect of H$_2$O$_2$ and NaClO Concentration

The formation of the more stable chloro-complexes PtCl$_6^{2-}$ and PdCl$_4^{2-}$ requires a higher redox potential, instead of the noted value of 368 mV with 8.0 mol/L HCl. Hence, H$_2$O$_2$ was added to the lixiviant solution to improve the conditions for metal complexation. The effect of H$_2$O$_2$ addition in terms of volume proportionate to 8.0 mol/L HCl solution ranging from 0.5 vol% to 5.0 vol% was investigated by Ilyas et al. (2020). The addition of H$_2$O$_2$ creates a vigorous reaction and a favourable oxidative environment (as per a high redox potential) to form the chloro-complexes of palladium, platinum and rhodium (Bard, 1985). Consequently, the effect of the change in redox potential was reflected in the leaching behavior of precious metals. The results showed (Figure 3.8) that the leaching of palladium and platinum was increased by the addition of H$_2$O$_2$ and further improved when the dosage was increased from 0.5 vol% to 5.0 vol%. Leaching of palladium increased from 60% (with 0.5 vol% H$_2$O$_2$) to reach 90% (with 3.0 vol% H$_2$O$_2$), while platinum leaching improved from 38% to ~ 81% with the same proportion of H$_2$O$_2$ addition. A further increase in H$_2$O$_2$ dosage (above 3.0 vol%) did not much improve leaching of the precious metals, which accorded with the recorded Eh values of the system.

The effect of NaClO addition was also examined for the NaClO-HCl-H$_2$O$_2$ system by Harjanto et al. (2006). Here NaClO was selected as a promoter in a 5mol/L HCl-containing leaching system together with H$_2$O$_2$ (1%). As shown in Table 3.1, the addition of NaClO (0–5 %), along with H$_2$O$_2$, to the leaching solution gives a Pt, Pd, and Rh dissolution in the range of 86.1–88.8%, 95.8–98.7% and 72.0–76.9%, respectively. The addition of 3% NaClO yields a Pt, Pd and Rh dissolution of 87.7%, 98.7 and 76.9% respectively, which was higher than the HCl–H$_2$O$_2$ system (5 mol/L HCl, 1% H$_2$O$_2$) but lower than the 7 mol/L HCl and 1% H$_2$O$_2$-containing system. The

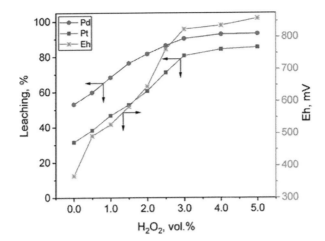

FIGURE 3.8 Leaching behavior of precious metals from exhausted DOC and changes in redox potential of the system as a function of H_2O_2 addition (condition: pulp density, 5%; acid concentration, 8.0 mol/L HCl; temperature, 55°C; time, 2 h; and agitation speed, 400 rpm).

Source: Adopted with permission from Ilyas et al. (2020).

TABLE 3.1
Consumption and products of leaching in the various chloride based leaching solutions

Conditions		Leaching solution		
		NaClO + HCl + H_2O_2	HCl + H_2O_2	NaClO + HCl
Pulp density	(g/L)	500	500	500
Pretreated mass	(g)	1000	1000	1000
Solution volume	(L)	2	2	2
Reagents		**Consumption/kg**	**Consumption/kg**	**Consumption/kg**
NaClO	(mL)	60	-	60
Water	(mL)	1040	-	1107
HCl (12 kmolm⁻³)	(mL)	833	1933	833
H_2O_2 (30%)	(mL)	66.7	66.7	-
PGM products		**Production g/kg**	**Production g/kg**	**Production g/kg**
Pt	(g)	3.32	3.62	3.30
Pd	(g)	5.74	5.82	5.62
Rh	(g)	1.84	2.05	1.62
PGM extraction		**Production (%)**	**Production (%)**	**Production (%)**
Pt	(%)	87.7	95.5	87.1
Pd	(%)	98.7	100	96.6
Rh	(%)	76.9	85.6	67.9
Average of PGM dissolution	(%)	87.8	93.7	83.9

Source: Modified from Harjanto et al. (2006).

Detailed composition of the leaching solutions is as follows: (pretreated mass by hydrogen reduction was used throughout; NaClO-HCl-H_2O_2 = 3 vol% NaClO-5 kmolm⁻³ HCl-1 vol% H_2O_2; HCl-H_2O_2 = 11.6 kmolm⁻³ HCl–1 vol% H_2O_2; NaClO-HCl = 3 vol% NaClO-5 kmolm⁻³ HCl).

results from leaching by the NaClO-HCl-H₂O₂ system also suggest that the presence of NaClO (up to 3%) is effective in increasing the dissolution of Pt, Pd and Rh by about 3–5%.

3.3.3 Effect of Temperature and Contact Time

In general, an increase in chlorine mass transfer rate by elevation of the temperature should increase gold-leaching efficiency (Nicol, 1980; Viñals et al., 1995). But in contrast, the solubility of chlorine (as $Cl_2(aq)$) decreases with an increase in the temperature (from 7×10^{-3} M Cl_2 to 2.5×10^{-3} M Cl_2 at 20–60°C temperatures, respectively) due to the lower absorbability of gases at higher temperatures. In chlorine leaching of spent printed circuit boards, therefore, copper extraction is found to decrease with an increase in temperature. At the initial stage of gold leaching, the lowest concentration of residual chlorine was mainly responsible for slower kinetics for the reactions which accelerated after 40 min and after a 2 h prolonged leaching the gold extraction was found to be independent of the effect of temperature (Figure 3.9). Such behavior is accounted for by the favourable diffusion rate of hypochlorous species at higher temperatures. The diffusion coefficients of $Cl_2(aq)$, HOCl and OCl– also confirm the suitability of temperature at 50°C (Kim et al., 2016; Lee and Srivastava, 2016).

While considering HCl as leaching medium, the effect of leaching temperature and time was investigated by Harjanto et al. (2006), who concluded that an

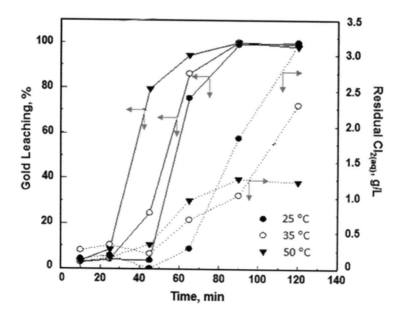

FIGURE 3.9 Gold leaching rate at different temperatures and corresponding residual chlorine in HCl-leached solution (experimental conditions: 2.0 M HCl solution; electro-generation rate of Cl_2 at 714 A/m² current density; pulp density 17 g/L; temperature 25°C; particle size −3/+2 mm).

insignificant effect on leaching of precious metals was observed over 65°C and above 1h of leaching time.

A detailed study by Ilyas et al. (2020) indicated that temperature (25–70°C, using 8.0 mol/L HCl with 3.0 vol% H_2O_2 for 2 h duration) can significantly promote the solid–liquid mass transfer; however, a higher temperature may cause faster degradation of H_2O_2. Experimental results indicated a significant effect on leaching while temperature increased from 25°C to 55°C; thereafter, no remarkable change was observed. This commonly reveals the exothermic nature of the leaching process that might proceed through the change in reaction rate.

In order to establish dissolution kinetics and mechanism, leaching studies were carried out by the same group of researchers at different temperatures (25–70°C), with time variation from 10 min to 180 min. Results (Figure 3.10 a and b) show the progress of leaching with respect to elapsed time, which could indicate that dissolution of precious metals significantly increased with time and temperatures. Palladium efficacy of maximum 96% was obtained for 180 min of leaching at 70°C (Figure 3.10 a), whereas up to 90% was obtained for platinum in similar conditions (Figure 3.10 b). Interestingly, the leaching data at 55°C and 70°C were observed to be almost the same, decomposition of H_2O_2 at a higher temperature (>55°C) is known to be fast. This phenomenon can be ascribed to the shifting of leach kinetics from diffusion control at low temperatures to chemical control at higher temperatures.

3.3.4 Effect of Pulp Density

The possibilities for maximum mass transfer into bulk solution from an exhausted diesel oxidative catalyst was investigated by Ilyas et al. (2020), who carried out leaching experiments at different pulp densities (from 5 to 20 wt./vol.%) at optimum conditions of: HCl concentration, 8.0 M; H_2O_2 addition, 3 vol%; temperature, 55°C; time, 3 h; and agitation speed, 400 rpm. The results revealed that that the leaching

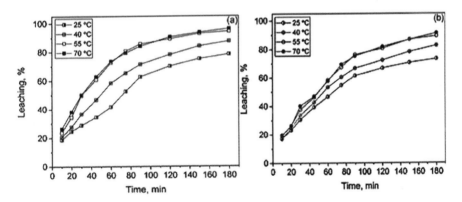

FIGURE 3.10 Leaching behavior of palladium (a) and platinum (b) from spent catalyst at different temperatures as a function of time (condition: pulp density, 5%; acid concentration, 8.0 mol/L HCl; H_2O_2 addition dosage, 3%; and agitation speed, 400 rpm).

Source: Modified from Ilyas et al. (2020).

efficiency of precious metals was the same with 5% and 8% pulp density (>94% palladium and ~90% platinum). Thereafter, increasing pulp density to 12% and above could result in decreased efficiency of precious metals in HCl solution. Leaching was found to decline to 91.5% palladium and ~86% platinum with a pulp density of 12%, with a much greater decline to 68.7% palladium and 60.4% platinum when the pulp density was increased up to 20%. This phenomenon of decreased leaching efficiency at higher pulp density can be ascribed to the lower availability of surface area per unit volume to the solution (Habashi, 1969).

Similar phenomena were observed by other researchers while performing experiments with spent catalytic converters at varied pulp densities (100 to 700 g/L), as in Table 3.1. It was observed that the dissolution of Pt and Rh decreases at higher pulp density. Only a slight decrease of Pd dissolution was observed during the leaching with pulp density higher than 100 g/L. The decrease of Rh dissolution is higher than that of Pt or Pd at pulp density higher than 100 g/L. This is understandable, since the amount of powder became excessive at high pulp density. One can assume that to some extent higher pulp density would reduce the agitation efficiency. In addition, leach lixiviant may not reach some PM particles at higher pulp densities, as these are shielded by the support materials (Graham et al., 2003; Harjanto et al., 2006).

3.4 BROMIDE, IODIDE AND AQUA REGIA LEACHING OF PRECIOUS METALS FROM URBAN MINE SOURCES

Bromide, iodide and aqua regia leaching of precious metals from spent printed circuit boards and catalytic converters has been studied by various researchers and found to have both advantages and processing problems (von Michaelis, 1987; Kalocsai, 1984; Baghalha, 2012; Brent and Atluri, 1998; Syed, 2012 ; Yannopoulos, 1991).

3.4.1 BROMIDE LEACHING OF PRECIOUS METALS

Bromine as a lixiviant for gold was firstly described in 1846 (von Michaelis, 1987). Liquid bromine exothermally reacts with gold to form Au_2Br_6 of dimeric structure, as with Au_2Cl_6. It forms $[LAuBr_3]^-$ type complexes with nitrogen-donor ligands. The monobromide of gold, like its corresponding monochloride, is sensitive to moisture, decomposing to auri- and auro-bromide complexes, such as $[LAuBr]^-$ and $[AuBr_2]^-$.

The leaching kinetics of gold with bromine is greatly accelerated in the presence of a protonic cation (e.g., NH_4^+) and an oxidizing reagent (Kalocsai, 1984). Rapid leaching of gold is possible at nearly neutral pH conditions, whereas the high redox potential requirement ($E^0 = 0.97V$ vs. SHE), compared with gold cyanidation (-0.57V vs. SHE), for stabilization of gold bromide complex can be achieved by the addition of a strong oxidant like bromine. Bromine can be introduced to the slurry (as bromide) with hypochlorite, or chlorine used as oxidants to convert the bromide to bromine as follows:

$$2Br^- + Cl_2 \rightarrow 2Cl^- + Br_2 \tag{3.30}$$

$$2Br^- + ClO^- + 2H^+ \rightarrow Br_2 + Cl^- + H_2O \tag{3.31}$$

After completion of the leaching reaction, the unconsumed bromine gets converted to bromide ions. The dissolution of gold was shown to depend on the bromine/bromide ratio and the associated minerals in the ore (Pesic and Sergent, 1992; van Meersbergen et al., 1993). The presence of base metals (like Cu, Zn, Al as their sulphates) has no effect on leaching, but Fe^{2+} and Mn^{2+} undergo oxidization, increasing the bromine consumption. Hence, investigations have sought alternative oxidants (like Fe^{3+}, H_2O_2 and NaOCl) to eliminate the associated problems, including corrosive reactions and high-vapour pressure, but with limited success (Trindade et al., 1994; Sparrow and Woodcock, 1995). Organic bromides (N-halo hydantoins such as Geobrom 3400) can be used to reduce the problems of vapour loss.

3.4.2 IODIDE LEACHING OF PRECIOUS METALS

Gold–iodide complexes are the most stable halide complexes in aqueous solutions following the order: $I^- > Br^- > Cl^-$ (Nicol et al., 1987). As can be seen from the Eh-pH diagram of Au-I_2-H_2O system shown in Figure 3.11, the stability region of AuI_2^- complex occupies a wider pH range (up to 13) than other halides (Hiskey and Atluri, 1988; Baghalha, 2012).

In the presence of iodide gold oxidizes to form AuI_2^- at redox potential 0.51 V; above 0.69 V the AuI_4^- complex is formed, whose stability region is greater than the $AuCl_4^-$ and $AuBr_4^-$. Iodine solubilizes in pure water as (Marken, 2006):

$$I_{2(s)} \rightarrow I_{2(aq)} \tag{3.32}$$

An increase in I^- concentration increases the overall solubility of iodine, forming the tri-iodide at a pH below 9 (Davis et al., 1993):

$$I_{2(aq)} + I^- \rightarrow I_3^- \tag{3.33}$$

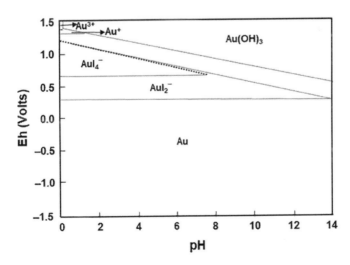

FIGURE 3.11 Eh-pH diagram of gold complexes in iodide media at 25°C (5×10^{-4} M Au; 0.1 M iodine).

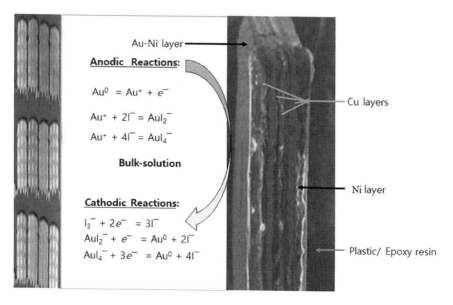

FIGURE 3.12   Electrochemical mechanism of iodide leaching of gold.
Source: Modified from Ilyas et al (2020).

Going above pH 9, the reactions for the formation of hypoiodite and iodite ion can be written as (Davis et al., 1993):

$$I_3^- + H_2O \rightarrow IO^- + 2I^- + 2H^+ \tag{3.34}$$

$$3I_3^- + 3H_2O \rightarrow IO_3^- + 8I^- + 6H^+ \tag{3.35}$$

The presence of tri-iodide ions in an iodide solution above 1.0×10^{-3} M (Marken, 2006) acts as oxidant for the electrochemical (mechanism shown in Figure 3.12) leaching of gold as follows (Baghalha, 2012):

$$2Au + I_3^- + I^- \rightarrow 2AuI_2^- \tag{3.36}$$

$$2Au + 3I_3^- \rightarrow 2AuI_4^- + I^- \tag{3.37}$$

As per the wide range of pH for soluble species of gold in iodine solution (Figure 3.12), the leaching of gold has been investigated under a wider pH range than other halides. Gold extraction increases as pH increases up to pH 9.0, decreasing rapidly thereafter.

The predominant formation of oxidized species of iodine IO_3^- instead of I_3^- is mainly responsible for this (Davis et al., 1993). Hence, the leaching rate of gold depends on the iodine and iodide concentrations in the solution, which are not greatly affected by changes in pH up to 9.0.

The species AuI_4^- is meta-stable as the iodide ion converted to iodine (Sparrow and Woodcock, 1995) gets reduced as AuI_2^-. The $[I_3^-]/[I^-]$ couple present in solution can be determined by the Nernst equation, as follows (Hiskey and Atluri, 1988):

$$E = 0.54 - 0.03 \log \frac{\left[I^-\right]^3}{\left[I_3^-\right]} \qquad (3.38)$$

In a decreased concentration of iodine, the AuI_2^- and AgI_2^- complexes become unstable, leading to a decline in the leaching efficiency of gold. Additionally, the hydroxide precipitation of base metals on gold surfaces hinders the leaching process. The maximum gold leaching was obtained with an iodine/iodide mole ratio of 1:5. The excessive I^- under acidic environment can precipitate gold as AuI; precipitating the residual base metal (Pb_2O as PbI_2 and CuO as CuI) passivates on the surface of gold hinders the formation of AuI_2^-.

In the presence of oxidant, iodide leaching of gold is advantageous in two ways:

(i) increased recovery of gold, and

(ii) reduced consumption of iodine.

An addition of 1% H_2O_2 causes gold leaching to increase up to 95%; however, a further addition of H_2O_2 may precipitate iodine, reducing the leaching yield. Hence, leaching conditions of the oxidant/iodide molar ratio, concentration and pH need to be optimized to avoid surface passivation by AuI and to maximize the leaching rate. The leaching reaction of gold in iodide solution in the presence of H_2O_2 can be written as:

$$2Au + 4I^- + H_2O_2 \rightarrow 2AuI_2^- + 2OH^- \qquad (3.39)$$

Alternatively, hypochlorite has been used, achieving maximum leaching at a $[OCl^-]/[I^-]$ molar ratio of 0.25 (Davis and Tran, 1991). I_3^- formed by reacting hypochlorite with iodide actively complexes the gold, giving higher efficiency of gold extraction.

3.4.3 AQUA REGIA LEACHING OF PRECIOUS METALS

In the case of metal dissolution with aqua regia, the nascent chlorine (Cl_2) and nitrosyl chloride (NOCl) formed provide a high oxidation potential, and the high chloride-ion concentration acts as the complexing agent (Burkin, 2001). HNO_3 and HCl generate these species through the following reactions (Massucci et al., 1999):

$$NO_3^- + 4H^+ + 3e^- \leftrightarrow NO + 2H_2O \qquad (3.40)$$

$$HNO_3 + 3HCl \leftrightarrow NOCl + Cl_2 + 2H_2O \qquad (3.41)$$

$$2NOCl_{(gas)} \rightarrow 2NO_{(gas)} + Cl_{2(gas)} \qquad (3.42)$$

$$NOCl + H_2O \leftrightarrow HNO_2 + HCl \qquad (3.43)$$

Srivastava and Lee found gold (Au^{3+})-soluble species formed according to the mechanism given below.

$$Au + NO_3^- + 4H^+ \rightarrow Au^{3+} + 2H_2O + NO \tag{3.44}$$

$$Au^{3+} + 4Cl^- \rightarrow AuCl_4^- \tag{3.45}$$

$$Au + HNO_3 + 4HCl \rightarrow HAuCl_4 + 2H_2O + NO \tag{3.46}$$

Park and Fray (2009) proposed a process of recycling high-purity PMs (Au, Ag, and Pd) from WPCBs using aqua regia. Optimum S/L ratio was 1/20 g/mL and leach time 3 h. Au, Ag, and Pd recoveries were 97%, 98%, and 93%, respectively.

In this study Au was recovered as nanoparticles to improve the value. Ag is relatively stable in aqua regia, so it remained unreacted due to the formation of an AgCl black surface which prevents Ag dissolution in aqua regia. Pd forms a red cubic structural precipitate ($Pd(NH_4)_2Cl_6$) with aqua regia. Zn dissolved in aqua regia helped Pd precipitation. A solvent extraction using toluene, dodecane thiol, and sodium borohydride was employed to selectively recover Au. Extracted Au was converted to nanoparticles (round-shaped: 20 nm). However, the application of aqua regia in extraction of PMs is limited in a lab scale because aqua regia is strongly oxidative and corrosive, and the waste water from leaching is too acidic to be dealt with.

Further leaching studies of Pt, Pd, and Rh from spent catalysts indicated that platinum is usually soluble in aqua regia. The spent catalytic sample combines the oxidizing action of HNO_3 with the complexing ability of HCl to form platinum hexachloride salt (Eq. (3.47).

$$3Pt + 18HCl + 4HNO_3 \leftrightarrow 3H_2PtCl_6 + 4NO + 8H_2O \tag{3.47}$$

Palladium is readily soluble in aqua regia and partially soluble in hydrochloric acid containing no oxidizing agents. It is soluble in chlorine and is also the only PM that is readily soluble in nitric acid. The reactions are:

$$Pd + 2HCl + Cl_2 \leftrightarrow H_2PdCl_6 \tag{3.48}$$

$$3Pd + 18HCl + 4HNO_3 \leftrightarrow 3H_2PdCl_6 + 4NO + 8H_2O \tag{3.49}$$

$$Pd + Cl_2 \leftrightarrow PdCl_2 \tag{3.50}$$

It is apparent from the above reactions that the stable state for platinum is tetravalent while that of palladium is divalent. Palladium metal is slightly attacked in HCl solution in the presence of oxygen, and the attack is enhanced by increasing the hydrochloric acid concentration and temperature. In contrast, palladium is not acted upon by alkaline solutions, even in the presence of an oxidizing agent.

The dissolution of rhodium is extremely difficult since it is a very noble metal. Generally, rhodium is first fused with potassium bisulphate to produce water-soluble rhodium sulphate. After alloying sulphate salt with a ten-fold excess of zinc or lead, this alloy is treated with hydrochloric or nitric acid. After removing the solution, the residue is dissolved easily in aqua regia to yield rhodium chloride (Eq. (3.51).

$$Rh + 6HCl + HNO_3 \leftrightarrow H_3RhCl_6 + NO + 2H_2O \qquad (3.51)$$

Rhodium is insoluble in nitric acid but when alloyed with zinc dissolves in a mixture of boiling hydrochloric and nitric acids. Rhodium partially dissolves in HCl solution bubbled with air at high pressure at ambient temperature. It also dissolves in HCl with H_2O_2 present as oxidant. The presence of dissolved palladium in HCl solution under strongly oxidizing conditions has been shown to enhance rhodium dissolution at temperatures around 60°C (Ginzburg et al., 1990).

Tanaka Noble Metal Ind. (Tadashi, 1982) has taken out a patent for the recovery of metals from spent catalysts containing 1000 ppm Pt, 200 ppm Pd, and 300 ppm Rh in aqua regia. The recoveries of Pt, Pd, and Rh were 99.0, 100, and 86.7%, respectively. Bonucci and Parker (1984) dissolved Pt along with Pd from a crushed spent automotive catalyst in an agitated reactor in HCl solution using nitric acid as oxidant at 95°C. The alumina co-dissolution was reduced by thermal pre-treatment of the catalyst without affecting Pt solubility. The rhodium present in the catalyst could be selectively dissolved with sulphuric acid, leaving Pt and Pd in the residue. Muraki and Mitsui (1986) patented a process for recovering Pt and Pd loaded on granular or honeycomb Al_2O_3, SiO_2 or carbon support by leaching with aqua regia. Perte et al. (1988) patented a process for the recovery of Pt along with Rh from a spent catalyst using aqua regia leaching. The solution is purified by ion exchange to obtain a pure solution, which is then treated with ammonium hydroxide to obtain salts of hexa-chlorocomplexes. The salts are then reduced with hydrazine hydrate to produce Pt–Rh powder, which is washed to produce high-purity product (98%). Tyson and Bautista (1987) leached Pt and Pd of spent catalysts within a given particle range (−60+70 mesh to −120+140 mesh) with 3791 ppm Pt and 1306 ppm Pd in a packed bed reactor using different HCl: HNO_3 concentration ratios. Based on these studies, a kinetic expression was determined empirically for the experimental data. The reaction rate was initially high but dropped quickly with time for both metals. The leaching extent was 90% and 70% for Pt and Pd, respectively, in 5 h. Jafarifar et al. (2005) investigated two alternative methods for leaching the Pt/Rh bimetallic catalyst, widely used in the reforming process for the production of high-octane fuels containing 0.2% Pt, 0.43% Re, and other impurities. In the first method, the sample was refluxed with aqua regia at a liquid/solid ratio of 5 for 2.5 h. In the second case, 150 W microwave radiation was used with aqua regia at a liquid/solid ratio of 2 for 5 min. After leaching, Pt was recovered as diammonium hexachloroplatinate after separating Rh. The recoveries of Pt were 96.5% and 98.3% using the first and second method, respectively.

Rh was recovered as potassium perrhenate with 94.2% and 98.9% recovery using the first and second methods, respectively. Commercial spent reforming catalysts were studied in aqua regia solution under atmospheric pressure at 100°C for the dissolution of Pt by Baghalha et al. (2009), who showed that particle sizes b100 μm and agitation speeds >700 rpm eliminated the internal and external mass transfer resistances, respectively. The Pt extraction rate was increased significantly by increasing the L/S mass ratio and the reaction temperature. The activation energy for the platinum surface dissolution reaction of 72.1 kJ/mol indicates that Pt extraction in aqua regia solution is controlled by surface chemical reactions. The reaction order was 1.5 for Pt concentration in solid and 1.3 for the hydrogen ion molarity in solution.

3.5 LIMITATIONS, CHALLENGES AND ENVIRONMENTAL IMPACT OF HALIDE LEACHING

Though the highly corrosive acidic environment can be tackled by special stainless steel and rubber-lined equipment and difficulties in transportation can be handled by in-situ chlorine generation, the poisonous nature of chlorine is still a problem to be controlled to avoid any health risk. The use of chlorine for commercial operations has been successfully established in Nevada, with safety measures, since 1971 (Marsden and House, 2006), and was recently employed by Sumitomo Metal Mining Co. in the leaching of precious metals (Brent and Atluri, 1998). But obtaining selectivity other than controlled ORP leaching seems to be difficult, and without it, in the highly oxidizing environment of acidic media, the maximum of base dissolved in leach liquor can present big challenges during downstream processing. Moreover, control of ORP at production level would be challenging, as Cu^{2+} itself provides a favourable oxidizing environment for gold leaching. Temperature plays an important role in chlorine adsorption in HCl solution, hence controlled temperature reactions are required to lower operational costs. Adsorptive dissolution of chlorine has already been identified as playing a major role in chlorine leaching; therefore, it would be interesting to look at replacing HCl with other cheap and comparatively less corrosive reagents like NaCl.

Iodine has been identified as a good oxidant (<11 pH) and better than HOCl with higher leaching kinetics of gold (Davis and Tran, 1991). Nevertheless, iodine continues to be underemployed as a lixiviant for gold leaching, maybe largely because of cost (Syed, 2012 ; Yannopoulos, 1991). Besides this, the non-toxic and non-corrosive nature of iodine and the stability of gold–iodide complex at a wide range of pH can be advantageous if the research community regards it as a 'green' alternative to the highly toxic cyanidation process. This possibility may be similar to the one presented by Kim et al. (2016) for the selective chlorine leaching of gold in two stages (by controlling the potential). Controlled chlorine leaching at the front followed by iodide leaching at the back end may be an alternative, subject to process costs and compatibility of the two media at the two different stages.

ACKNOWLEDGEMENTS

This work was supported by the Brain Pool Programme through the National Research Foundation of Korea (NRF) funded by the Ministry of Science and ICT (Grant No. 2019H1D3A2A02101993) and the Basic Science Research Programme through the National Research Foundation of Korea (NRF) funded by the Ministry of Education (Project no. 2020R1I1A1A01074249).

REFERENCES

Avraamides, J. (1982). Prospects for alternative leaching systems for gold: a review. *Proceedings, Symposium on Carbon-in-Pulp Technology for the Extraction of Gold*, Melbourne: Australasian Institute of Mining and Metallurgy, pp. 369–391.

Baghalha, M. (2012). The leaching kinetics of an oxide gold ore with iodide/iodine solutions. *Hydrometallurgy*, 113–114: 42–50.

Baghalha, M., Gh, H. K. and Mortaheb, H. R. (2009) Kinetics of platinum extraction from spent reforming catalysts in aqua-regia solutions. *Hydrometallurgy*, 95(3-4), 247–253.

Bard, A. J. (1985). In R. Parsons and J. Jordan, (eds) *Standard potentials in aqueous solutions*. New York: Marcel Dekker, pp. 339–365, 383–385.

Birloaga, I., De Michelis, I., Ferella, F., Buzatu, M., and Vegliò, F. (2013). Study on the influence of various factors in the hydrometallurgical processing of waste printed circuit boards for copper and gold recovery. *Waste management*, 33(4): 935–941.

Bonucci, J. A. and Parker, P. D. (1984) Recovery of platinum group metals from automobile catalytic converters. In *Proceedings AIME-IPMI Precious Metals Symposium, Los Angeles*, pp. 465–481.

Brent, H.J., Atluri, V.P. (1998) Dissolution chemistry of gold and silver in different lixiviants. *Mineral Processing and Extractive Metallurgy Review*, 4: 95–134.

Burkin, A. R. (2001). *Chemical hydrometallurgy: Theory and principles*. Singapore: World Scientific.

Chao, M. S. (1968). The diffusion coefficients of hypochlorite, hypochlorous acid, and chlorine in aqueous media by chronopotentiometry. *Journal of the Electrochemical Society*, 115(11): 1172–1174.

Davis, A., Tran, T., Young, D.R. (1993). Solution chemistry of iodide leaching of gold. *Hydrometallurgy*, 32: 143–159.

Davis, A., Tran, T. (1991) Gold dissolution in iodide electrolytes. *Hydrometallurgy*, 26: 163–177.

Filmer, A.O., Lawrence, P.R., Hoffman, W. (1984). A Comparison of Cyanide, Thiourea and Chlorine as Lixiviants for Gold. *Australian Inst. of Mining and Metallurgy, Regional Conference: Proceedings on Gold Mining, Metallurgy and Geology*. October 1984, pp. 1–8.

Finkelstein, J. J. (1972). The Goring Ox: Some Historical Perspectives on Deodands, Forfeitures, Wrongful Death and the Western Notion of Sovereignty. *Temp. LQ*, 46: 169.

Finkelstein, N. P., and Hancock, R. D. 1974. A new approach to the chemistry of gold. *Gold Bulletin*, 7(3): 72–77.

Ginzburg, S.L., Ezerskaya, N.A., Prokof'eva, L.V., Fedorenko, N.V. (1990).In *Analytical chemistry of the platinum metals* P. Shelnitz (ed.). New York: John Wiley and Sons, pp. 10–80.

Graham, G. W., O'Neill, A. E., and Chen, A. E. (2003). Pd encapsulation in automotive exhaust-gas catalysts. *Applied Catalysis A: General*, 252(2): 437–445.

Habashi, F. (1969). *Principles of extractive metallurgy: Hydrometallurgy*, vol. I. New York: Gordon and Breach, Science Publishers Inc.

Harjanto, S. et al., (2006). Leaching of Pt, Pd and Rh from automotive catalyst residue in various chloride based solutions. *Materials Transactions*, 47(1): 129–135.

Hiskey, J.B. and V.P. Atluri (1988). Dissolution chemistry of gold and silver in different lixiviants. *Mineral Processing and Extractive Metallurgy Review*, 4:95–134.

Ilyas, S., Srivastava, R. R., Kim, H., Cheema, H. A. (2020) Hydrometallurgical recycling of palladium and platinum from exhausted diesel oxidation catalysts. *Separation and Purification Technology*. doi:10.1016/j.seppur.2020.117029.

Ilyas, S., Lee, J. C. (2018). *Gold metallurgy and the environment*. Boca Raton, FL: CRC Press. https://doi.org/10.1201/9781315150475

Jafarifar, D., Daryanavard, M. R. and Sheibani, S. (2005) Ultra fast microwave-assisted leaching for recovery of platinum from spent catalyst. *Hydrometallurgy*, 78(3-4): 166–171.

Kalocsai, G. I. Z. (1984). Improvements in or relating to the dissolution of noble metals. *Austral. Provisional Patent 30281/84.*

Kim, M. S., Park, S. W., Lee, J.C., and Choubey, P.K. (2016). A novel zero emission concept for electrogenerated chloride leaching and its application to extraction of platinum group metals from spent automotive catalyst. *Hydrometallurgy*, 159: 19–27.

Lee, J.C., Srivastava, R.R. (2016). Leaching of gold from spent/end-of-life mobile phone-PCB using "greener reagents". In *Recovery of gold from secondary source*. World Scientific, pp. 7–56.

Marken, F. (2006). The electrochemistry of halogens. In: A. J. Bard, M. Stratmann, F. Scholz, C.J. Pickett (eds), *Encyclopedia of electrochemistry, inorganic chemistry*. Chap. 9, Vol. 7. Wiley-VCH, pp. 291–297.

Marsden, J.O., House, C.L. (2006). *The chemistry of gold extraction*, 2nd edition. Colorado: Society of Mining, Metallurgy, and Exploration. Inc. .

Massucci, M., Clegg, S. L. and Brimblecombe, P. (1999) Equilibrium partial pressures, thermodynamic properties of aqueous and solid phases, and Cl_2 production from aqueous HCl and HNO_3 and their mixtures. *The Journal of Physical Chemistry A*, 103(21): 4209–4226.

Meersbergen, V.M.T., Lorenzen, L., van Deventer, J.S.J. (1993). The electrochemical dissolution of gold in bromine medium. *Miner. Eng.* 6: 1067–1079.

Michaelis, V. H. (1987). The prospects for alternative leach reagents. Can precious metal producers get along without cyanide? *Eng. Min. J.*, 188(6): 42–47.

Muraki, M. and Mitsui, Y. (1986). Method for collecting platinum and palladium from platinum catalyst. *Japanese patent, 61110731*, A2.

Nicol, M. J. (1980). The anodic behaviour of gold. *Gold Bulletin*, 13(2): 46–55.

Nicol, M. J., Paul, R. L., Fleming, C. A. (1987). *The chemistry of the extraction of gold.* Mintek.

Nicol, W. M. (1976). *U.S. Patent No. 3 972,725.* Washington, DC: U.S. Patent and Trademark Office.

Park, Y. J., Fray, D. J. (2009). Recovery of high purity precious metals from printed circuit boards. *Journal of Hazardous Materials*, 164: 1152–1158.

Perte, E., Ghiara, C., Marc, M., Ceuca, O. and Crucin, O. (1988) *Romania patent, 94014 B1.*

Pesic, B., Sergent, R.H. (1992). Dissolution of gold with bromine from refractory ores preoxidized by pressure oxidation. In: Hager, J. (ed.), *Proceedings, EDP '92 Congress. The Minerals, Metals and Materials Society*, Warrendale, PA, USA. pp. 99–114.

Pourbaix, M. (1974) *Atlas of electrochemical equilibria in aqueous solution.* National Association of Corrosion Engineers, Houston, Texas, p.551.

Putnam, G.L. (1944). Chlorine as a solvent in gold hydrometallurgy. *Engineering and Mining Journal* 145(3): 70–75.

Radulescu, O., Gorban, A. N., Zinovyev, A., and Lilienbaum, A. (2008). Robust simplifications of multiscale biochemical networks. *BMC systems biology*, 2(1), 86.

Syed, S. (2012). Recovery of gold from secondary sources – a review. *Hydrometallurgy*, 115–116: 30–51.

Sergent, J., Ohta, S., and Macdonald, B. (1992). Functional neuroanatomy of face and object processing: a positron emission tomography study. *Brain*, 115(1): 15–36.

Snoeyink, P.L., Jenkins, D. (1979). *Water chemistry*. New York: John Wiley.

Sparrow, G.J., Woodcock, J.T., (1995). Cyanide and other lixiviant leaching systems for gold with some practical applications. *Miner. Process. Extract. Metall. Rev.: Int. J.* 14, 193–247.

Tadashi, K. (1982). Method for recovering platinum group metal from residual catalyst. *Japanese patent, 57155333*, Tanaka Noble Metal Ind.

Takeno, N. (2005). Atlas of Eh-pH diagrams, Intercomparison of thermodynamic databases, Geological Survey of Japan Open File Report No. 419. Available from: (http://www.gsj. jp/GDB/openfile/files/no0419/openfile419e.pdf 2005).

Tran, P., Zhang, X. K., Salbert, G., Hermann, T., Lehmann, J. M., and Pfahl, M. (1992a). COUP orphan receptors are negative regulators of retinoic acid response pathways. *Molecular and Cellular Biology*, 12(10): 4666–4676.

Tran, T., Davis, A., and Song, J. (1992b). Extraction of gold in halide media. In *Proc. Int. Conf. Ext. Met. Gold and Base Metals*, pp. 323–327.

Tran, T., Lee, K., Fernando, K. (2001). Halide as an alternative lixiviant for gold processing – an update. In Young, C.A., Twidwell, L.G., Anderson, C.G. (eds), *Cyanide: Social, industrial and economic aspects*. Warrendale, PA: The Minerals, Metals and Materials Society, 501–508.

Trindade, R.B.E., Rocha, P.C.P., Barbosa, J.P. (1994). *Dissolution of gold in oxidized bromide solutions. Hydrometallurgy '94*. London: Chapman & Hall, pp. 527–540.

Tyson, D. R. and Bautista, R. G. (1987) Leaching kinetics of platinum and palladium from spent automotive catalysts. *Separation Science and Technology*, 22(2-3): 1149–1167.

Viñals, J., Nunez, C., and Herreros, O. 1995. Kinetics of the aqueous chlorination of gold in suspended particles. *Hydrometallurgy*, 38(2): 125–147.

Yen, W.T., Pindred, R.A., Lam, M.P. (1990). Hypochlorite leaching of gold ore. In: Hiskey, J.B., Warren, G.W. (eds), *Hydrometallurgy Fundamentals, Technology and Innovations*. Littleton, CO: The Society for Mining, Metallurgy and Exploration, Inc., pp. 415–436.

Yannopoulos, J.C. (1991) *The Extractive Metallurgy of Gold*. Van Nostrand Reinhol, USA.

4 Urban Mining of Precious Metals with Cyanide as Lixiviant

Rajiv Ranjan Srivastava
Center for Advanced Chemistry, Institute of Research and
Development, Duy Tan University, Da Nang 550000, Vietnam

Sadia Ilyas
Mineral Resources and Energy Engineering, Jeonbuk National
University, Jeonju, Jeonbuk 54896, Republic of Korea

Nimra Ilyas
Institute of Microbiology, University of Agriculture Faisalabad
(UAF), 38040, Pakistan

Hyunjung Kim
Mineral Resources and Energy Engineering, Jeonbuk National
University, Jeonju, Jeonbuk 54896, Republic of Korea

Department of Environment and Energy, Jeonbuk National
University, Jeonju, Jeonbuk 54896, Republic of Korea

CONTENTS

4.1 URBAN MINING OF PRECIOUS METALS WITH CYANIDE AS LIXIVIANT: AN OVERVIEW

Cyanide has featured prominently as a leach lixiviant for over 100 years, due to its relatively low cost and higher extraction efficiency than previously used chlorination and amalgamation which had only 55–65% extraction efficiency. Cyanidation of PMs is a milestone in PM metallurgy and can be considered a wonderful development in the processing of PMs containing ores and urban mines (waste electric and electronic equipment and spent catalysts, etc.). Table 4.1 describes various historical developments in the cyanidation of precious metals.

TABLE 4.1
Salient historical developments in the cyanidation process

Chemists	Scientific developments	Development time
Johann Conrad Dippel	Discovery of 'Berlin/Prussian blue' via heating dry blood with potash and subsequent treatment with iron vitriol	1704
Pierre Joseph Macquer	Discovery of potassium ferrocyanide via boiling Prussian blue with alkali to separate the iron and concentrated solution yields yellow crystals of $K_3[Fe(CN)_6]$	1752
Carl Wilhelm Scheele	Discovery of blue acid via heating Prussian blue with dilute H_2SO_4; the dissolution of gold with cyanide was known to the Swedish chemist Carl Wilhelm Scheele	1782
Joseph Louis Gay-Lussac	Discovery of HCN via liquefying the blue acid gas	1811
Leopold Gmelin	Discovery of potassium ferricyanide via action of chlorine into a solution of potassium ferrocyanide	1822
George Elkington	In gold electroplating the necessary bath was introduced for recovery of gold from cyanide solution	1836
Bagration	Solvent action of aqueous solution of alkali cyanide on gold was investigated	1843
Elsner	The role of atmospheric oxygen was established in gold cyanidation	1846
Micheal Faraday	Cyanide dissolution of gold was investigated	1857
John Stewart MacArthur	MacArthur–Forrest process was established for gold extraction by suspending the crushed ore in a cyanide solution; up to 96% of pure gold was recovered	1887
Guido Bodländer	Formation of H_2O_2 as an intermediate product during cyanidation was observed	1896
i) Charles W. Merrill ii) Thomas B. Crowe	Merrill–Crowe process introduced to improve the MacArthur–Forrest process by precipitating gold with Zn-dust instead of using the Zn-shavings	1900

Table 4.1: Salient historical developments in the cyanidation process

Cyanide leaching of PMs from various urban mined sources has been a tremendous help in metal extraction; however, cyanide leaching of the noblest metal, gold, was for a long time a mystery due to its significant dissolution at room temperature in a dilute cyanide solution (0.01–0.1%), in contrast to other metals that were found to dissolve faster in a more concentrated solution. Similarly, there were doubts about the role of oxygen in the gold cyanidation process.

With almost 60 years' experience of the cyanidation process, these queries have been answered by the understanding that the electrochemical behavior of the process was similar to that of a galvanic cell. This has been demonstrated by introducing air from one direction on the surface of a small gold sphere embedded in a KCN gel. It was observed that the surface in direct contact with oxygen acted as the cathode while the surface less exposed to oxygen acted as the anode. By this means, oxygen carries electrons from the gold surface while gold ions are rapidly complexed by the cyanide ions in solution.

MacArthur used zinc shavings to precipitate gold from the cyanide solution by analogy with the 'transmutation' of iron into copper. Later, Charles Washington Merrill (1869–1956) introduced zinc dust in around 1900, significantly contributing to making the process more efficient. Further improvements were made by Thomas Bennett Crowe, who removed air from the solution by passing it through a vacuum tank before introducing the zinc, in what is known as the Merrill–Crowe process (Habashi, 1967).

Later studies also reported platinum, palladium, and rhodium cyanidation from various spent sources like catalytic converters (Atkinson et al., 1992; Chen and Huang, 2006; Chen et al., 2005; Hancock et al., 1977; Kuczynski et al., 1995; Desmond, 1991; Sibrell et al. 1994; Shams et al., 2004). At room temperature and pressures, the reaction between cyanide and PMs (Pt, Pd, Rh) did not occur because of poor kinetics. But at elevated temperatures (120–180°C), cyanidation of these metals was similar to gold. Atkinson et al. (1989) investigated the leaching behavior of platinum from virgin and spent monolith automotive catalysts with 5% NaCN and 1% promoter at pH 11.8 and 80°C in 1 h and observed 75% and 95% recovery of platinum, respectively, which increased further with a rise in temperature. Huang (2006) reported the recovery of Pt along with Pd and Rh from spent automotive catalysts by pressure alkaline treatment followed by cyanide leaching. These studies showed that the PGM metals are liberated from their carrier under high-temperature and pressure treatment with NaOH. The pre-treated material is then ground for subsequent leaching in cyanide solution. Under optimized conditions, metal recoveries were 96% Pt, 98% Pd, and 92% Rh.

4.2 CYANIDATION OF PRECIOUS METALS FROM URBAN MINE SOURCES

Among the precious metals, gold cyanidation has been widely investigated and several theories have been put forward (Habashi, 1987a, b; Cornejo and Spottiswood, 1984).

Elsner's oxygen theory: Elsner (1846) was the first to recognize the essential role of oxygen for gold leaching in cyanide solution:

$$4Au + 4NaCN + O_2 + H_2O \rightarrow 4NaAu(CN)_2 + 4NaOH \tag{4.1}$$

Janin's hydrogen theory: Janin (1888, 1892) was convinced about the evolution of hydrogen gas during cyanide leaching of gold according to the equation below:

$$2Au + 4NaCN + 2H_2O \rightarrow 2NaAu(CN)_2 + 2NaOH + H_2 \qquad (4.2)$$

Maclaurin (1893) and Christy (1896), after careful experimental investigations, concluded the necessity of oxygen in cyanide leaching process as stated in Elsner's theory.

Bodländer's hydrogen peroxide theory: Bodländer (1896) proposed a two-step gold leaching process with cyanide lixiviant according to the following equations.

$$2Au + 4NaCN + O_2 + 2H_2O \rightarrow 2NaAu(CN)_2 + 2NaOH + H_2O_2 \qquad (4.3)$$

$$2Au + 4NaCN + H_2O_2 \rightarrow 2NaAu(CN)_2 + 2NaOH \qquad (4.4)$$

The formation of H_2O_2 as an intermediate product was proved by its detection in leaching solution. The overall equation of the above two reactions was as per Elsner's equation.

Cyanogen formation: Christy (1896) observed the liberation of cyanogen gas formed by the action of oxygen with sodium cyanide solution, which can be the active agent for attacking the gold and facilitating dissolution. The two-step reaction can be represented as:

$$\frac{1}{2}O_2 + 2NaCN + H_2O \rightarrow (CN)_2 + 2NaOH \qquad (4.5)$$

$$2Au + 2NaCN + (CN)_2 \rightarrow 2NaAu(CN)_2 \qquad (4.6)$$

Later, Skey (1897) and Park (1898) concluded that the aqueous cyanogen does not exert the least solvent action on gold.

Cyanate formation: McArthur (1905) assumed the effectiveness of potassium cyanate for gold cyanidation which he believed to be formed by the oxidation of cyanide with supplied oxygen. Nevertheless, the assumption was refuted by Green (1913), who evidenced that cyanate had no action on gold dissolution. Some thermo-dynamic evidence was given by Barsky et al. (1934), whose calculations of the free energies for auro- and argento-cyanide complexes favoured Eisner and Bodländer's equations, while Janin's equation was found unfeasible thermodynamically.

Corrosion theory: Boonstra (1943) argued that gold cyanidation is similar to the metal corrosion process. He pointed out that dissolved oxygen in cyanide solution is reduced to hydroxyl ion and hydrogen peroxide, making it a reaction of an electro-chemical nature. On that basis, Bodländer proposed the following sequential steps:

$$O_2 + 2H_2O + 2e^- \rightarrow H_2O_2 + 2OH^- \qquad (4.7)$$

$$H_2O_2 + 2e^- \rightarrow 2OH^- \qquad (4.8)$$

$$Au \rightarrow Au^+ + e^- \qquad (4.9)$$

$$Au^+ + CN^- \rightarrow AuCN \qquad (4.10)$$

$$AuCN + CN^- \rightarrow Au(CN)_2^- \qquad (4.11)$$

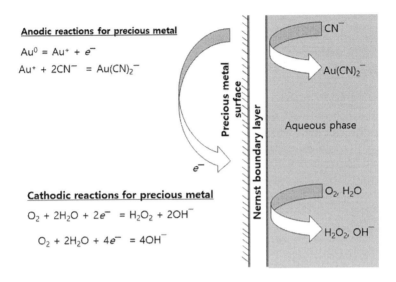

Anodic reactions for precious metal

$$Au^0 = Au^+ + e^-$$

$$Au^+ + 2CN^- = Au(CN)_2^-$$

Cathodic reactions for precious metal

$$O_2 + 2H_2O + 2e^- = H_2O_2 + 2OH^-$$

$$O_2 + 2H_2O + 4e^- = 4OH^-$$

Precious metal surface

Nernst boundary layer

e^-

Aqueous phase

CN^-

$Au(CN)_2^-$

O_2, H_2O

H_2O_2, OH^-

FIGURE 4.1 A typical electrochemical leaching mechanism of precious metals in cyanide solution.

Overall, it was concluded that in the case of its extraction from urban mined sources like printed circuit boards, the gold cyanidation process involves heterogeneous reactions at the interfaces of solid and liquid (Figure 4.1).

The dissolution is supposed to follow the sequential steps: i) absorption of oxygen in the cyanide solution and solubilization therein; ii) transportation of cyanide ions and dissolved oxygen towards interface; iii) diffusion of cyanide ions and dissolved oxygen (reactants) onto solid surfaces through the Nernst boundary layer; iv) occurrence of electrochemical reactions; v) de-sorption of the solubilized gold–cyanide complex and other reaction products from the solid surface; and vi) transportation of the reaction products to the bulk solution.

Electrochemically, the oxygen removes electrons from one part of the gold surface, the cathodic zone, while the gold releases electrons at another part, the anodic zone. Accordingly, the solubilization/leaching rate is a function of the cyanide concentration at low cyanide concentrations. At high cyanide concentrations, however, the solubilization rate depends on the soluble concentration of oxygen. Hence, the solubilization rate increases linearly with increasing concentration of cyanide until maximum solubilization of gold is reached; beyond that, a slight retarding effect occurs. The activation energy for solubilizing the gold in cyanide solution via mass-transport control is calculated in the range of 8–20 kJ/mol (Habashi, 1967). The selectivity of free cyanide for gold solubilization and the extremely high stability of the cyanide complexes are the key advantages of the process.

One of the major questions concerning the leaching of Pt, Pd, and Rh in a cyanide system is the speciation of these metals in solution. Detailed UV spectroscopy was conducted for the identification of the Pt, Pd, and Rh species by Sibrell et al. (1994). This is because many transition metal complexes show characteristic UV spectra due to electronic transitions. The most common complexes observed under the conditions used in the catalyst leaching process by the same group of researchers were tetracyanoplatinate(II), $[Pt(CN)_4]^{2-}$, tetracyanopalladate(II), $[Pd(CN)_4]^{2-}$, and hexacyanorhodate(III), $[Rh(CN)_6]^{3-}$. The Pt and Pd complexes have square planar geometries, while the Rh complex has an octahedral one. The potassium salts of these cyanide complexes were obtained for use as standards in the UV analysis. Solutions of the Pt, Pd, and Rh complexes were also generated by leaching samples of pure, elemental Pt, Pd, and Rh blacks (powder that appears black) under conditions identical to the catalyst samples, to form the same species in solution. The spectra of the leach solutions from the blacks were then compared with the spectra from solutions containing the Pt, Pd, and Rh standards. For the Pt and Pd species, the results were fairly clear-cut. Comparison of the spectra of the Pt species (see Figure 4.2) shows close similarity, demonstrating the presence of a tetracyanoplatinate(II) complex.

The UV spectra of the Pd species (Fig. 4.2) matches with the standard and confirms the presence of the tetracyanopalladate(II) species. For the Rh complex, the situation was different.

The spectra for the Rh black leach solution and the hexacyanorhodate(III) standard (shown in Figure 4.4) were not as distinctive as those of the Pt and Pd complexes (Figure 4.4).

Although the spectra appeared to be similar, the evidence was not conclusive that the Rh was indeed in this form. Therefore, additional samples of Rh complexes were examined by the same group of researchers. These included the ammonia complex, $[Rh(NH_3)_5Cl]Cl_2$, the nitrite complex, $K_3Rh(NO_2)_6$, the acetate complex, $[Rh(CH_3COO)_2]_2$, and the chloride complex $RhCl_3 \cdot xH_2O$. Each of these compounds

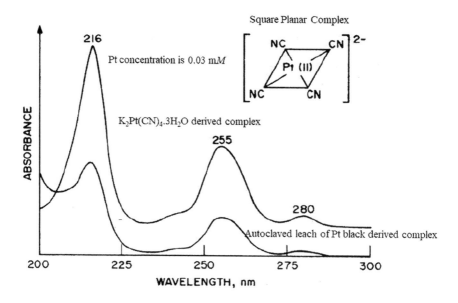

FIGURE 4.2　Ultraviolet spectroscopic elucidation of tetracyanoplatinate(II).

Source: Modified from Sibrell et al. (1994).

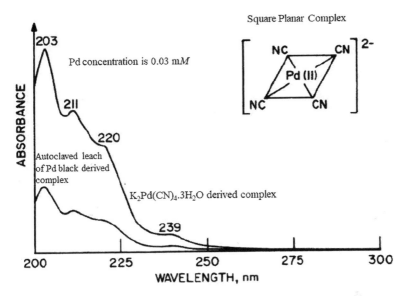

FIGURE 4.3   Ultraviolet spectroscopic elucidation of tetracyanopalladate(II).
Source: Modified from Sibrell et al. (1994).

gave UV spectra with distinctive peaks that did not agree with the leach solution spectra. Mixed ligand complexes were also prepared by reaction of the chloro- salt with ammonia, sodium nitrite, and sodium cyanide in various combinations in water. However, none of the UV spectra of any of these compounds matched that of the Rh leach solution. The hexacyano complex was still the closest match, despite its ill-defined spectrum.

During autoclave leaching of Rh black, it was observed that, immediately after leaching, the solution had a yellow colour, but this colour had disappeared by the following day. The yellow colour could be made to reappear if the solution was reheated in the autoclave to 160°C. Further investigation showed that the yellow colour was enhanced by leaching under an inert helium atmosphere, rather than air, as in the usual procedure. However, this increase in colour was not accompanied by an increase in Rh recovery to the solution. The yellow complex was also shown to be air sensitive: the yellow colour could be maintained by placing the solution fresh out of the autoclave into an air-tight bottle. The solution was analyzed by UV spectroscopy, and the resulting spectra are shown in Figure 4.4.

Since the solution was exposed to air while the spectra were being recorded, the yellow colour faded with time, which is apparent in Figure 4.4. Also associated with the complex was a pair of bands in the UV region of the spectra, at 324 and 366 nm, with a much higher absorbance than the band at 425 nm that was responsible for the yellow colour. This distinctive doublet in the UV region, combined with the air sensitivity of the complex, enabled its identification as tetracyanorhodate(I), $[Rh(CN)_4]^{3-}$. Sharpe (1976) gives the wavelengths of the maxima in the $[Rh(CN)_4]^{3-}$ spectrum as 322 and 365 nm. Additional tests were conducted to ascertain the conditions necessary for the formation of the Rh^{+1} complex. A sample of leach solution that had

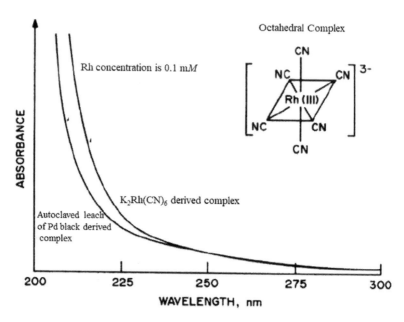

FIGURE 4.4   Ultraviolet spectroscopic elucidation of hexacyanorhodate(III).
Source: Modified from Sibrell et al. (1994).

previously been shown to contain the Rh^{+1} complex, but from which the yellow colour had faded, was boiled to drive off ammonia, then reheated in the autoclave to 160°C. The Rh^{+1} complex was observed when the autoclave was cooled and opened, indicating that ammonia was not required for the formation of the Rh^{+1} complex. Another sample of the same leach solution was treated with hydrogen peroxide, to oxidize the formate to carbonate. After heating in the autoclave to 160°C for 1 h, the autoclave was cooled and opened. No Rh^{+1} was observed. Sodium formate was added back to this solution, which was then reheated in the autoclave. The Rh^{+1} complex was again present when the autoclave was opened. These results show that the presence of formate results in the formation of the Rh^{+1} complex. This was later confirmed by heating a solution of potassium hexacyanorhodate(III), $K_3Rh(CN)_6$, both in the absence and in the presence of formate. The Rh^{+1} complex was formed only when formate had been added. In cyanide leaching at elevated temperatures, formate will always be present due to hydrolysis of the cyanide. One possible mechanism for Rh^{+1} formation is as an intermediate in the oxidation of elemental Rh to Rh^{+3}. In the presence of free cyanide, hydride would be formed, which may be oxidized to hexacyanorhodate(III). In the later stages of leaching, when the free cyanide concentration was low, the Rh^{+1} complex would accumulate, with no way to convert to the higher oxidation state. However, this mechanism does not require the presence of formate and therefore does not seem to be supported by the experimental results. A more likely mechanism for the formation of the Rh^{+1} complex is reduction of hexacyanorhodate(III) by the formate to give the hydride complex. This in turn reacts in a manner termed reductive elimination that forms the Rh^{+1} complex. Thus, in Rh black leach solutions, each of these three species may be present. This would also explain why Rh extraction was not increased when the Rh^{+1} complex was observed, since it was formed from species already in solution. One possible consequence of the formation of the Rh^{+1} complex is re-precipitation of some of the Rh, by the following disproportionation reaction:

$$3\left[Rh(CN)_6\right]^{3-} \rightarrow \left[Rh(CN)_6\right]^{3-} + 2Rh + 6CN^- \qquad (4.12)$$

If this was the case, the Rh concentration would be expected first to increase with time as the Rh was solubilized, and then to decrease as the Rh^{+1} complex was formed and disproportionation took place. Therefore, an additional group of autoclave leaching tests was performed concerning the effect of time at temperature for leaching of the Rh black. Leaching tests were done with no holding time at temperature and 30 min at temperature, for comparison with the standard 60 min leaching time at temperature. Surprisingly, it was found that essentially all of the leaching had taken place by the time the solution reached the target temperature of 160°C. Extraction of the Rh from Rh black was about 30% for all three cases. There was no evidence of the yellow Rh^{+1} complex after 0 min at 160°C, but the complex was present after 30 and 60 min at temperature. Since the Rh concentration in solution did not decrease when the Rh^{+1} complex was formed, no significant disproportionation can have taken place.

The Rh^{+1} complex has so far not been observed in the leaching of automobile exhaust catalysts. This is a marked contrast to the leaching behavior of the elemental Rh samples. Often, catalyst leach solutions are brown tinted and could be masking the yellow colour of the complex. However, even when leaching virgin catalysts, where the leaching solution was colourless, the Rh^{+1} complex was not observed. A leach solution generated from a catalyst was reheated separately to 160°C in an

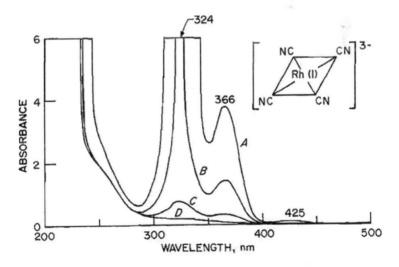

FIGURE 4.5 Ultraviolet spectroscopic elucidation of tetracyanorhodate(I).

Source: Modified from Sibrell et al. (1994).

autoclave. Interestingly, under those conditions, the solution had a yellow colour, demonstrating the presence of the Rh^{+1} complex. It is possible that in the presence of the catalyst, the Rh^{+1} species are re-oxidized as they are formed.

The cyanidation process was later studied by Chen and Huang (2006) to recover Pt, Pd, and Rh from spent automotive catalysts containing 818.3 g/t Pt, 516.7 g/t Pd, and 213.8 g/t Rh. As the leaching was slow at room temperature and pressure, these studies were carried out at elevated temperatures and pressures showing a cyanide leaching order of Pt>Pd>Rh due to the metal bonding strength of their complexes tetracyanoplatinate(II), tetracyanopalladate(II), and hexacyanorhodate(III) in the order $Rh(CN)_6^{3-}$>$Pd(CN)_4^{2-}$ >$Pt(CN)_4^{2-}$. The Pt and Pd complexes have square planar geometries, while the Rh complex is octahedral.

Huang (2004) reported the recovery of Pt along with Pd and Rh from spent automotive catalysts by pressure alkaline treatment followed by cyanide leaching. These studies showed that PMs are liberated from their carrier under high-temperature and pressure treatment with NaOH. The pretreated material is then ground for subsequent leaching in cyanide solution. Under optimized conditions, the metal recoveries were 96% Pt, 98% Pd, and 92% Rh. In the cyanide dissolution of Pt, Pd, and Rh, the reaction rate has been proposed to be controlled by a surface chemical reaction, similar to the gold-cyanide reaction mechanism (Wadsworth et al., 2000). However, the reaction occurs at higher temperatures than with gold because the metallic bonding strength of Pt, Pd, and Rh is higher than that of gold and a surface oxide passivating layer is present. For pressure cyanide leaching of Pt, Pd, and Rh, the following chemical reactions were concluded to occur.

$$2Pt + 8NaCN + O_2 + 2H_2O \rightarrow 2Na_2\left[Pt\left(CN\right)_4\right] + 4NaOH \qquad (4.13)$$

$$2Pd + 8NaCN + O_2 + 2H_2O \rightarrow 2Na_2\left[Pd\left(CN\right)_4\right] + 4NaOH \qquad (4.14)$$

$$4Rh + 24NaCN + 3O_2 + 6H_2O \rightarrow 4Na_3\left[Rh\left(CN\right)_6\right] + 12NaOH \qquad (4.15)$$

In the foregoing experiments on cyanide leaching of Pt, Pd, and Rh from spent auto-catalysts (Huang, 2004), it was observed that the (above-mentioned) cyanide leaching order was unaffected by a change in cyanide concentration, dissolved oxygen, and temperature.

4.3 EFFECT OF VARIOUS PROCESS PARAMETERS

The effect of various process parameters on the efficiency of gold leaching in cyanide solution has been widely discussed and studied.

4.3.1 EFFECT OF EH-PH ON CYANIDATION

Figure 4.6 presents the aqueous chemistry of precious metal in cyanide solution and shows that $Au\left(CN\right)_2^-$, aurous-cyanide ions occur predominantly in the wider pH range while the Au^{3+}, auric, ions are in a very limited area. The stability field of Au^0 at relatively low potential value (Eh) covers the whole pH range, as does the stability

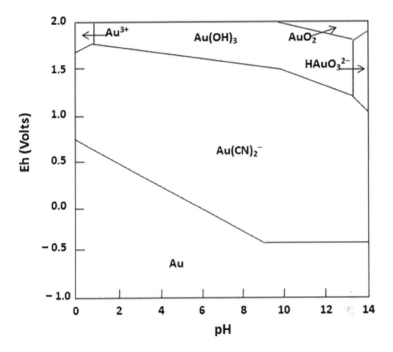

FIGURE 4.6   Eh-pH diagram of the Au-CN-H$_2$O system at 25°C and 1 atm.

of water. At high Eh values, Au^0 can form gold peroxide or hydrated auric oxide (insoluble oxides) which are unstable thermodynamically and hence powerful oxidants. The oxidizing power of these compounds depends on the acidity of the system and declines with an increase in pH. At very low Eh values, hydrogen cyanide (HCN) and cyanide ions (CN$^-$) are stable species, the latter being predominant at pH > 9.24, whereas cyanate (CNO$^-$) is the only stable species at a higher Eh value.

As Figure 4.6 shows, [Au(CN)$_2$]$^-$ (aurous cyanide complex), has substantial stability, extending into a large area of the Au-H$_2$O stability fields. The presence of extensive stability fields for this compound, especially at pH > 9.2, where the formation of HCN can be totally avoided, makes leaching in cyanide solution feasible. Although solid aurous cyanide, AuCN, and the auric cyanide complex, [Au(CN)$_4$]$^-$, have been reported, the aurous cyanide complex, [Au(CN)$_2$]$^-$ is the only stable complex of gold cyanidation. It has been found that the introduction of cyanide in aqueous systems drastically reduces the stability fields of zero-valence gold and its oxides.

4.3.2 Effect of Cyanide Concentration on Cyanidation

The gold cyanidation rate increases linearly with an increase in cyanide concentration until the maximum point is reached (Wadsworth et al., 2000; Marsden and House, 1992; Kondos et al., 1995; Ling et al., 1996; Deschênes et al., 2003). A retarding effect on gold solubilization was observed with further increase in cyanide concentration (Figure 4.7) (Maclaurin, 1893; Barsky et al., 1934).

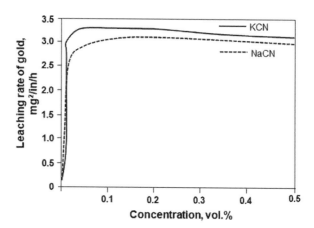

FIGURE 4.7   Effect of cyanide (KCN and NaCN) concentration on leaching rate of gold.
Source: Modified from Ilyas and Lee (2018)

At a high concentration cyanide ion undergoes hydrolysis, resulting in an increase in alkalinity which suppress the leaching of gold.

$$CN^- + H_2O \rightarrow HCN + OH^- \tag{4.16}$$

Further investigations by various researchers indicated that the use of 400 to 500 ppm sodium cyanide could result in a similar rate of gold leaching that is independent of the cyanide concentration, if it exceeds 0.075% potassium cyanide or 0.06% sodium cyanide in the lixiviant solution (Ling et al., 1996; Deschênes et al., 2003; Ellis and Senanayake, 2004). In fact, an excess of cyanide causes needless consumption of cyanide, which does not favour leaching reactions (Kondos et al., 1995). Large amounts of cyanide would create cyanide complexes of impurities. On the other hand, a higher cyanide concentration may be needed in view of its competition with other kinds of associated impurities (Marsden and House, 1992), but a decrease in cyanide concentration ultimately controls the extra cost of effluent treatment at industrial scale (Ling et al., 1996; Deschênes et al., 2003). In conclusion, therefore, a lesser or higher concentration of cyanide than the optimal level may negatively affect the gold cyanidation process. Like gold, the dissolution rate of other precious metals increases with increasing cyanide concentration until it reaches a plateau. There was a small decrease in recovery of Pt, Pd, and Rh at further increased concentrations of NaCN (Figure 4.8).

The reason for the decreased leaching with the increase in NaCN concentration shown in Figure 4.8 is believed to be due to the surface chemical reaction process whereby both CN^- and O_2 need to be absorbed on the surface of metal. If the concentration of CN^- is too high, many active sites on the metal surface will be occupied by CN^-, which will not favour the absorption of O_2. The existence of an optimum ratio between the concentration of cyanide and oxygen was also observed in the cyanide leaching of gold (Gu, 1994).

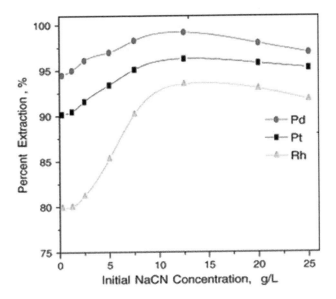

FIGURE 4.8   Effect of cyanide concentration on leaching of Pt, Pd, and Rh.
Source: Adopted with permission from Chen and Huang (2006).

4.3.3 Effect of Alkali on Cyanidation

The addition of alkali in cyanide solution has both accelerating and retarding effects on gold dissolution. The purposeful addition of alkali has following advantages: (i) it prevents the hydrolysis loss of cyanide; (ii) it prevent cyanide loss by the action of carbon dioxide in air; (iii) decomposition of bicarbonates occurs in the mill water prior to cyanidation; (iv) it neutralizes acidic compounds (such as ferric salts, ferrous salts, and magnesium sulphate) in the mill water before adding to the cyanide circuit; and (v) neutralization of acidic constituents—pyrite, alkalis ($CaO/NaOH/Na_2CO_3$)—added in the gold cyanidation process. The use of lime additionally promotes the settling of fine particles to obtain a clear leach liquor that can be separated easily from the pulp.

Although the use of an alkali is essential in cyanidation, several researchers have found that the addition of alkalis like sodium hydroxide and particularly calcium hydroxide retards the cyanidation leaching of gold. Barsky et al. (1934) investigated the effects of calcium hydroxide and sodium hydroxide on the rate of gold dissolution in cyanide solutions containing 0.1% NaCN and found a decreased leaching rate when calcium hydroxide was added with a solution pH ~11. Leaching was almost nil at pH $\geq$ 12.2. The effect of NaOH was less pronounced, with the leaching rate starting to be slower at pH > 12.5. However, leaching was more rapid at pH 13.4 using NaOH than in a solution containing a similar concentration of cyanide by using calcium hydroxide at pH 12.2. The effect of calcium ion on leaching was then investigated by adding $CaCl_2$ and $CaSO_4$ to a cyanide solution. Neither of these salts affected the leaching rate to any appreciable extent. The solubility of oxygen in cyanide solutions with various amounts of $Ca(OH)_2$ also did not show any appreciable difference.

It is thus concluded that a decrease in leaching rate using NaCN solutions caused by the addition of $Ca(OH)_2$ is not due to either lower solubility of oxygen or the presence of calcium ions. Habashi (1967) attributed the retarding effect of $Ca(OH)_2$ to formatting calcium peroxide onto the gold surface, which prevents the cyanidation reaction. Notably, calcium peroxide is supposed to form by the reaction of lime with H_2O_2 accumulating in the solution.

Moreover, cyanide exits as HCN gas in the less alkaline region (pH < 9.2) where the formation of insoluble AuCN along with hydrogen peroxide is possible, as per the reaction below:

$$2Au + 2HCN + O_2 \rightarrow 2AuCN + H_2O_2 \qquad (4.17)$$

To avoid the formation of AuCN, therefore, the cyanide solution should be alkaline, which can control the decomposition of cyanide ions via hydrolysis and also in the presence of atmospheric CO_2.

$$CN^- + H_2CO_3 \rightarrow HCN + HCO_3^- \qquad (4.18)$$

To prevent the formation of insoluble AuCN, and avoid the adverse effect on the leaching rate of a very high pH, it is necessary to carefully optimize the leaching pH, which is usually maintained between 11 and 12.

4.3.4 EFFECT OF DISSOLVED OXYGEN ON CYANIDATION

Pure oxygen was first introduced in the gold cyanidation process by Air Products, South Africa in the 1980s (Stephens, 1988) and then also practised in Canadian plants (McMullen and Thompson, 1989). The Lac Minerals plants were the first to demonstrate a faster leaching rate associated with dissolved oxygen and lead nitrate. Deschênes et al. (2003) investigated the effect of dissolved oxygen as presented in Figure 4.9, from which it was concluded that dissolved oxygen concentration is not much related to cyanide consumption; rather, rapid leaching kinetics can be achieved.

Oxygen-assisted leaching was adopted quickly in industry with the technological advancement for improving oxygen mass transfer, e.g., the use of Degussa's peroxide-assisted leach or pressure acid leaching, PAL, and Kamyr's carbon-in-leach-with-oxygen process, CILO (Loroesch et al., 1988; Elmore et al., 1988; Revy et al. 1991; Kondos et al., 1995; Liu and Yen, 1995). Numerous efforts have been made to develop an efficient device for enhancing oxygen dispersion (Jara and Harris 1994; Sceresini, 1997; McLaughlin et al., 1999). The practice of continuous oxygen monitoring and control stabilizes process performance and compensates for disturbances related to changes in oxygen requirements. A better design of oxygen probes has added further robustness to the control and operation strategy in leaching (McMullen and Thompson, 1989). The FILBLAST Gas-Shear Reactor has been employed to improve gas mass transfer efficiency via an improved dissolved oxygen concentration and reduced oxygen consumption, which could enhance the leaching rate of gold in cyanide solution.

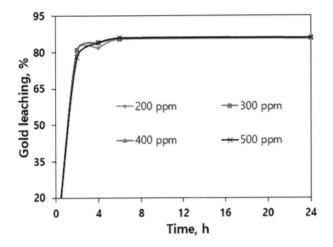

FIGURE 4.9   Effect of dissolved oxygen concentration on gold cyanidation at pH 11.2 with 500 ppm NaCN concentration and time 24 h.

Source: Modified from Deschênes et al., 2003; Ilyas and Lee, 2018.

Overall, the role of oxygen is critical in gold cyanidation and the maximum dissolved oxygen content of a dilute cyanide solution is 8.2 ppm at room temperature and atmospheric pressure that corresponds to 0.27×10^{-3} mole per litre. Mostly cyanide leaching of gold is performed at pH ~11, where the dissolved O_2 concentration remains ~6 ppm. A decrease in O_2 concentration (particularly below 4 ppm) reduces the leaching rate drastically. In contrast, leaching increases remarkably when the concentration of dissolved oxygen rises above 10 ppm. An oxygen-enriched operation (12–18 ppm O_2) is beneficial for achieving high throughput at the commercial level.

The effect of O_2 pressure on platinum dissolution was investigated by Chen and Huang (2006) for a fixed NaCN concentration. In this series of experiments, O_2 pressure ranging from 0.02 to 2.5Mpa was used. The rate was observed to increase with increasing O_2 pressure, subsequently reaching a plateau value that is independent of O_2 pressure. The reason for the increased dissolution with the increase of O_2 concentration is believed to be the surface chemical reaction process where O_2 needs to be absorbed on the surface of the metal. If the concentration of O_2 is high, the Pd dissolution increases. In aqueous solution, the cyanide ion was oxidized successively to cyanate and carbon dioxide. However, more rapid oxidation of free cyanide may have an effect on the leaching rate. Cyanide oxidation was found to be first order with respect to hydroxyl ion and zero order with respect to cyanide ion in the rate-determining step. Optimum dissolution was obtained with oxygen pressure between 1.1 and 1.3 MPa (Figure 4.10).

Technically, neither the concentration of dissolved oxygen alone nor the concentration of free cyanide ions alone are important in practice but it is the molar ratio of two concentrations that should be 6.

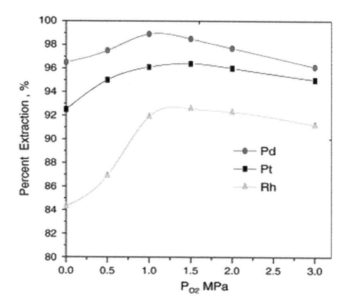

FIGURE 4.10   Effect of oxygen on Pt, Pd and Rh cyanidation at 6.25 g/L NaCN, 160°C and 1 h. *Source*: Adopted with permission from Chen and Huang (2006).

4.3.5 EFFECT OF TEMPERATURE ON CYANIDATION

Generally, reaction kinetics are expected to increase with a rise in temperature but the temperature has a dual effect on gold cyanidation. An increase in temperature increases the activity of cyanide solution, thus increasing the rate of gold leaching but decreasing the amount of dissolved oxygen in the solution, which ultimately decreases the gold leaching rate. Therefore, there should be an optimum temperature for the maximum rate.

Maximum cyanide leaching of gold in 0.25% KCN at 85°C showed half the amount of dissolved oxygen at this temperature compared with room temperature (Figure 4.11).

Interestingly an increase in temperature to 100°C slightly reduced leaching, although no dissolved oxygen was observed at that temperature. This leaching trend can be attributed to the lower capacity of an electrode to adsorb/retain hydrogen in a heated solution. Hence, the maximum opposing electromotive force (EMF) due to polarization reduces for the heated solution until the EMF of gold leaching exceeds the polarization EMF, allowing gold leaching even in the absence of dissolved oxygen. Polarization can be prevented either by oxygen oxidizing the hydrogen at the gold surface to favour leaching at low temperatures, or by heat dislodging the hydrogen from the gold surface to favour leaching without oxygen. The activation energy of gold and silver leaching ranges from 2–5 kcal/mole, which is typically the diffusion-controlled reaction.

For Pt, Pd, and Rh, when the reaction temperature was higher than 160°C, the percentage of Pd leached decreased rapidly because $Pd(CN)_4^{2-}$ is not stable at high

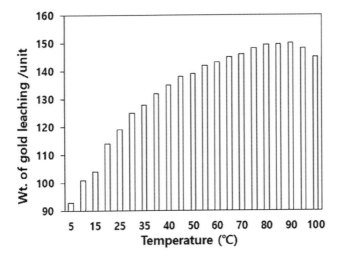

FIGURE 4.11 Effect of temperature on gold cyanidation with 0.25% KCN solution under aeriation.

Source: Modified from Julian and Smart (1921).

temperature and is easily decomposed to Pd metal. In contrast, the Pt and Rh cyanide complexes remained relatively stable in solution at 180°C but showed a slight decrease in concentration (Figure 4.11).

At these high temperatures, free cyanide is readily hydrolyzed and oxidized and decomposes more quickly than complexed cyanide. The thermal decomposition reactions of Pt, Pd, and Rh are as follows.

$$Pt(CN)_4^{2-} + 1.5O_2 + 7H_2O \rightarrow Pt + 4NH_3 + 4CO_2 + 2OH^- \tag{4.19}$$

$$Pd(CN)_4^{2-} + 1.5O_2 + 7H_2O \rightarrow Pd + 4NH_3 + 4CO_2 + 2OH^- \tag{4.20}$$

$$Rh(CN)_6^{3-} + 2.25O_2 + 10.5H_2O \rightarrow Rh + 6NH_3 + 6CO_2 + 3OH^- \tag{4.21}$$

The higher temperature stability of $Pt(CN)_4^{2-}$ than of $Pd(CN)_4^{2-}$ can be explained by the higher thermodynamic and kinetic stability of heavy platinum group metal complexes than that of light ones even with the same valence state, same complexing agent, and same geometrical structure (Chen, 1995). On the other hand, the higher stability of $Rh(CN)_6^{3-}$ than $Pd(CN)_4^{2-}$ can be explained by the chemical reactivity of the cyanide complex with different geometrical structures. $Pd(CN)_4^{2-}$ has a square planar structure, allowing O_2 to attack the central ions along the Z-axis. However, $Rh(CN)_6^{3-}$ has an octahedral structure, and the central ion is surrounded by cyanide ions. Therefore, the bond between CN^- and the central atom needs to be broken before reaction with O_2 can occur (Chen and Huang, 2006).

4.3.6 Effect of Agitation and Particle Size on Cyanidation

The precious metal cyanidation rate depends on the mixing pattern and the thickness of the diffusive layer (Marsden and House, 1992). Consequently, the agitation rate must be sufficient to properly suspend all solid particles in the lixiviant solution. When stirring speed is increased, the leaching kinetics increases. An intense mixing pattern reduces the thickness of the diffusive layer and improves the rate of mass transfer of oxygen and cyanide, allowing feasible saturation of pulp (Ellis and Senanayake, 2004). Ling et al. (1996) investigated whether smaller particle size could enhance the rate of gold leaching due to the larger available surface area and longer contact time between solid and lixiviant. At optimal aeration and agitation conditions, the maximum rate of gold leaching was determined to be 3.25 mg/cm^2/h. This equals a penetration of 1.68 microns on each side of a flat 1 cm^2 gold particle, or a total reduction in thickness of 3.36 microns hourly. At this rate, a gold particle of 37 microns thickness would take about 11 h to completely leach out in the solution (Kondos et al., 1995).

4.3.7 Effect of Associated Metal Ions on Cyanidation

Mostly gold occurs in native form, along with varying amounts of co-existing silver. As well as silver, several other metals such as copper, lead, zinc, etc., and some carbonaceous matter, are also present in gold-bearing urban mined sources. The presence of carbonaceous matter is a cause for concern, as it significantly adsorbs the gold-cyanide complex, causing operational loss. The metals that dissolve in cyanide solution either accelerate or retard the leaching.

Dissolved Fe and Cu form different respective cyanide complexes in leach liquors. Similarly, the presence of small amounts of lead also accelerate the leaching. The electrode potential value of these metals in the cyanide solution indicates that gold can displace these metal ions. The accelerating effect in the presence of these metal ions corresponds with the alteration in the surface character of the gold by alloying with displaced ions. A change in surface character may lead to a decreasing thickness of the boundary layer through which the reactants diffuse to reach the metallic surface. Oxygen is necessary for gold cyanidation leaching. Any side reaction that may deprive gold of its oxygen content in cyanide solution will lead to a decrease in the leaching rate. Metal impurities like silver, copper, zinc, and iron associated with gold may dissolve in a cyanide solution, causing depletion of the cyanide content from the lixiviant. Aluminosilicates, if present, form colloidal silica and alumina in alkaline pH as well as precipitating the iron. These are reaction products that have a strong adsorptive capacity for sodium cyanide, thus retarding the gold leaching. A large number of lead ions cause a retarding effect by forming an insoluble film of $Pb(CN)_2$ on the gold surface.

Although calcium ion has no effect on gold dissolution, at pH > 11.5 it retards gold cyanidation. Solutions kept alkaline by $Ca(OH)_2$, when compared with others at the same pH kept alkaline with KOH, hinder the leaching in the case of lime, as shown in Figure 4.11. The decrease is presumably due to the formation of calcium peroxide (as in Equation 4.22) on the gold surface, which prevents the reaction with cyanide.

$$Ca(OH)_2 + H_2O_2 \rightarrow CaO_2 + 2H_2O \qquad (4.22)$$

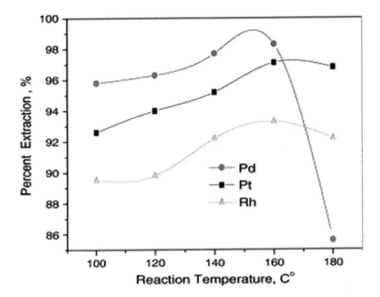

FIGURE 4.12 Effect of temperature on Pt, Pd, and Rh cyanidation at 6.25 g/L NaCN, 160°C , 1 h and O_2 pressure 1.5 MPa.

Source: Adopted with permission from Chen and Huang (2006).

The addition of ozone to the cyanide solution decreases the leaching rate. Apparently, a brick-red layer of gold oxide is responsible for the retarding effect. The oxidation of potassium cyanide to cyanate is also possible with ozone.

4.4 BIOGENIC CYANIDATION FOR PRECIOUS METAL LEACHING FROM URBAN MINE SOURCES

Cyanogenic micro-organisms form more than 50% of the soil microbial community. Formation of hydrocyanic acid by a variety of bacteria, fungi, and algae has been known for many years. Cyanogenic bacterial species like *Chromobacterium violaceum*, *Pseudomonas fluorescens*, *Pseudomonas aureofaciens*, *Pseudomonas aeruginosa*, *Pseudomonas plecoglossicida*, *Pseudomonas putida*, *Pseudomonas syringae*, *Bacillus megaterium*, archaea species like *Ferroplasma acidipholum*, *Ferroplasma acidarmanus*, and some fungal species such as *Marasmius oreades*, *Clitocybe* sp. and *Polysporus* sp. have been reported so far (Knowles, 1976; Askeland and Morrison, 1983; Paterson, 1990; Golyshina et al., 2000; Faramarzi and Brandl, 2006; Brandl et al., 2008; Hol et al., 2011). However, the application of fungi and archaea is limited, and commercially available microbial isolates (*Chromobacterium violaceum* and *Pseudomonas fluorescens*) are the most commonly studied.

Mostly, micro-organisms synthesize cyanide as a secondary metabolite (idiolites), or degrade cyanide to detoxify it, and/or to use it for growth as a source of carbon and nitrogen. Cyanogenic micro-organisms play a functional role in the development of α-amino acid derivatives exploited in complex compounds of lipids and proteins, as well as biological membranes (Castric, 1981; Merchant, 1998; Kita et al., 2006; Faramarzi et al. 2020). In producer strains, cyanide has no apparent function in primary metabolism, and is generally considered a secondary metabolite. Typically, cyanide is only formed in the mid-to-late exponential growth phase (idiophase), by HCN synthase activity. Cyanogenesis is very strictly regulated in bacteria, so that the local concentrations of cyanide are usually less than 1 mM and can be tolerated by many living cells (Faramarzi et al., 2004).

4.4.1 The Metabolic Pathway of Biogenic Cyanidation

Glycine is mainly responsible for acting as an immediate metabolic precursor of cyanide in proteobacteria, and a stoichiometric formation of HCN and CO_2 occurs via oxidative decarboxylation according to the following equation (Michaels et al., 1965; Wissing, 1974; Castric, 1977):

$$C_2H_5NO_2\left(glycine\right) \xrightarrow{-2H} C_2H_3NO_2\left(Imino\ acetic\ acid\right) \xrightarrow{-2H} HCN + CO_2 \quad (4.23)$$

Using the substrate of radiolabelled [1-14C] glycine or, [2-14C] glycine, cyanide can be derived from the methylene carbon of glycine and CO_2 from the carboxyl group of glycine in the cyanogenic bacteria *Chromobacterium violaceum*, *Pseudomonas fluorescens* and *Pseudomonas aeruginosa* (Askeland and Morrison, 1983). The C–N bond is retained during the reaction (Brysk et al., 1969) without any possible transamination or deamination reactions. In *Pseudomonas aeruginosa*, threonine can be metabolized to glycine to serve as a precursor to biocyanidation, but less effectively (Castric, 1977). In vitro, the enzyme complex converting glycine to HCN and CO_2, HCN synthase appears to be membrane associated, both in a *Chromobacterium violaceum* and *Pseudomonas* sp. that can be solubilized by detergents (Wissing, 1974; Wissing and Andersen, 1981; Bunch and Knowles, 1982). The HCN synthase is very sensitive to oxygen and can easily be altered, while glycine protects the *Pseudomonas* and *Chromobacterium* enzymes somewhat from the toxicity exhibited by oxygen (Castric, 1981; Wissing and Andersen, 1981; Bunch and Knowles, 1982). Hence, the HCN synthase has been purified only partially from a *Pseudomonas* sp. In crude extracts, HCN synthase of *Pseudomonas* sp., and *Chromobacterium violaceum* can use artificial electron acceptors to oxidize glycine (Wissing, 1974; Castric, 1981; Bunch and Knowles, 1982). In vivo the natural electron acceptor is oxygen, but oxygen is not strictly required for cyanogenesis by the *Chromobacterium violaceum* in which fumarate can be the terminal electron acceptor.

4.4.2 Bioleaching with Biogenic Cyanide

Biogenic cyanide, produced as described above, can be utilized for leaching precious metals from various urban mine sources likes SPCBs and SCCs. Although the leaching of precious metals in cyanide via complexation from SPCBs is similar to chemical cyanidation leaching, overall the bio-cyanidation leaching of gold can be divided into three types of process—(i) one-step bioleaching, (ii) two-step bioleaching, and (iii) spent medium bioleaching—mainly based on whether the material is added directly or indirectly into the media, or cells are separated from the culture after reaching maximum cell density and cyanide production and material is added into the cell-free media (spent media). A prior decrease in the copper content of spent material is suggested for preference to achieve improved bioleaching of gold (Rohwerder et al. 2003). The external addition of $FeSO_4$ and $MgSO_4$ to the medium, and the presence of Na_2HPO_4 and $Pb(NO_3)_2$ is found to enhance the rate of cyanogenesis (Bosecker, 1997; Hoque and Philip, 2011; Brandl et al., 2001; Ilyas and Lee, 2014).

In contrast to two-step bioleaching where microbes consume the oxygen, spent medium bioleaching utilizes oxygen complexed with metals in the absence of bacteria. As no consumption of cyanide is done by the bacteria in spent media leaching, the full strength of the biogenic cyanide can be utilized in complexing with precious metals, in contrast to two-step bioleaching where growth/cyanide production is coupled with the leaching process. Various leaching modes, process and growth conditions were chosen by researchers according to the culture type and nature of the spent material. Mostly SPCBs require pretreatment to remove other base metals prior to biogenic cyanidation, and SCCs require pressure cyanidation after accumulation of biogenic cyanide for efficient leaching of precious metals. Faramarzi et al. (2004) applied different cyanogenic bacterial strains of *Bacillus megaterium, Pseudomonas fluorescens, and Chromobacterium violaceum* under optimum conditions (Luria-Bertani medium supplemented with glycine 0.75 g L^{-1}) in the presence of nickel- and gold-containing solids.

Pradhan and Kumar (2012) reported effective bioleaching of precious metals from electronic waste using cyanogenic bacterial strains *Chromobacterium violaceum, Pseudomonas aeruginosa*, and *Pseudomonas fluorescens* under optimized cyanide-forming conditions via both single and mixed cultures of cyanogenic bacteria. *Chromobacterium violaceum* as a single culture was capable of leaching more than 79%, 69%, and 46% of copper, gold, and zinc, respectively; and a mixture of *Chromobacterium violaceum* and *Pseudomonas aeruginosa* demonstrated metal mobilization of more than 83%, 73%, and 49%, respectively (Pradhan and Kumar, 2012).

The effects of various experimental conditions, such as pH, incubation technique, particle size, and bio-oxidative treatment, were investigated in bioleaching of low-grade ores containing gold by *Chromobacterium violaceum*. Optimal cyanide production conditions were determined as a pH level of 9 and glycine concentration of 5 g L^{-1} within 2 days of incubation (Shin et al., 2013).

The bioleaching potential of *Chromobacterium violaceum*, applying two-step bioleaching and spent medium leaching, and using bacterial cell-free metabolites, was compared; results showed higher recovery of gold from electronic scrap material via the spent medium approach (Natarajan and Ting, 2014).

Li et al. (2015) investigated several factors influencing gold leaching efficiency, such as dissolved oxygen, base metals, particle size, and nutrients, especially several metal ions serving as catalysts in metabolism. Gold recovery from electronic scrap material by bioleaching was also studied, using cyanogenic bacterium in a 200 -mL

Luria-Bertani medium at 0.5% of pulp density and a pH level of 9, and shaking it in an incubator shaker at 30°C with 200 rpm. It was found that in two-step bioleaching, dissolution of gold improved from 1.63 (0.13 mg/L) to 13.62% (1.43 mg/L) after 7 days.

Tran et al. (2011) investigated the catalytic roles of metal ions (Na^+, Mg^{2+}, Fe^{2+}, and Pb^{2+}) and the effect of Na_2HPO_4 nutrient addition on cyanide generation efficiency by the bacterium in gold extraction from mobile phone PCB waste. The addition of $MgSO_4$ (4 mmol L^{-1}) to the growth medium raised gold leaching efficiency within 8 days at a pH level of 11.0.

Arshadi and Mousavi (2015) reported simultaneous extraction of gold and copper at about 36.81% and 13.26%, respectively, using pure culture of *Bacillus megaterium* as a leaching agent under optimum conditions, including an initial pH of 10, pulp density of 2 g L^{-1}, and glycine concentration of 0.5 g/L.

Pham and Ting (2009) compared gold bioleaching from electronic waste containing copper and gold using *Pseudomonas fluorescens* and *Chromobacterium violaceum* under a wide range of pulp densities (0.5–8% w/v). *Chromobacterium violaceum* produced more cyanide than *Pseudomonas fluorescens* in the absence of electronic waste, but *Pseudomonas fluorescens* indicated a higher growth rate, increased cyanide production, and more efficient gold leaching at all pulp densities.

Cyanogenic *Chromobacterium violaceum, Pseudomonas plecoglossicida, and Pseudomonas fluorescens* were used to mobilize gold, silver, and platinum in the presence of various wastes containing metals including silver-containing jewellery, gold-containing electronic scrap, or platinum-containing car catalysts. Copper complex was detected during treatment of electronic waste due to the high copper content (100 g kg^{-1}) in the scrap, and only small amounts of platinum (0.2%) were leached from a spent car catalytic converter after 10 days (Brandl et al., 2008).

Motaghed et al. (2014) studied platinum and rhenium extraction from a spent refinery catalyst using *Bacillus megaterium* as a cyanogenic bacterium. Response surface methodology was used to optimize two main factors, and maximum platinum and rhenium recovery of 15.7% and 98%, respectively, were achieved under optimum conditions including an initial glycine concentration of 12.8 g L^{-1} and 4% (w/v) pulp density after 7 days.

Tay et al. (2013) showed enhanced gold recovery by a lixiviant metabolically engineered strain of *Chromobacterium violaceum,* which produced more cyanide and recovered twice as much gold from electronic scrap as from wild bacteria.

4.4.3 Factors Influencing Efficiency of Biogenic Cyanide Production

Optimum conditions for production of cyanide by bacteria depend on the concentration of glycine in the growth medium. Growth of *Pseudomonas aeruginosa* on nutrient broth resulted in formation of a high level of cyanide when glycine was used as a nitrogen source. In addition, a synergistic effect of methionine and glycine was observed on formation of cyanide in a chemically defined medium. Using adapted cells in a growth medium containing glycine and methionine showed that cyanide production was stimulated by fumarate, malate, or succinate and decreased by 2,

4-dinitrophenol, and sodium azide. A mixture of methionine and glycine increased stimulation of cyanide formation compared to growth on peptone. Both yield and rate of cyanide synthesis in bacterial growth media are maximal at the start of the stationary phase, and no cyanide was produced during logarithmic growth phases (Castric, 1974).

In addition, the growth of *Pseudomonas aeruginosa* under very low aeration caused a dramatic decline in cyanide production. Synthetic electron acceptors such as 2, 6-dichlorophenol indophenol, methylene blue, phenazine methosulphate, and ferricyanide stimulated cyanide formation. Dissolved oxygen concentrations less than 20 µM in the culture medium induced cyanogenesis in *Pseudomonas aeruginosa* (Kralik and Castric, 1979). Batch cultures of *Pseudomonas aeruginosa* were found to be able to form only low levels of cyanide during logarithmic growth with adequate aeration, and reduction of aeration rapidly increased hydrogen cyanide production (Castric et al., 1981). Partially purified HCN synthase required exogenous electron acceptors, such as phenazine methosulphate, for activity, whereas oxygen allowed only a limited response (Castric, 1994).

4.5 LIMITATIONS, CHALLENGES, AND THE ENVIRONMENTAL IMPACTS OF CYANIDE LEACHING

For cyanidation, three main types of cyanides can be considered; (i) free cyanides, (ii) weak acid-dissociable cyanides (WADs), and (iii) strong acid-dissociable cyanides (SADs). However, the German Standard Method only differentiates between releasable cyanides (hydrocyanic acid, their alkali, and alkaline earth salts, including cyanide complexes of Ag, Zn, Cd, and Cu) and strong cyanide complexes (of cobalt, nickel, iron, and gold). Hence, the term total cyanides includes free cyanides, WADs, SADs, cyanate ion, OCN^-, thiocyanate ions, $SCNO^-$, and cyanogen chloride, $ClCN$ (Oelsner et al. 2001). The chemical name for hydrogen cyanide, HCN, includes hydrogen cyanide, hydrocyanic acid, and prussic acid which, depending on the pH and redox potential, can exist in either the free or complex forms. With the increase in the stability of cyanide compounds, the ability to release/form free cyanide in solution decreases. This is advantageous for halting cyanide mobility, but disadvantageous in the treatment/remediation of effluent as the cyanide ions form stable ferrous $[Fe(CN)_6^{4-}]$ and ferric $[Fe(CN)_6^{3-}]$ cyano-complexes. Although cyanide losses (either in the atmosphere during handling or via generated effluent) during urban mining of precious metals are far less than in mining practices from native ore sources, the International Cyanide Management Code has imposed a limit of 50 ppm cyanide solution for gold mining in order to control losses (Riani, et al. 2007).

When cyanides are discharged to the environment, their ability to undergo a number of processes—dissolution, adsorption, precipitation, (bio)oxidation, and biodegradation—along with a variety of metal complexes makes it difficult to trace their path in soil, water, or air. These processes often occur simultaneously, and depending on the prevailing physical or chemical conditions, result in degradation or attenuation of cyanides. The toxicity of cyanides is a function of the dissociation of free cyanides into the environment. Dissociation reduces with increasing stability of the cyanide complex, from weak complexes to strong complexes. The stability constants of the cyanide complexes with lead, silver, copper, and nickel are less than for ion complexes, which release HCN more easily and are therefore more toxic (Oelsner et al., 2001). The cyano-complexes of copper and zinc in WADs are insoluble in water but soluble in ammonia solution. The production of ammonia from natural attenuation would, therefore, result in the dissolution of copper and zinc in cyanide solution. This results in an increase in bioavailability and cyanide concentration within a specific environment. Except for the volatilization of the free cyanide, the released cyanides may still be available to drive other chemical processes under suitable conditions. This holds true for photolysis, precipitation, and complexation processes.

Cyanide is a toxic substance that can be inhaled, ingested orally (through contaminated water or food), or diffused through the skin. Cyanide prevents the uptake and subsequent transportation of oxygen to cells (Logsdon et al., 1999). If iron, which co-ordinates the uptake and transport of oxygen to the cells, is consumed by cyanide, failure of the respiratory system, rapid breathing convulsions, loss of consciousness, and suffocation can occur if there is no medical intervention, although the body can detoxify small concentrations of cyanide to less toxic cyanate, preventing the accumulation of cyanide in the body. Cyanide diffusion through the skin is supported by the small molecular size of HCN and the fact that cyanide dissolves readily in lipids of the human body (Simeonova and Fishbein, 2004). Concentrations of 20–40 ppm HCN in the air are toxic; increasing the concentration up to 250 ppm (1–3 mg CN per kg body weight) causes death within minutes. The LD_{50} (lethal dose-50) values representing the toxicity of cyanide and its derivatives are given in Table 4.2.

TABLE 4.2
Boiling point, exposure limit, and toxicity of various cyanide derivatives

Substance	B.P. (oC)	Exposure limit	LD50	Cyanide release
Bromobenzylcyanide	Solid	---	3.5 g/g	+
Cyanamide	Solid	2 mg/g	1.0 g/g	0
Cyanide salts	Solid	5 mg/g	2.0 mg/g	+
Cyanoacetic acid	108	---	2.0 g/g	0
Cyanogen	Gas	10 ppm	13.0 mg/g	+
Cyanogen chloride	61	0.3 ppm	13.0 mg/g	+
Ferric-cyanide	Solid	----	1.6 g/g	0
Ferroc-cyanide	Solid	----	1.6 g/g	0
Hydrogen cyanide	26.5	10 ppm	0.5 mg/g	+
Malonitrile	Solid	3 ppm	6.0 mg/g	+
Methylcyano-acrylate	Liquid	2 ppm	----	+
Methyliso-cyanate	39	0.02 ppm	2 ppm	-
Nitoprusside	Solid	----	10 mg/g	+
O-Tolunitrile	204	----	0.6 g/g	0

Source: Lowehein and Moran (1975); Ilyas and Lee (2018).

Cyanide undergoes a number of redox reactions in the open, forming various cyanide species of different toxicity levels, especially at a higher concentration. These compounds include:

Cyanogen Chlorides: toxic compounds, formed as intermediates during the chlorine oxidation of cyanides to cyanates. In the presence of ammonia, another class of toxic compounds, chloramines, are formed.

Cyanogens: produced in acidic environments when free cyanide encounters oxidants like oxidized copper minerals; nevertheless their formation is not expected in alkaline conditions.

Cyanates: usually formed as intermediate products via the reaction of cyanide with oxidants (ozone, hypochlorite, chlorine, hydrogen peroxide) during oxidative degradation of cyanides.

Thiocyanates: formed by the action of cyanide with sulphur or sulphur-containing chemical species that remain present in mineral ores. They persist in acid mine drains for decades after the closure of the mines.

Nitrate and Ammonia: chemical dissociation of cyanides and cyanide derivatives generates a large number of nitrates and ammonia, toxic to aquatic organisms, as degradation products.

For protection of aquatic resources from cyanide toxicity, the contaminated water must be detoxified before its discharge. The US Environmental Protection Agency (USEPA) has set limits of 200 ppb and 50 ppb cyanide in drinking water and for aquatic-biota, respectively (Gurbuz et al., 2004). The US health service has proposed a maximum permitted limit for cyanide in effluent of 0.2 mg/L, with 0.01 mg/L as a guideline. Swiss and German regulatory standards for cyanide are 0.01 mg/L for drinking or surface water and 0.5 mg/L for effluent. For cyanide disposal in Mexico it is 0.2 mg/L. The minimal national standard (MINAS) for the discharge of cyanide set by India's central pollution control board (CPCB) is 0.2 mg/L, so in order to avoid the toxicity of cyanide, it is important for industrial waste water to be treated by one of following methods: ion exchange, electrowinning, hydrolysis distillation, membrane treatment, electro dialysis, acidification, volatilization, flotation, addition of metal ions, alkali chlorination, hypochlorite oxidation of cyanides, hydrogen peroxide process, ozone treatment of cyanides, photolytic degradation, heterogeneous photo-catalysis, and the INCO process (Ilyas and Lee, 2018; Dash et al., 2008; IAEA 2002; Ahmaruzzaman, 2011; Sorokin et al., 2001; Kim et al., 2003; Wang et al., 2006; Carrillo-Pedroza and Soria-Aguilar, 2001a, b; Australia Environment, 2003; Ozomax, 2005; Volesky and Naja, 2005; Oelsner et al., 2001; EPRI Environmental Community Center, 1997; Miller, 2003; Davies et al., 1998; Barr et al. 2007; Latkowska and Figa, 2007;Bucsh et al., 1980; Young et al., 1984; Botz, 1999; Durney, 1984; Logsdon et al. 1999; Young and Jordan, 1995; Iordache et al. 2003; EPA 1994; Terry et al., 2001; Scott, 1984; Lemos et al. 2006; USEPA, 1994; Gogate and Pandit, 2004; Botz and Mudder, 2000; Simovic et al, 1985; Aguado et al. 2002).

Leaching with biogenic cyanide can be a potential alternative to chemical cyanidation, as biogenic cyanide is destroyed by the same type of micro-organisms, if they remain in excess, through a combination of hydrolytic, oxidation, reduction, and substitution processes. On the hydrolytic pathway, there is direct cleavage of the

C–N bond, eliminating the possibility of further reactivity. The decomposition can be catalyzed by the cyanidase-forming by-products formic acid and ammonia (hydrolysis) or by cyanide hydratase forming the formamide by-product (hydration) (Dumestre et al., 1997). In the oxidative pathway, monoxygenase enzymes catalyze the cyanides to cyanates that can be further hydrolyzed to ammonia and carbon dioxide dioxygenase enzymes (Knowles, 1976).

$$HCN + H_2O \xrightarrow{\text{monoxygenase}} HCONH_2 \tag{4.24}$$

$$HCN + O_2 + H^+ + NAD(P)H \xrightarrow{\text{monoxygenase}} HOCN + NAD(P)^+ + H_2O \tag{4.25}$$

$$HCN + O_2 + 2H^+ + NAD(P)H \xrightarrow{\text{dioxygenase}} CO_2 + NH_3 + NAD(P)^+ \tag{4.26}$$

Although the anaerobic conditions for destroying cyanide are uncommon, numerous microbes follow this route to form ammonia and methane as the destructive products (Kao et al., 2003; Ilyas and Lee, 2018), as in the reactions below:

$$HCN + 2H^+ + 2e^- \xrightarrow{\text{reductive pathway}} CH_2NH + H_2O + NAD(P)^+ = CH_2O \tag{4.27}$$

$$CH_2NH + 2H^+ + 2e^- \xrightarrow{\text{reductive pathway}} CH_3^- NH + 2H^+ + 2e^- = CH_4 + NH_3 \tag{4.28}$$

ACKNOWLEDGEMENTS

This work was supported by the Brain Pool Programme through the National Research Foundation of Korea (NRF) funded by the Ministry of Science and ICT (Grant No. 2019H1D3A2A02101993) and the Basic Science Research Programme through the National Research Foundation of Korea (NRF) funded by the Ministry of Education (Project no. 2020R1I1A1A01074249).

REFERENCES

Aguado, J., Grieke, R.V., López-Muñoz, M., Marugán, J. (2002). Removal of Cyanides in Wastewater by Supported Tio2-Based Photocatalysis. *Catal Today* 75:95–102.

Ahmaruzzaman, M. (2011). Industrial wastes as low-cost potential adsorbents for the treatment of wastewater laden with heavy metals. *Advances in Colloid and Interface Science.* 166(1):36–59.

Arshadi, M. and Mousavi, S. M. (2015) Enhancement of simultaneous gold and copper extraction from computer printed circuit boards using Bacillus megaterium. *Bioresource Technology*, 175, 315–324.

Ashurst, K., Finkelstein, N. (1970). The influence of sulphydryl and cationic flotation reagents on the cyanidation of native gold. Mintek.

Askeland, R.A., Morrison, S.M. (1983). Cyanide production by *Pseudomonas fluorescens* and *Pseudomonas aeruginosa. Appl Environ Microbiol.* 45:1802–1807.

ASTI, A.S. (2007). *Cyanide Wastes.* Orange, CA: Advanced Sensor Technologies, Inc..

Atkinson, G. B., Desmond, D. P., Kuczynski, R. J. and Walters, L. A. (1989). Recovery of PGM from virgin automotive catalyst by cyanide leaching. In *Proceeding Seminar of Int'l Precious Metals Institute Las Vegas Nevada*, pp. 109–115.

Atkinson, G. B., Kuczynski, R. J. and Desmond, D. P. (1992) Cyanide leaching method for recovering platinum group metals from a catalytic converter catalyst *U.S. Patent, 5,160,711*. Washington.

Australia Environment. (2003). Cyanide Management. Australia. Baker, A.J., 1970, 1985. Wastewater Treatment Controls. Retrieved 1 Dec 2010 from Ftp://Ftp.Unicauca.Edu. Co/Facultades/FIET/DEIC/Materias/Instrumentacion%20Inustrial/Instrument%20 Engineers'%20Handbook,%20Fourth%20Edition,%20Volume%20Two%20 Process%20Control%20and%20Optimization/1081ch8_39.Pdf.

Avraamides, J. (1989). Cip carbons–selection, testing and plant operations. In: *Gold Forum on Technology and Practices-World Gold*, Pp. 288–292.

Barr, G., Willy, G., David, J., Keith, M. (2007). *The New Cesl gold process*. Perth, WA, Australia: Cominco Engineering Services Ltd.

Barsky, G., Swainson, S., Hedley, N. (1934). Dissolution of gold and silver in cyanide solutions. *Trans. AIME*. 112: 660–677.

Bodländer, G. (1896). Ueber abnorme Gefrierpunktserniedrigungen. *Zeitschrift für Physikalische Chemie*. 21: 378–382.

Boonstra, B. (1943). Über die Lösungsgeschwindigkeit von Gold in Kalium Cyanid-lösungen. *Korros. Metallschutz*. 19: 146–151.

Bosecker, K. (1997). Bioleaching: metal solubilization by microorganisms. *FEMS Microbiology reviews*, 20(3–4): 591–604.

Botz, M. (1999). *Overview of cyanide treatment methods*. Washington, DC: The Gold Institute. 20036.

Botz, M.M. and Mudder, T.I. (2000). Modeling of natural cyanide attenuation in tailings impoundments. *Minerals and Metallurgical Processing*. 17(4):228–233.

Brandl, H., Bosshard, R., Wegmann, M. (2001). Computer-munching microbes: metal leaching from electronic scrap by bacteria and fungi. *Hydrometallurgy*. 59(2): 319–326.

Brandl, H., Lehmann, S., Faramarzi, M. A., and Martinelli, D. (2008). Biomobilization of silver, gold, and platinum from solid materials by HCN-forming microorganisms. *Hydrometallurgy*. 94: 14–17.

Brysk, M.M., Lauinger, C., Ressler, C. (1969). Biosynthesis of cyanide from [2-14C-15N] glycine in *Chromobacterium violaceum*. *Biochim Biophys Acta*. 184:583–588.

Bucsh, O.R., Spottiswood, D.J., Lower, G.W. (1980). Ion-Precipitate Flotation Of Iron-Cyanide Complexes. *Water Pollution Control Federation*. 52 (12): 292–293.

Carrillo-Pedroza, F.R. and Soria-Aguilar, M.J. (2001a). Destruction of cyanide by ozone in two gas-liquid contacting systems. *EJMP & EP (European Journal of Mineral Processing and Environmental Protection)*, 1(1):55–63.

Carrillo-Pedroza, F., Soria-Aguilar, M. (2001b). Destruction Of Cyanide By Ozone In Two Gas-Liquid Contacting Systems. *The European Journal of Mineral Processing and Environmental Protection*. 1: 55–61.

Castric, P.A. (1977). Glycine metabolism by *Pseudomonas aeruginosa*: hydrogen cyanide biosynthesis. *J Bacteriol*. 130:826–831.

Castric, P.A. (1981). The metabolism of hydrogen cyanide by bacteria. In: Vennesland, B., Conn, E.E., Knowles, C.J., Westley, J., Wissing, F. (eds), *Cyanide in biology*. London: Academic, pp. 233–261.

Chen, J. (1995). *The Fundamental Theory and Practice on Chemical Hydrometallurgical Processes of Platinum Group Metals*. Kunming, China: Yunnan Science and Technology Press.

Chen, J., and Huang, K. (2006) A new technique for extraction of platinum group metals by pressure cyanidation. *Hydrometallurgy*, 82: 164.

Chen, J., Huang, K. and Chen, Y. R. (2005). Hydrometallurgical leaching method for extracting platinum, palladium, copper and nickel from the sulfide flotation concentrates containing platinum metals. *South African Patent*, 5141.

Christy, S. (1896). The solution and precipitation of the cyanide of gold. *Trans. AIME.* 26: 735–772.

Cornejo, L.M. and Spottiswood, D.J. (1984). Fundamental aspects of the gold cyanidation process: a review. *Mineral Energy Resource. (United States).* 27(2):1–18.

Dash, R.B., Balomajumder, C., Kumar, A. (2008). Treatment of metal cyanide bearing wastewater by simultaneous adsorption and biodegradation (SAB). *Journal of Hazardous Materials* 152(1): 387–396.

Davis, W.M. (1880). Depositing gold from its solutions. *U.S. Patent.* 227:963.

Deschênes, G., Lacasse, S., Fulton, M. (2003). Improvement of cyanidation practice at Goldcorp red lake mine. *Minerals Engineering.* 16:503–509.

Deschênes G., Lastra R., Brown J. R., Jin S., May O., Ghali E. (2000). Effect of lead nitrate on cyanidation of gold ores: progress on the study of the mechanisms. *Minerals Engineering.* 13:1263–1279.

Desmond, D. P. (1991) *High-temperature cyanide leaching of platinum-group metals from automobile catalysts–laboratory tests*, US Department of the Interior, Bureau of Mines, 9384.

Dumestre, A., Chone, T., Portal, J., Gerard, M., Berthelin, J. 1997. Cyanide degradation under alkaline conditions by a strain of fusarium solani isolated from contaminated soils. *Applied and Environmental Microbiology.* 63(7): 2729–2734.

Durney, J.L. (1984). *Electroplating engineering handbook*, 4th Edition. Van Nostrand Reinhold, Springer USA.

Eisler, R., Wiemeyer, S.N. (2004). Cyanide hazards to plants and animals from gold mining and related water issues. In *Reviews of environmental contamination and toxicology.* New York: Springer, 21–54.

Ellis, S., Senanayake, G. (2004). The effects of dissolved oxygen and cyanide dosage on gold extraction from a pyrrhotite-rich ore. *Hydrometallurgy.* 72:39–50.

Elmore, C., Brison, R., Kenny, C. (1988). The kamyr cilo process. *Perth Gold* 88: 197.

Elsner, L. (1846). Beobachtungen über das Verhalten regulinischer Metalle in einer wässrigen Lösung von Cyankalium. *Advanced Synthesis & Catalysis.* 37: 441–446.

EPA: US, U.E. (1994). *Treatment of cyanide heap leaches and tailings.* Washington, DC: Office of Solid Waste, Special Waste Branch.

EPRI Environmental Community Center (1997). *Membrane technologies for water and wastewater treatment.* Palo Alto, CA: Electric Power Research Institute.

Faramarzi, M. A., Brandl, H. (2006). Formation of water-soluble metal cyanide complexes from solid minerals by *Pseudomonas plecoglossicida. FEMS Microbiology Letters.* 259: 47–52.

Faramarzi, M. A., Mogharabi-Manzari, M., and Brandl, H. (2020). Bioleaching of metals from wastes and low-grade sources by HCN-forming microorganisms. *Hydrometallurgy* 191:105228. doi: 10.1016/j.hydromet.2019.105228

Faramarzi, M. A., Stagars, M., Pensini, E., Krebs, W., Brandl, H. (2004). Metal solubilization from metal-containing solid materials by cyanogenic *Chromobacterium violaceum. Journal of Biotechnology.* 113: 321–326.

Gogate, P.R., Pandit, A.B. (2004). A review of imperative technologies for wastewater treatment I: oxidation technologies at ambient conditions. *Advances in Environmental Research.* 8(3):501–551.

Golyshina, O. V., Pivovarova, T. A., Karavaiko, G. I., Kondrat'eva, T. F., Moore, E. R.B., Abraham, W. R., Lunsdorf, H., Timmis, K. N., Yakimov, M. M., Golyshin, P. N. (2000). *Ferroplasma acidiphilum* gen. nov., sp. nov., an acidophilic, autotrophic, ferrous-iron-oxidizing, cell-wall-lacking, mesophilic member of the Ferroplasmaceae fam. nov., comprising a distinct lineage of the Archaea. *Int J Syst Evol Microb*, 50: 997–1006.

Green, M. (1913). The action of oxidisers in cyaniding. *Journal of Chemical Metallurgy & Mining Society* 13: 355.

Gu, Y.Y. (1994) The optimal ratio between the concentration of CN^- and O_2 in gold cyanide leaching process. *Gold*, 15 (6): 50–52.

Gurbuz, N., Ozdemir, I., Demir, S., Cetinkaya, B. (2004). Improved palladium catalysed coupling reactions of aryl halides using saturated N-heterocarbene ligands. *Journal of Molecular Catalysis. A: Chemical.* 209(1).

Habashi, F. (1967). Kinetics and mechanism of gold and silver dissolution in cyanide solution. Montana College of Mineral Science and Technology.

Habashi, F. (1987a). One hundred years of cyanidation. *CLM. Bull.* 80(905):108–114.

Habashi, F. (1987b). One hundred years of cyanidation. *Can. Min. Metall. Bull.* 80: 108–114.

Hancock, R. D., Finkelstein, N. P. and Evers, A. (1977). A linear free-energy relation involving the formation constants of palladium (II) and platinum (II). *Journal of Inorganic and Nuclear Chemistry*, 39(6), 1031–1034.

Hol, A., van der Weijden, R. D., Weert, G. V., Kondos, P., Buisman, C. J.N. (2011). Processing of Arsenopyritic gold concentrates by partial biooxidation followed by bioreduction. *Environmental Science and Technology.* 45: 6316–6321.

Hoque, M. E., Philip, O. J. (2011). Biotechnological recovery of heavy metals from secondary sources—An overview. *Materials Science and Engineering: C.* 31(2): 57–66.

Huang, K. 2004. Extraction of platinum group metals by pressure cyanation. PhD dissertation, Kunming University of Science and Technology.

IAEA. (2002). *Application of ion exchange processes for the treatment of radioactive waste and management of spent ion exchangers.* Vienna: IAEA in Austria.

Ilyas, S., Lee, J.-C. (2014). Biometallurgical recovery of metals from waste electrical and electronic equipment: a review. *ChemBioEng Reviews.* 1(4): 148–169.

Ilyas, S., Lee, J.-C. (2018). *Gold metallurgy and the environment.* Boca Raton: CRC Press, doi:10.1201/9781315150475.

Iordache, I., Nechita, M., Aelenei, N., Rosca, I., Apostolescu, G., Peptanariu, M. (2003). Sonochemical enhancement of cyanide ion degradation from wastewater in the presence of hydrogen peroxide. *Polish Journal of Environmental Studies.* 12 (6): 735–737.

Janin, A. (1892). The cyanide process. *Min. M. Ind.* 249.

Janin Jr, L. (1888). Cyanide of potassium as a lixiviate agent for silver ores and mineral. *Eng. J.* 46: 548–549.

Jara, J., Harris, R. (1994). A new device to enhance oxygen dispersion in gold cyanidation. In: *Proceedings, Annual Meeting of the Canadian Mineral Processors*, Paper 94. Canadian Institute of Mining, Metallurgy and Petroleum (CIM), Montreal.

Julian, H.F. and E. Smart. (1921). *Cyaniding gold and silver ores.* London: Griffin.

Kao, C. M., Liu, J. K., Lou, H. R., Lin, C. S., Chen, S. C. (2003). Biotransformation of cyanide to methane and ammonia by Klebsiella oxytoca. *Chemosphere.* 50(8): 1055–1061.

Kim, Y. J., Qureshi, T. I., Min, K. S. (2003). Application of advanced oxidation processes for the treatment of cyanide containing effluent. *Environmental Technology.* 24: 1269–1276.

Kita, Y., Nishikawa, H., Takemoto, T. (2006). Effects of cyanide and dissolved oxygen concentration on biological Au recovery. *Journal of Biotechnology*, 124: 545–551.

Knowles, C. J. (1976). Microorganisms and cyanide. *Bacteriological Reviews.* 40(3): 652.

Kondos, P. D., G. Deschênes and R. M. Morrison. (1995). Process optimization studies in gold cyanidation. *Hydrometallurgy.* 39:235–250.

Kuczynski, R.J., Atkinson, G.B. and Dolinar, W.J. (1995). *High temperature cyanide leaching of platinum-group metals from automobile catalysts-pilot plant.* US Bureau of Mines RI 9543.

La Brooy, S., Komosa, T., Muir, D. (1991). Selective leaching of gold from copper-gold ores using ammonia-cyanide mixtures. In *Proceedings of 5th Aus IMM Extractive Metallurgy Conference.*

Latkowska, B., Figa, J. (2007). Cyanide Removal from Industrial Wastewaters. *Polish Journal of Environmental Study.* 16 (2A): 748–752.

Lemos, F., Gonzoga, S., Dutra, J. (2006). Copper electrowinning from gold plant waste streams. *Minerals Engineering.* (19): 388–398.

Li, J., Liang, C. and Ma, C. (2015) Bioleaching of gold from waste printed circuit boards by Chromobacterium violaceum. *Journal of Material Cycles and Waste Management,* 17(3), 529–539.

Ling, P., Papangelakis, V.G., Argyropoulos, S.A., Kondos P. D. (1996). An improved rate equation for cyanidation of a gold ore. *Canadian Metallurgical Quarterly.* 35:225–234.

Liu, G.O., Yen, W.T. (1995). Dissolution kinetics and carbon adsorption for the cyanidation of gold ores in oxygen-enriched slurry. *CIM Bull.* 88(986): 42–48.

Logsdon, M.J., Hagelstein, K., Mudder, T.I. (1999). *The management of cyanide in gold extraction.* Ottawa, Ontario: International Council on Metals and the Environment.

Loroesch, J., Knorre, H., Merz, F., Gos, S. and Marais, H.J. (1988). The Degussa PAL system- a future technology in cyanidation. *Perth Gold.* 88:202.

Lowehein, F.A. and Moran, M.K. (1975).*Faith, Keys and Clark's industrial chemicals.* New York: John Wiley and Sons.

Maclaurin, R.C. (1893). The dissolution of gold in a solution of potassium cyanide. *Journal of the Chemical Society, Transactions.* 63: 724–738.

Marsden, J., House I. (1992). *The chemistry of gold extraction.* New York: Ellis Horwood.

McArthur, J.S. (1905). Gold extraction by cyanide: a retrospect. *Journal of the Society of Chemical Industry.* 24:311–315.

McLaughlin, J.D., Quinn, P., Agar, G.E., Cloutier, J.Y., Dube, G., Leclerc, A. (1999). Oxygen mass transfer rate measurements under different hydrodynamic regimes. *Ind. Mine´ r. –Les Tech.* 76(3–4): 121–126.

McMullen, J., Thompson, R. (1989). Practical use of oxygen for gold leaching in Canada. In *Randol Gold & Silver Recovery Innovations: Phase IV Workshop,* Sacramento, California, Pp. 99–100.

Merchant, B. (1998). Gold, the noble metal and the paradoxes of its toxicology. *Biologicals,* 26: 49–59.

Michaels, R., Hankes, L.V., Corpe, W.A. (1965). Cyanide formation by nonproliferating cells of *Chromobacterium violaceum. Arch Biochem Biophys.* 111:121–125.

Miller, J.D. (2003). *Treatment of cyanide solutions and slurries using air-sparged hydrocyclone (Ash) technology.* Salt Lake, UT: The Office of Industrial Technologies, Energy Efficiency and Renewable Energy, U.S. Department of Energy.

Motaghed, M., Mousavi, S. M., Rastegar, S. O. and Shojaosadati, S. A. (2014). Platinum and rhenium extraction from a spent refinery catalyst using Bacillus megaterium as a cyanogenic bacterium: statistical modeling and process optimization. *Bioresource Technology,* 171, 401–409.

Natarajan, G. and Ting, Y. P. (2014). Pretreatment of e-waste and mutation of alkali-tolerant cyanogenic bacteria promote gold biorecovery. *Bioresource Technology,* 152, 80–85.

Oelsner, K., Dornid, D., Uhlemann, R. (2001). Degradation of complex cyanides. Bioservice Waldenburg. Saxon State Ministry of the Environment and Agriculture.

Ozomax. (2005). Advanced Oxidation Process. Ozomax. Pargaa, J., Shuklab, S., Carrillo-Pedrozac, F., (2003). Destruction of Cyanide Waste Solutions Using Chlorine Dioxide. *Ozone and Titania Sol.* 23: 183-191.

Park, J. (1898). Notes on the action of cyanogen on gold. *Trans. Am. Inst. Min. Metall. Pet. Eng.* 6: 120.

Paterson, C. J. (1990). In: Arbriter, A., and Han, K. N. (eds) *Gold: Advances in Precious Metals Recovery.* New York: Gordon and Breach, Ch. 1: 49–116.

Pham, V. A. and Ting, Y. P. (2009). Gold bioleaching of electronic waste by cyanogenic bacteria and its enhancement with bio-oxidation. *Advanced Materials Research,* 71, 661–664.

Pradhan, J. K. and Kumar, S. (2012). Metals bioleaching from electronic waste by Chromobacterium violaceum and Pseudomonads sp. *Waste Management & Research*, 30(11), 1151–1159.

Revy, T., Watson, S., Hoecker, W. (1991). Oxygen assisted cyanidation of gold in Australia. In *Randol Gold Forum '91, Cairns, Australia*. Golden, CO: Randol International, pp. 317–324.

Riani, J.C., Leao, V.A., Silva, C.A.D., Silva, A.M., Bertolino, S.M., Lukey, G.C. (2007). The elution of metal cyanocomplexes from poly acrylic and polystere based ion exchange resins using nitrate and thiocyanate eluants. *Brazlian Journal of Chemical Engineering* 24(3): 421–431.

Rohwerder, T., Gehrke, T., Kinzler, K., Sand, W. (2003). Bioleaching review part A: progress in bioleaching: fundamentals and mechanisms of bacterial metal sulfide oxidation. *Applied Microbiol Biotechnology*, 63: 239–248.

Sceresini, B., (1997). The Filblast cyanidation process–a maturing technology. In *Randol Gold Forum* 97:173–179.

Scott, S.J. (1984). An overview of cyanide treatment methods for gold mill effluents. *Conference on Cyanide and the Environment*, Tucson, AZ. Geotechnical Engineering Program, Colorado State University.

Shams, K., Beiggy, M. R. and Gholamipour Shirazi, A. (2004). Optimum conditions for platinum removal from dehydrogenation spent catalysts using cyanide leaching method followed by ion exchange. *Applied Catalyst*, 258, 227–234.

Sharpe, A.G. (1976). *The chemistry of cyano complexes of the transition metals*. Organometallic Chemistry - A Series of Monographs. London-New York-San Francisco: Academic Press, pp. 243–264.

Shin, D., Jeong, J., Lee, S., Pandey, B.D., Lee, J.-C. (2013) Evaluation of bioleaching factors on gold recovery from ore by cyanide-producing bacteria. *Miner. Eng*. 48: 20–24.

Sibrell, P. L., Atkinson, G. B. and Walters, L. A. (1994). *Cyanide leaching chemistry of platinum-group metals. Report of investigations*. Bureau of Mines, Reno Research Center, United States.

Simeonova, F.P., Fishbein, L. (2004). *Hydrogen cyanide and cyanides: human health aspects*. Geneva: World Health Organization.

Simovic, L. and Snodgrass, W.J. (1999). Techniques for Evaluating a Mathematical Model for the Natural Degradation of Cyanide from Gold Mill Effluents.

Simovic, L. Snodgrass, W. J. Murphy, K. L. Schmidt, J. W. (1985). Development of a model to describe the natural degradation of cyanide in gold mill effluents. In van Zyl, Dirk (ed.), *Cyanide and the environment; Proceedings of a conference, Tucson, Arizona*. 11–14 December 1984. Colorado State University Geotechnical Engineering Program, v. 2, p. 413–432.

Skey, W. (1897). A note on cyanide process. *Eng. And Min. J*. 63.

Sorokin D.Y., Tourova, T. P., Lysenko, A. M., Kuenen, J. G. (2001). Microbial thiocyanate utilization under highly alkaline conditions. *Applied Biochemistry Microbiology*. 67: 528–538.

Stephens, T. (1988). The use of pure oxygen in the leaching process in South African gold mines. In *Perth International Gold Conference*. Golden, CO: Randol International, pp. 191–196.

Tay, S. B., Natarajan, G., bin Abdul Rahim, M. N., Tan, H. T., Chung, M. C. M., Ting, Y. P. and Yew, W. S. (2013). Enhancing gold recovery from electronic waste via lixiviant metabolic engineering in Chromobacterium violaceum. *Scientific Reports*, 3, 2236.

Terry, I.M., Botz, M.M., Smidth, A. (2001). *Chemistry and treatment of cyanidation wastes*. London: Mining Journal Books Limited, 2nd Edition.

Tran, C. D., Lee, J. C., Pandey, B. D., Jeong, J., Yoo, K. and Huynh, T. H. (2011). Bacterial cyanide generation in presence of metal ions (Na^+, Mg^{2+}, Fe^{2+}, Pb^{2+}) and gold bioleaching from waste PCBs. *Journal of Chemical Engineering of Japan*, 44, 692–700.

Volesky, B., Naja, G. (2005). Biosorption application strategies. *16th Internat. Biotecnol. Symp. Compress Co.*, Cape Town, South Africa.

Wadsworth, M. E., Zhu, X., Thompson, J.S., Pereira, C. J. (2000). Gold dissolution and activation in cyanide solution: kinetics and mechanism. *Hydrometallurgy.* 57:1–11.

Wang, L.K., Hung, Y.-T., Howard, H.L., Constantine, Y. (2006). *Handbook of industrial and hazardous waste treatment.* New York: Marcel Dekker, Inc.

Wissing, F. (1974). Cyanide formation from oxidation of glycine by a *Pseudomonas* species. *J Bacteriol.* 117:1289–1294.

Wissing, F., Andersen, K.A. (1981). The enzymology of cyanide production from glycine by a *Pseudomonas* species. In: Vennesland, B., Conn, E. E., Knowles, C. J., Westley, J., Wissing, F. (eds), *Cyanide in biology*, London: Academic, pp. 275–288

Young, G., Douglas, W., Hampshire, M. (1984). Carbon in pulp process for recovering gold from acid plant calcines at president brand. *Mining engineering.* 36: 257–264.

Young, C. A., Jordan, T. S. (1995). Cyanide remediation: Current and past technologies. *Conference on hazardous waste research.* Manhattan, Kansas: Department of Metallurgical Engineering, Montana Tech.

5 Urban Mining of Precious Metals with Thiosulfate and Thiourea as Lixiviant

Sadia Ilyas
Mineral Resources and Energy Engineering, Jeonbuk National University, Jeonju, Jeonbuk 54896, Republic of Korea

Huma Munir
Department of Chemistry, Government College University Faisalabad, 38040, Pakistan

Hyunjung Kim
Mineral Resources and Energy Engineering, Jeonbuk National University, Jeonju, Jeonbuk 54896, Republic of Korea

Department of Environment and Energy, Jeonbuk National University, Jeonju, Jeonbuk 54896, Republic of Korea

Rajiv Ranjan Srivastava
Center for Advanced Chemistry, Institute of Research and Development, Duy Tan University, Da Nang 550000, Vietnam

CONTENTS

5.1 URBAN MINING OF PRECIOUS METALS WITH THIOSULFATE AND THIOUREA: AN OVERVIEW

For precious metal leaching from spent printed circuit boards, the useful sulphur-based thio-compounds are thiosulfate and thiourea. Apart from the complications in solution chemistry exhibited by the instability of thio-compounds and many other reactions which simultaneously take place during gold leaching, these thio-compounds have chemical similarities to enable gold to be leached in an oxidizing environment (Ilyas and Lee, 2014).

5.2 THIOSULFATE LEACHING OF PRECIOUS METALS

Thiosulfate, with the chemical symbol, $S_2O_3^{2-}$ and tetrahedral molecular shape, is an oxyanion of sulphur and can be derived by replacing one oxygen atom with a sulphur atom in a sulphate anion (Schmidt, 1962) as indicated in Figure 5.1.

The sulphur-to-sulphur (S—S) distance indicates a single bond, implying that the sulphur bears a significant negative charge and the S—O interactions have a more double-bond character. Thiosulphate can be produced from the reaction of elemental sulphur and sulphite at elevated temperature:

$$S + SO_3^{2-} \rightarrow S_2O_3^{2-} \tag{5.1}$$

Under alkaline conditions, thiosulphate can be produced as a product of the reaction between sulphur or sulphide and hydroxide (Shieh et al., 1965):

$$S_8 + 8NaOH \rightarrow 2Na_2S_2O_3 + 4NaHS + 2H_2O \tag{5.2}$$

$$2(NH_4)_2 S_5 + 6NH_4OH + 6O_2 \rightarrow 5(NH_4)_2 S_2O_3 + 3H_2O \tag{5.3}$$

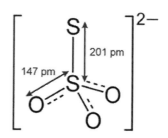

FIGURE 5.1 Tetrahedral structure of thiosulphate ion with bond angles.

The thiosulphate anion is a metastable donor of sulphur, and undergoes dispropor-tionation to form sulphite and sulphur or an active sulphur species. It is sometimes regenerated from tri-, tetra-, or penta-thionates in an alkaline aqueous ammonia solu-tion (Zhang and Dreisinger, 2002; Aylmore and Muir, 2001; Naito et al., 1970):

$$4S_4O_6^{2-} + 6OH^- \rightarrow 2S_3O_6^{2-} + 5S_2O_3^{2-} + 3H_2O \qquad (5.4)$$

$$2S_4O_6^{2-} \rightarrow S_3O_6^{2-} + S_5O_6^{2-} \qquad (5.5)$$

$$2S_5O_6^{2-} + 6OH^- \rightarrow 5S_2O_3^{2-} + 3H_2O \qquad (5.6)$$

$$S_3O_6^{2-} + 2OH^- \rightarrow SO_4^{2-} + S_2O_3^{2-} + H_2O \qquad (5.7)$$

$$S_3O_6^{2-} + NH_3 + OH^- \rightarrow SO_3NH_2^- + S_2O_3^{2-} + H_2O \qquad (5.8)$$

Thiosulphate is a divalent soft ligand (type A) which tends to form stable complexes with low-spin d^{10} ($Au^+, Ag^+, Cu^+, Hg^{2+}$) and d^8 ($Au^{3+}, Pt^{2+}, Pd^{2+}$) metal ions (Livingstone, 1965; Wilkinson and Gillard, 1987). Mostly, the thiosulphate ion acts as a unidentate ligand via the terminal sulphur atom, establishing strong σ bonds with a metal ion which are stabilized by $p\pi$–$d\pi$ back-bonding (back donation). Thiosulphate ligands may also act as a bidentate ligand through sulphur and an oxygen atom and as a bridg-ing ligand via the terminal sulphur atom, usually resulting in an insoluble complex (Figure 5.2) (Gmelin, 1973; Livingstone, 1965; Ryabchikov, 1943; Zhao et al., 1998).

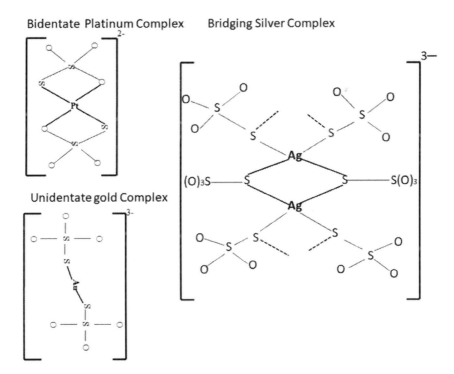

FIGURE 5.2   Unidentate, bidentate and bridging complexes of thiosulphate with precious metals.

The recovery of gold using thiosulphate was first proposed early in the 1900s (White, 1900). The compatibility of an environmentally benign thiosulphate ligand to be complexed with gold along with the achievable faster kinetics, as with cyanidation, are some of the basic characteristics that make thiosulphate the prime alternative candidate in gold metallurgy. Especially in the case of secondary wastes containing carbonaceous material, the in-situ adsorption of anionic gold cyanide complex onto the carbonaceous matter can be avoided using thiosulphate as lixiviant. The affinity order of gold adsorption on the carbon surface is: $SCN^- > SC(NH_2)_2 > CN^- \ S_2O_3^{2-}$. Although thiosulphate exhibits the anionic species, possibly $Au(S_2O_3)^-$ and $Au(S_2O_3)_2^{3-}$, it shows less affinity for reductive adsorption of the thiosulphate complex than with the adsorption of cyanide and chloride complexes on the carbon surface, leading the way towards treat carbonaceous ores in an environmentally benign manner.

5.2.1 Mechanism of Thiosulphate Leaching of Precious Metals From Urban Mine Sources

Thiosulphate $(S_2O_3)^{2-}$ has been widely accepted as the best suitable reagent and alternative to cyanide and aqua regia lixiviant for gold leaching from various primary and secondary sources. The chemistry of the gold–thiosulphate system is complex and needs an oxidizing atmosphere to keep reactions under control. Copper, which has self-catalytic behavior, is commonly used as an oxidizing agent. The compulsion to maintain the alkaline condition in the thiosulphate system to prevent its decomposition by acid is fulfilled in an ammoniacal medium; under such conditions copper can easily form ammine complexes to catalyze the reaction kinetics (Aylmore and Muir, 2001). In the case of gold extraction from spent printed circuit boards, the amount of copper and the reduced interference of foreign metals due to its inability to form soluble ammine complexes is another reason for its usefulness for thiosulphate leaching. Gold alloyed with nickel followed by nickel and copper layers can easily be

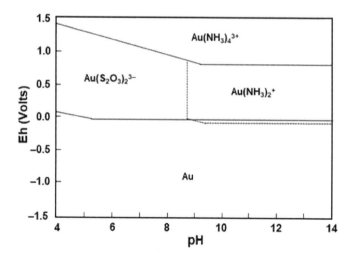

FIGURE 5.3   Eh–pH diagram of the Au–$(S_2O_3)^{2-}$–H_2O system (conditions: 5×10^{-4} M Au, 1M $S_2O_3^{2-}$, 1M NH_3/NH_4^+ at 25°C).

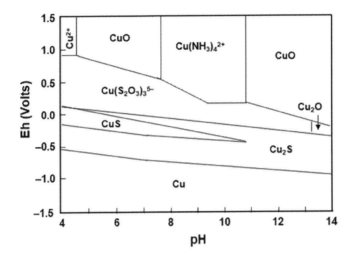

FIGURE 5.4   Eh–pH diagram of the Cu—$(S_2O_3)^{2-}$–H_2O system (conditions: 0.5 M Cu^{2+}, 1M $S_2O_3^{2-}$, 1M NH_3/NH_4^+ at 25°C).

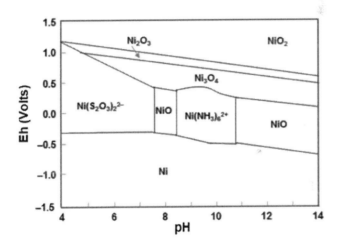

FIGURE 5.5   Eh–pH diagram of the Ni—$(S_2O_3)^{2-}$–H_2O system (conditions: 0.35 M Ni^{2+}, 1M $S_2O_3^{2-}$, 1M NH_3/NH_4^+ at 25°C).

liberated to leach in ammoniacal solution as all three metals form their ammine complexes (Chen et al., 1996; Srivastava et al., 2013). The potential-pH diagrams of Au, Cu, and Ni are given in Figures 5.3, 5.4 and 5.5, respectively.

There are so many entities for potential gold leaching in this complex system, including the simultaneous presence of thiosulphate and ammonia, the redox couple Cu^{1+} and Cu^{2+} and the stability of thiosulphate itself under certain pH conditions, that understanding the aqueous chemistry is vitally important. The two gold–thiosulphate complexes are known to form as $Au(S_2O_3)^-$ and $Au(S_2O_3)_2^{3-}$, the latter complex being the more stable (Johnson and Davis, 1973). The plausible reaction with O_2 used as oxidant can be written as follows:

$$4Au + 8S_2O_3^{2-} + O_2 + H_2O \rightarrow 4\left[Au\left(S_2O_3\right)_2\right]^{3-} + 4OH^- \qquad (5.9)$$

But the above reaction has been found to exhibit slow kinetics due to passivation by sulphur deposited on the gold surfaces by the decomposition of thiosulfate(Pedraza et al., 1988). Introducing the ammonia prevents such passivation by preferential adsorption onto gold surfaces over the thiosulphate, and gold can be leached as follows (Chen et al., 1996; Jiang et al., 1993):

$$Au\left(NH_3\right)^{2+} + 2S_2O_3^{2-} \rightarrow \left[Au\left(S_2O_3\right)_2\right]^{3-} + 2NH_3 \qquad (5.10)$$

However, the formation of a gold–ammine complex is only possible at higher temperatures (Meng and Han, 1993), and >80°C is economically not a good choice, with a high rate of ammonia decomposition at an elevated temperature (>60°C). This has been encountered in the catalytic action of copper ions in gold–thiosulphate–ammonia leaching (Tyurin and Kakowski, 1960). The leaching of gold that occurs under the oxidizing environment of Cu^{2+} and Ni^{2+} has been found to be 18–20 times more beneficial with enhanced kinetics (Ter-Arakelyan 1984), also at a temperature <60°C (Tozawa et al., 1981). Moreover, gold–thiosulphate–ammonia leaching in the presence of copper and nickel is an electrochemical reaction, in which the $Cu(NH_3)_4^{2+}$ is converted to $Cu(NH_3)^{2+}$ to support the formation of the oxidized product $[Au(S_2O_3)_2]^{3-}$; the reverse oxidation of Cu^{1+} to Cu^{2+} occurs in the presence of O_2 (Byerley et al., 1973). The reactions that take place, in this case, are as follows:

$$Au + 2S_2O_3^{2-} \rightarrow \left[Au\left(S_2O_3\right)_2\right]^{3-} + e^- \qquad (5.11)$$

$$Cu\left(NH_3\right)_4^{2+} + 3S_2O_3^{2-} + e^- \rightarrow \left[Cu\left(S_2O_3\right)_3\right]^{5-} + 4NH_3 \qquad (5.12)$$

$$2Cu\left(NH_3\right)_4^{2+} + 8S_2O_3^{2-} \rightarrow 2\left[Cu\left(S_2O_3\right)_3\right]^{5-} + S_4O_6^{2-} + 8NH_3 \qquad (5.13)$$

$$2Cu\left(NH_3\right)_4^{2+} + 8NH_3 + O_2 + H_2O \rightarrow 2Cu\left(NH_3\right)_4^{2} + 8S_2O_3^{2-} + OH^- \qquad (5.14)$$

In contrast to the ore bodies, the liberation of gold from the spent printed circuit boards is depends to a great extent on how the alloyed nickel with the gold layer behaves in the ammonia–thiosulphate system. This makes the system much more complicated than the earlier complexed system of Au–Cu–NH₃/NH₄–S₂O₃ in solution; hence it has scarcely been described. The thermodynamic stability of the Cu^{2+}-thiosulphate complex is higher than that of $Cu(NH_3)_4^{2+}$; for this reason , the $Cu(NH_3)_4^{2+}$ is reduced to a Cu^{2+}–thiosulphate complex, causing oxidation of thiosulphate to degrade as tetrathionate. This condition does not arise in the presence of nickel, which also controls thiosulphate consumption during the whole process of gold leaching from spent printed circuit boards. Gold leaching can be catalyzed by the nickelous oxide under similar Eh–pH condition to the ammonia–thiosulphate system (Figure 5.5). The probable mechanism of these complicated electrochemical reactions and phenomena is presented in Figure 5.6.

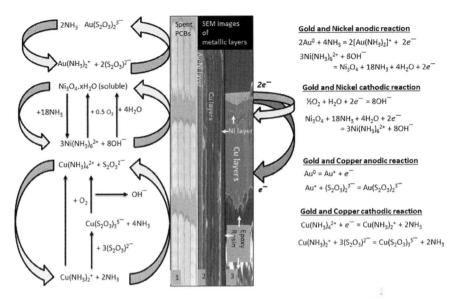

FIGURE 5.6 Probable electrochemical mechanism for gold–thiosulphate leaching from spent printed circuit boards.

It can be seen that the thiosulphate ions react with Au^{1+} on the anodic surface of gold and enter the solution to form $Au(S_2O_3)_2^{3-}$ which is catalyzed by the Cu^{2+}–Cu^{1+} ammine complexes. The reduction of $Cu(NH_3)_4^{2+}$ transfers two ammonia ligands to form the kinetically favoured diaminoaurate(I) complex, which subsequently exchanges the ligands with free thiosulphate ions to form the thermodynamically more stable auro-thiosulphate complex. At the same time, gold leaching is boosted by the oxidation reaction of the Ni^{2+}–ammine complex to form Ni_3O_4, and then the reduction of Ni_3O_4 with oxidation of gold as the $Au(NH_3)_2^+$ complex. The predominant cathodic reactions are dependent on the relative concentrations of the species.

Plenty of previously reported work suggests that the Au–Cu–NH_3–S_2O_3 leaching process is diffusion controlled. But leaching of gold from spent printed circuit boards (in which Au is alloyed with Ni) has been found to be chemically controlled, indicating that other entities influence gold leaching, and the presence of nickel in the system as per the electrolytic mechanism shown in Figure 5.6 may account for this. It can easily be seen that together with gold, all the nickel was leached in ammoniacal thiosulphate solution, and only after this is the copper layer exposed to the lixiviant.

Moreover, the leaching rate drastically decreased ($\sim$20% leaching after 9 h) whed 15mM Cu^{2+} was used instead of 20 mM. Leaching of shredded printed circuit boards also showed reduced efficacy of gold leaching (30.3%),compared to 78.8% leaching of the spent printed circuit boards unit under the same condition of 0.1 M $(NH_4)_2S_2O_3$, 40mM $CuSO_4$, 40 g L^{-1} solid–liquid ratio and pH 10.0–10.5 (Tripathi et al., 2012).

5.2.2 Effect of Various Process Parameters

A handful of research works have studied gold leaching from spent printed circuit boards in ammoniacal thiosulphate solutions. It is important to understand the influence of different factors.

5.2.2.1 Effect of Temperature

The role of temperature in the leaching kinetics of precious gold extraction from spent printed circuit boards is well established. A study conducted by Ha et al. (2014) with constant parameters of 10 nM $CuSO_4$, 60 nMNa$_2$S$_2$O$_3$, 0.2 MNH$_4$Cl, and 0.26 M NH_3 and at various leaching temperatures (in the range of 20–50°C) found that at the lowest temperature (20°C), the rate of gold leaching was also lowest and only <50% gold was extracted in 5 min, whereas at ≥40°C, all the gold was leached within 2 min (Figure 5.7). This difference in the leaching kinetics as a function of temperature is corroborated by the reduction rate of Cu^{2+} to Cu^{1+}.

The rate of reduction for Cu^{2+} to Cu^{1+} at 50°C was 3.9 times higher than that at 30°C (Figure 5.7). The reaction rate at the reagent concentration range of 40–60mM thiosulfate, 5–7mM Cu^{2+} and 0.22–0.247 M ammonia was given as follows:

$$R_1 = K\left[\left(S_2O_3^{2-}\right)\right]^{0.40} \times \left[\left(Cu^{2+}\right)\right]^{0.25} \times \left[\left(NH_3\right)\right]^{1.64} \tag{5.15}$$

While at the concentration range of 60–70mM thiosulfate, 7–9 mM Cu^{2+}, and 0.247–0.263 M ammonia, the gold leaching rate is expressed as higher reagent concentration ranges than those given above follow zero-order kinetics (Senanayake, 2004).

$$R_2 = K\left[\left(S_2O_3^{2-}\right)\right]^{0.22} \times \left[\left(Cu^{2+}\right)\right]^{0.16} \times \left[\left(NH_3\right)\right]^{0.72} \tag{5.16}$$

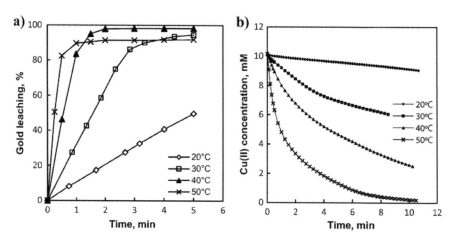

FIGURE 5.7 The extraction kinetics of gold and reduction rate of Cu(II) to Cu(I) at leaching temperatures of 20–50°C. Experimental conditions: 10mM $CuSO_4$; 60mM $Na_2S_2O_3$; 0.2 M NH_4Cl; 0.26 M NH_3; 10 mL/min nitrogen sparging rate.

Source: Adopted with permission from Ha et al. (2014).

5.2.2.2 Effect of Ammonia

Gold complexation with thiosulphate exhibits slow kinetics due to decomposition of thiosulphate to sulphur which passivates onto the gold surface, hindering leaching (Pedraza et al., 1988; Jiang et al., 1993; Chen et al., 1996). Alkaline solutions must be used to prevent thiosulphate dissolution, hence the use of ammonia which also prevents surface passivation and enhances gold complexation as follows (Chen et al., 1996; Jiang et al., 1993; Abbruzzese et al., 1995; Tozawa et al., 1981; Meng and Han, 1993; Tyurin and Kakowski, 1960):

$$Au\left(NH_3\right)^{2+} + 2S_2O_3^{2-} \rightarrow \left[Au\left(S_2O_3\right)_2\right]^{3-} + 2NH_3 \qquad (5.17)$$

The role of ammonia in gold–thiosulfate leaching has been mainly identified for the stabilization of copper as a cupric ammine complex to catalyze gold oxidation, which is helpful in further complexation with thiosulphate (Grosse et al., 2003). Higher ammonia concentration may cause the formation of solid species of copper like CuO, Cu2O, and (NH4)5Cu(S2O3)3 that impede gold dissolution by getting coated on the gold surfaces. This behavior was confirmed by Ha et al. (2010) when leaching spent printed circuit boards with thiosulphate in the presence of 0.1–0.4 M ammonia in solution.

Improved leaching efficacy was obtained with 0.3M ammonia at copper concentrations between 15mM and 30mM and $S_2O_3^{2-}$ concentration of 0.14 M, whereas less gold was obtained in solution at lower ammonia concentration (<0.3 M). This can be understood by gold passivation with the decomposed products of thiosulphate at lower ammonia concentrations. It is clear from the Eh–pH diagram (Fig. 5.3) that gold leaching greatly depends on thiosulphate concentration at solution pH < 9.0. For a similar kind of observation, thiosulphate concentration in the leach liquor of spent printed circuit boards as a function of pH (8.0–11.0) was analyzed by Tripathi et al. (2012). The results indicated that an increase in pH up to 10.5 gave the highest solubility of thiosulfate, ~0.1 M, which decreased to 0.08 M at pH 11.0. This behavior of thiosulphate as a function of pH matched well with the experimental results of previous studies, where the maximum rate of gold leaching was determined as 2.393×10^{-5} mol.m^{-2}.s^{-1} at 0.265 M NH$_3$ level (Ha et al., 2014). It is imperative to mention that in spent printed circuit boards, gold remains alloyed with nickel, therefore the formation of nickel ammine complexes also need to be considered. The Eh–pH diagram of the nickel-thiosulphate system (Figure 5.5) reduces the possibility of the formation of Ni(NH$_3$)$_6^{2+}$ at lower pH/ ammonia concentrations. This adversely affects the liberation of gold from the Au–Ni alloy phase. The positive effect of NH$_3$ among the terms analyzed here on gold leaching from spent printed circuit boards is shown in Figure 5.8.

5.2.2.3 Effect of Copper and Other Associated Metal Ions

The catalytic action of Cu^{2+} in securing gold leaching in thiosulphate solution was first reported by Tyurin and Kakowski (1960) A leaching rate 18 to 20 times higher than that obtained without employing Cu^{2+} was achieved (Ter-Arakeyan 1984). The reported increase in dissolution of gold in copper thiosulphate solutions containing

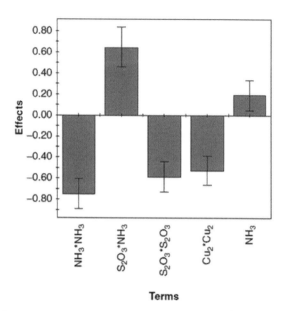

FIGURE 5.8 The effects of ammonia on the initial rate of thiosulphate leaching of gold from spent printed circuit boards.

Source: Adopted with permission from Ha et al. (2014).

ammonia has been attributed to the formation of $Cu(NH_3)_4^{2+}$ complexes. Results reported by various researchers were clearly attributed to the catalytic effect of copper in the gold leaching (Langhans et al., 1992). By varying the copper concentration in the range of 5–30 mM, it was found that going above 15mM Cu has no further effect on gold leaching (Figure 5.9).

The independence of gold leaching from Cu concentration above 15 mM is corroborated by the switching over of the gold leaching mechanism from diffusion control (at lower Cu concentration) to chemical control (at higher Cu concentration) (Jeffrey, 2001). In addition to this, the stability region of copper species $Cu(NH_3)_4^{2+}$ and $Cu(S_2O_3)_3^{5-}$ is very much concentration dependent (Aylmore and Muir, 2001), and at very high Cu concentration, precipitation of tenorite occurs. Therefore, in such a complex system of gold leaching, any excess of copper should be encountered by ammonia addition. Otherwise, the thiosulphate oxidized product, tetrathionate, may be formed (Flett et al., 1983), which could result in high reagent consumption and a decrease in gold leaching from the spent printed circuit boards.

Overall, in a thiosulphate leach liquor, the formation of gold and silver thiosulphate complexes occurs via the catalytic oxidation of the zero-valent metal by a suitable soluble metal complex, which is typically the $[Cu(NH_3)_4]^{2+}$ complex acting as the primary oxidant (Jiang et al., 1993; Li et al., 1995; Tozawa et al., 1981). In ammoniacal thiosulphate liquors, metal ions can form a range of complexes. In the case of copper, Cu^+ has commonly been reported as $[Cu(S_2O_3)_3]^{5-}$, yet at concentrations of thiosulphate below 0.05 M, the primary complex is expected to be $[Cu(S_2O_3)_2]^{3-}$ (Naito et al., 1970; Zipperian et al., 1988). Cu^{2+} exists predominantly

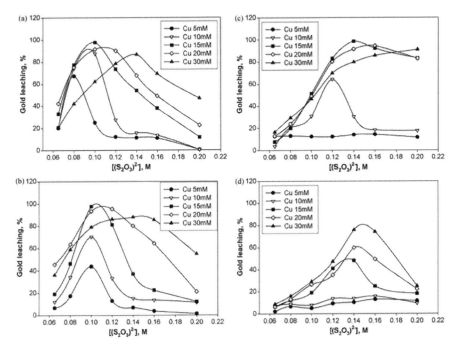

FIGURE 5.9   The effect of copper concentration on gold leaching from spent printed circuit boards in the thiosulphate system.

Source: Adopted with permission from Ha et al. (2010).

as $[Cu(NH_3)_4]^{2+}$, although some other ammine species may form (Byerley et al., 1973, 1975). In unfavourable conditions, the precipitation of $Cu_2S_2O_3$ or mixed salts of cuprous-ammonium thiosulphate may occur (Chen et al., 1996; Flett et al., 1983). Soluble thiosulphate complexes are also known for a number of heavy metals, with their stepwise stability constants and coordination numbers (Benedetti and Boulëgue, 1991; Gmelin, 1965, 1969, 1972, 1973; Hubin and Vereecken, 1994; Livingstone, 1965; Novakovskii and Ryazantseva, 1955; Tykodi, 1990; Vasil'ev et al., 1953; Vlassopoulos and Wood, 1990; Wilkinson and Gillard, 1987; Williamson and Rimstidt, 1993).

Apart from the formation of anionic thiosulphate complexes, some metal cations are expected to form ammine complexes (Smith and Martell, 1976). Several copper and palladium complexes bearing both ammine and thiosulphate ligands are also known, although their stability constants and solubility remain unknown (Wilkinson and Gillard, 1987). Based on stability constants, it can be predicted that many important metals will form thiosulphate complexes in preference to their corresponding ammine complexes. Thiosulphate complexes are expected to predominate for Au^+, Ag^+, Fe^{2+}, Hg^{2+}, and Pb^{2+}, whereas the metal ions Cu^+ and Cd^{2+} should be found as an equilibrium mixture of thiosulphate and ammine complexes. The remaining soluble metal ions should occur primarily as ammine complexes. The ligands of the aurothiosulphate complex are believed to be quite labile, as near-stoichiometric quantities of cyanide added to a thiosulphate liquor were found to rapidly form the corresponding aurocyanide complex (Lulham and Lindsay, 1991; Marchbank et al., 1996). This is especially significant when the rapid reaction between cyanide and thiosulphate ions is taken into account. The complexes $[Pd(S_2O_3)_4]^{6-}$ and $[Pt(S_2O_3)_4]^{6-}$ have aqueous solubilities above 10 ppb at pH 7 and 25°C, and quite low oxidation potentials (E^0) of –0.116 and –0.170 mV, respectively (Mountain and Wood, 1988; Plimer and Williams, 1988). However, they are not thermodynamically stable and slowly decompose into insoluble S-bridged oligomers (Anthony and Williams, 1994). Metals in higher oxidation states such as Au^{3+} and Fe^{3+} are readily reduced by thiosulphate ions and hence are not significant in leach liquors. Other anions from the leach liquor, such as chloride, hydroxide, or sulphate may also participate in metal ion solvation. Stable, soluble complexes bearing a mixture of ligands may be present, similar to the copper salts $[Cu(CN)_x(NH_3)_y]^{(1-x)}$ found in ammoniacal cyanide leach liquors (Muir et al., 1993). Both mercury and silver tend to form nearly insoluble sulphides, although complexation in excess thiosulphate tends to minimize this precipitation (Bean, 1997). Mostly Fe, TiO_2, and SiO_2 catalyze the oxidative degradation of thiosulphate ions into tetrathionate (Benedetti and Boulëgue, 1991; Xu and Schoonen, 1995). However, the side reactions and decomposition processes of many metal thiosulphate complexes are not well characterized, so it is essential to observe the natural degradation of thiosulphate via ubiquitous O_2, H_3O^+, trace Fe^{3+} and other oxidants prior to mineral leaching. One important example is Cu^{2+}, which also contributes to the essential gold oxidation step.

5.2.2.4 Effect of Oxygen

The completion of redox equilibrium between the cuprous-cupric couple, as described in the above electrochemical reactions, would require the conversion of the Cu^+ ion to Cu^{2+} to drive further leaching of gold. Oxygen supplied to the system causes the following reaction (Abbruzzese et al., 1995).

$$2Cu\left(S_2O_3\right)_3^{5-} + 8NH_3 + \frac{1}{2}O_2 + H_2O \rightarrow 2Cu\left(NH_3\right)_4^{2+} + 2OH^- + 6S_2O_3 \quad (5.18)$$

The amount of dissolved oxygen in thiosulphate solution of the ammoniacal medium directly affects the rapid oxidation of Cu^+ to Cu^{2+}, along with a little oxidation of thiosulphate forming sulphate and trithionate (Byerley et al., 1973). Notably, the oxidation of thiosulphate by oxygen in aqueous media under ambient temperature and pressure is known to be extremely slow and only prevails in the presence of Cu^{2+} ions and ammonia (Naito et al., 1970). In contrast to the presence of oxygen, Cu^{2+} ions oxidize thiosulphate ions initially to tetrathionate ions, which undergo a disproportionation reaction to subsequently yield the trithionate and thiosulphate ions. At low potentials where oxidants are deficient, in stagnant solutions, or in high copper-containing solutions, the decomposition of thiosulphate yields black precipitates of copper sulphides. Hence the precipitation of copper sulphides is related to the availability of oxygen in the system. The limited solubility of oxygen in aqueous medium and the slow reduction at the gold surface makes the use of oxygen without the copper catalytic reaction very slow, resulting in low gold dissolution.

5.2.3 Limitations, Challenges, and Environmental Impacts of Thiosulfate Leaching

Thiosulphate leach reactions are less favourable than gold cyanidation (Lee and Srivastava, 2016), hence high amounts are consumed to achieve the equivalent gold leaching rate. A thiosulphate leach solution requires a concentration of 5 to 20 g L^{-1} vs. 0.25 to 1 g L^{-1} cyanide in solution. Higher consumption of thiosulphate partially offsets its significantly lower cost, which is one-fifth of the cost of cyanidation. A poor affinity to adsorb the gold–thiosulfate complex onto carbon negates the use of conventional carbon-in-pulp (CIP) or carbon-in-leach (CIL) processes.

Thiosulphate may readily be oxidized or reduced according to the initial solution potential. Depending on the aqueous environment, thiosulphate can break down into sulphite, sulphate, trithionate, tetrathionate, sulphide, polythionates ($S_xO_y^{2-}$) and/or polysulphides x (S_X^{2-}). An important factor in thiosulphate stability is the pH of the solution, since thiosulphate rapidly decomposes in acidic media (Li et al., 1995). Certain metal ions and reagents also cause the breakdown of thiosulphate, as shown in Equations 5.19–5.23 (Abbruzzese et al., 1995; Briones and Lapidus, 1998; Williamson and Rimstidt, 1993; Tykodi, 1990; Xu and Schoonen, 1995).

$$4S_2O_3^{2-} + O_2 + 4H^+ \rightarrow 2S_4O_6^{2-} + 2H_2O \tag{5.19}$$

$$S_2O_3^{2-} + 2H^+ \rightarrow S^0 + SO_2 + 2H_2O \tag{5.20}$$

$$4S_2O_3^{2-} + O_2 + 2H_2O \rightarrow 2S_4O_6^{2-} + 4OH^- \tag{5.21}$$

$$S_2O_3^{2-} + CN^- + 0.5O_2 \rightarrow SCN^- + SO_4^{2-} \tag{5.22}$$

$$2\left[Fe(S_2O_3)\right]^+ \rightarrow 2Fe^{2+} + S_4O_6^{2-} \tag{5.23}$$

$$S_2O_3^{2-} + Cu^{2+} + 2OH^- \rightarrow SO_4^{2-} + H_2O + CuS \tag{5.24}$$

$$2Cu^{2+} + 2S_2O_3^{2-} \rightarrow 2Cu^+ + S_4O_6^{2-} \tag{5.25}$$

Notably, the anions trithionate ($S_3O_6^{2-}$) and tetrathionate ($S_4O_6^{2-}$), which are not known to have any lixiviating activity (Aylmore, 2001), can interfere with resin-based recovery methods by displacing metal complexes from ion-exchange sites (Fleming, 1998; O'Malley, 2001). In addition to the above reactions, thiosulphate is also consumed by peroxides, phosphines, polysulphides, permanganates, chromates, the halogens (chlorine, bromine, and iodine), and their oxyanions. In addition, certain species of fungi, microfauna, and microflora can digest thiosulphate ions (Xu and Schoonen, 1995). The degradation of thiosulphate ions may be caused, or catalyzed, by the presence of certain metal ions. Fe^{3+} ion accelerates the decomposition of thiosulphate by intramolecular electron transfer. The deep purple [$Fe(S_2O_3)$]$^+$ complex is formed, and decomposition occurs via reduction of the metal and concomitant oxidation and dimerization of the ligand to form the tetrathionate ion (Perez and Galaviz, 1987; Williamson and Rimstidt, 1993; Uri, 1947). Similarly, arsenic, antimony, and tin salts catalyze the formation of pentathionate from thiosulphates, while metallic copper, zinc, and aluminium result in the formation of sulphides (Bean, 1997; Xu and Schoonen, 1995).

The recyclability of thiosulphate solution strongly depends on the metal recovery technique employed, which may cause significant degradation of the liquor by oxidation, reduction, or contamination (Awadalla and Ritcey, 1991; Benedetti and Boulëgue, 1991). Ammonia, however, can be stripped from metal-depleted liquor (tailings) by exploiting its significant volatility (Marchbank et al., 1996). By-products and tailings from thiosulphate processing should consist primarily of low-toxicity metal hydroxides, oxides, sulphates, polythionates, polysulphides and/ or insoluble sulphides, although pilot studies to date have not directly addressed waste management. There are several reversible reactions in which thiosulphate is either consumed or regenerated, some of which play a vital role in leaching by recycling various breakdown products and regeneration of thiosulphate ions, as shown in Equations 5.26–5.43, where each reaction formulates the thiosulphate as product (Bean, 1997; Byerley et al., 1975; Fleming, 1998; Hu and Gong, 1991; Perez and Galaviz, 1987; Roy and Trudinger, 1970; Xu and Schoonen, 1995; Zipperian et al., 1988):

$$SO_3^{2-} + 2OH^- + S_4O_6^{2-} \rightarrow 2S_2O_3^{2-} + SO_4^{2-} + H_2O \tag{5.26}$$

$$3SO_3^{2-} + 2S^{2-} + 3H_2O \rightarrow 2S_2O_3^{2-} + 6OH^- + S^0 \tag{5.27}$$

$$SO_3^{2-} + S_5O_6^{2-} \rightarrow S_2O_3^{2-} + S_4O_6^{2-} \tag{5.28}$$

$$SO_3^{2-} + S_4O_6^{2-} \rightarrow S_2O_3^{2-} + S_3O_6^{2-} \tag{5.29}$$

$$2S_5O_6^{2-} + 6OH^- \rightarrow 5S_2O_3^{2-} + 3H_2O \tag{5.30}$$

$$2S_5O_6^{2-} + 6OH^- \rightarrow 5S_2O_3^{2-} + 3H_2O \tag{5.31}$$

$$4S_4O_6^{2-} + 6OH^- \rightarrow 5S_2O_3^{2-} + 2S_3O_6^{2-} + 3H_2O \tag{5.32}$$

$$2S_3O_6^{2-} + 6OH^- \rightarrow S_2O_3^{2-} + 4SO_3^{2-} + 3H_2O \tag{5.33}$$

$$4S_4O_6^{2-} + H_2S \rightarrow 2S_2O_3^{2-} + S^0 + 2H^+ \tag{5.34}$$

$$2S_2O_4^{2-} \rightarrow S_2O_3^{2-} + S_2O_5^{2-} \tag{5.35}$$

$$2S^{2-} + 4SO_4^{2-} + 8H^+ + 8e^- \rightarrow 3S_2O_3^{2-} + 6OH^- + H_2O \tag{5.36}$$

$$2S^{2-} + 2SO_2 + 2HSO_3^- \rightarrow 3S_2O_3^{2-} + H_2O \tag{5.37}$$

$$2S^{2-} + 3SO_2 + SO_3^{2-} \rightarrow 3S_2O_3^{2-} \tag{5.38}$$

$$2HS^- + 4HSO_3^- \rightarrow 3S_2O_3^{2-} + 3H_2O \tag{5.39}$$

$$S_6O_6^{2-} + 3SO_3^{2-} \rightarrow 3S_2O_3^{2-} + S_3O_6^{2-} \tag{5.40}$$

$$S^0 + SO_3^{2-} \rightarrow S_2O_3^{2-} \tag{5.41}$$

$$S_{(x)}^{2-} + SO_3^{2-} \rightarrow S_2O_3^{2-} + S_{(x-1)}^{2-} \tag{5.42}$$

$$S_3O_6^{2-} + S^{2-} \rightarrow 2S_2O_3^{2-} \tag{5.43}$$

Sulphite addition has been suggested by different researchers aiming at the regeneration of decomposed thiosulphate and lixiviating refractory MnO_2 (Flett et al., 1983; Groudev et al., 1996; Guerra and Dreisinger, 1999; Hemmati et al., 1989; Johnson and Bhappu, 1969; Langhans et al., 1992; Lulham and Lindsay, 1991). But the actual benefits of sulphite addition are questionable, due to the ready oxidation of sulphite by Cu^{2+}, producing Cu^+, sulphate and dithionate ions (Aylmore, 2001). Augmentation with excess sulphate to enhance thiosulphate stability (Gong et al., 1993; Hemmati et al., 1989; Hu and Gong, 1991), involving eight-electron redox reaction for the reduction of sulphate to thiosulfate, may not be feasible (as Equation 5.36). Apart from sulphide and sulphate, the breakdown products of thiosulphate are not known to form stable complexes with metal ions of interest (Aylmore, 2001; Smith and Martell, 1976). Metal sulphide complexes are generally sparingly soluble, while sulphate has negligible chelating ability, and complexes incorporating other polythionate ($S_xO_y^{2-}$) ligands are overwhelmed by the abundant thiosulphate ions. A number of authors have reported the in-situ synthesis of thiosulphate ions from sulphoxy compounds/ions during controlled oxidative leaching (Chen et al., 1996; Genik-Sas-Berezowsky et al., 1978; Groves and Blackman, 1995). As a by-product of the destruction of a sulphide matrix, the oxidation of native sulphur or sulphides may be the cheapest source of lixiviant generation (Equations 5.44–5.47) (Bean, 1997; Chen et al., 1996).

$$4S^0 + 6OH^- \rightarrow S_2O_3^{2-} + 2S^{2-} + 3H_2O \tag{5.44}$$

$$2NH_3 + SO_2 + S^0 + H_2O \rightarrow 2(NH_4)_2 S_2O_3 \tag{5.45}$$

$$2(NH_4)_2 S + 2SO_2 + O_2 \rightarrow 2(NH_4)_2 S_2O_3 \tag{5.46}$$

$$S_8 + 8NaOH \rightarrow 2(Na_2S_2O_3) + 2NaS_xH + H_2O \tag{5.47}$$

The reaction mechanism permitting this transformation appears to involve an attack on elemental sulphur by transitory polysulphide species (i.e., NaS_xH) (Bean, 1997; Aylmore and Muir, 2001). Recovering harmful sulphurous matter in this fashion also has the advantage of minimizing the environmental impact of the operation.

The formation of decomposition products can also be avoided by oxidation of thiosulphate to sulphate prior to discharge, but the oxidation cost is higher than cyanide oxidation (Lee and Srivastava, 2016). Recycling of thiosulphate solution can be a possibility; the build-up of polythionates is another issue, making it necessary to use a minimal reagent. Moreover, ammonia also poses environmental issues both in gaseous and liquid form. The threshold limiting value (TLV) for gaseous ammonia in air is 14 mg/m³ (Gos and Rubo, 2000), whereas its toxicity in water is similar to chlorine; hence, strict precautions are needed for thiosulphate leaching.

5.3 THIOUREA LEACHING OF PRECIOUS METALS

Thiourea belongs to a broad class of compounds with the general structure (R^1R^2N) $(R^3R^4N)C=S$. It is a planar organic sulphide with a C=S bond distance of 1.60 ± 0.1 Å. Although the chemical structure of thiourea is similar to that of urea, except that the oxygen atom is replaced by a sulphur atom, the properties of thiourea differ significantly from those of urea. Thiourea crystals can be dissolved in water or acid solution, and can then react with Au/Ag to produce a stable cationic complex or aurous ion.

Thiourea leaching of Au and Ag from spent printed circuit boards was carried out by Xu and Li (2011), and the influence of leaching time, reaction temperature, thiourea concentration, Fe^{3+} concentration, and material particle size on Au leaching rates were investigated. The results showed that Au and Ag leaching rates can reach 90.9% and 59.8%, respectively, under optimum leaching conditions.

Li et al. (2012) examined the thiourea leaching of Au and Ag from spent printed circuit boards with 24 L⁻¹ thiourea concentration and 0.6% of Fe^{3+} supplementation with 2 h of leaching time. The leaching efficiency of gold reached almost 89.7% along with 48.3% silver extraction within 2 h. In the absence of any ferric salt, it took 6 h to achieve the same extraction of gold in acidic thiourea solution. However, when the ferric ion concentration was higher than 0.01 M, gold recovery was lower. The iron present in printed circuit boards may also supply a part of iron during the leaching. In the case of silver leaching, there was no beneficial effect of ferric ions. Since gold has lower oxidation potential values than silver, it seems reasonable that the presence of an external oxidizing agent enhances gold dissolution. Birloaga et al. (2014) found that 69% of Au was extracted under conditions of 20 g L⁻¹ thiourea, 6 g L⁻¹ Fe^{3+} ions, and 10 g L⁻¹ H_2SO_4, as well as 600 rpm. Furthermore, under the same reagent conditions, multistage crosscurrent leaching was used to reduce the consumption of thiourea and improve the efficiency of Au leaching from spent printed circuit boards.

5.3.1 MECHANISM OF THIOUREA LEACHING OF PRECIOUS METALS FROM URBAN MINE SOURCE

The formation of gold complexes in thiourea solution can be better represented by the Eh-pH diagram (Figure 5.10) and probable electrochemical mechanism (Figure 5.11).

As can be seen from Figure 5.10, thiourea is unstable when decomposing in other than acid pH, hence the leaching of gold is most prominently performed in the pH range of 1–2 to form the only commonly existing cationic species of gold, $Au[SC(NH_2)_2]_2^+$ (Munoz and Miller, 2000). The electrochemical nature of the reaction, which yields up to 99% of gold, can be presented as:

$$Au + 2SC(NH_2)_2 = Au\left[SC(NH_2)_2\right]_2^+ + e^- \quad E = 0.38 \text{ V} \tag{5.48}$$

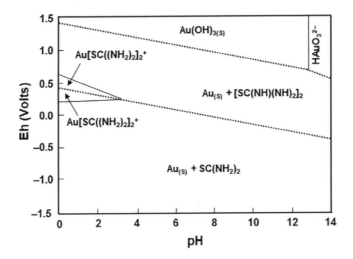

FIGURE 5.10 Eh–pH diagram of Au–SC(NH$_2$)$_2$–H$_2$O system (conditions: 5x 10^{-4} M Au, 0.5M SC(NH$_2$)$_2$ at 25°C).

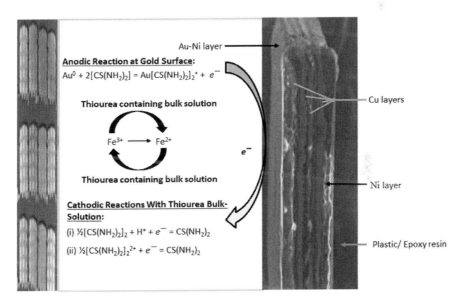

FIGURE 5.11 Probable electrochemical mechanism for gold–thiourea leaching from printed circuit boards.

The kinetics of Au dissolution in acidic thiourea solutions in the presence of a variety of oxidants, namely, H$_2$O$_2$, Fe$_2$(SO$_4$)$_3$, formamidine disulphide, oxygen, Na$_2$O$_2$, and MnO$_2$ have been studied by many authors. Among them all, the Fe^{3+} ion is found to be the most effective, preferably in an acidic sulphate solution rather than chloride/nitrate media (Plaskin and Kozhukhova, 1960; Songina et al., 1971). The reaction for gold leaching in thiourea and ferric ion solutions can be written as:

$$Au + 2SC(NH_2)_2 + Fe^{3+} \rightarrow Au\left[SC(NH_2)_2\right]_2^+ + Fe^{2+} \qquad (5.49)$$

In the presence of redox couple, Fe^{3+} and Fe^{2+}, gold leaching in thiourea solution has been found to be up to four times faster than oxidation by air purging (Huyhua et al., 1989). Deschênes and Ghali (1988) demonstrated the effect of ferric ion as an oxidizing agent during leaching of gold from chalcopyrite concentrate. Without any oxidizing agent, the thiourea solution provides an 80% gold extraction in 8 h. An addition of 2.0 g L^{-1} of this oxidant slightly improves the initial leaching kinetics but results in no real improvement in gold extraction. Increasing the concentration of oxidant to 5.0 g L^{-1} could increase leaching kinetics and result in extraction of > 93% gold in 7 h leaching.

The dissolution of precious metals from a spent printed circuit boards ash sample in acidic thiourea solutions with different concentrations of oxidant $Fe_2(SO_4)_3$ from 0 g L^{-1} to 7.5 g L^{-1} was also investigated by Batnasan et al. (2018), using a combined hydrometallurgical method consisting of high-pressure oxidative leaching and thiourea leaching. It was observed that increasing the oxidant concentration to 5 g L^{-1} resulted in an increase in the dissolution of Au and Pd, but a rapid decrease in Ag dissolution. The equations for dissolution of gold, silver, and palladium in acidic thiourea solutions in presence of Fe3+ ions can be generally described as follows;

$$Au + 2CS(NH_2)_2 + Fe^{3+} \rightarrow Au\left[CS(NH_2)_2\right]_2^+ + Fe^{2+} \qquad (5.50)$$

$$Pd + 4CS(NH_2)_2 + Fe^{3+} \rightarrow Pd\left[CS(NH_2)_2\right]_4^{2+} + Fe^{2+} \qquad (5.51)$$

$$Ag + 3CS(NH_2)_2 + Fe^{3+} \rightarrow Ag\left[CS(NH_2)_2\right]_3^+ + Fe^{2+} \qquad (5.52)$$

However, a further increase in Fe^{3+} ion (8.0 g L^{-1}) decreases gold extraction. Studies revealed that a lower dosage of Fe^{3+} is not adequate to oxidize the metal ions, whereas a higher dosage oxidizes thiourea itself to S^{2-}, S^0 and formamidine disulphide, which can suppress the leaching efficiency of gold. The oxidative degradation of thiourea into several degradation products can be written as:

$$2SC(NH_2)_2 + Fe^{3+} \rightarrow \left[SCN_2H_3\right]_2 + 2Fe^{2+} + 2H^+ \qquad (5.53)$$

$$\left[SCN_2H_3\right]_2 \rightarrow SC(NH_2)_2 + NH_2CN + S^0 \qquad (5.54)$$

$$SC(NH_2)_2 + Fe^{3+} + SO_4^{2-} \rightarrow \left[FeSO_4.SC(NH_2)_2\right]^+ \qquad (5.55)$$

The maximum dissolution of Au and Pd was found to be 68% and 7.1%, respectively, when the oxidant concentration was 5 g L^{-1}, whereas the Ag dissolution was 1.6%. It was observed that the trends with respect to silver dissolution in aqueous thiourea solutions in the presence of H_2SO_4 (0.25 M to 4 M) and $Fe_2(SO_4)_3$ oxidant (0 g/L to 7.5 g L^{-1}) exhibited quite similar profiles. This observation is probably related to formation of an insoluble silver–thiourea complex and silver sulphide (Ag_2S) under the oxidation conditions based on the following equations:

$$2Ag + \left(FeSO_4.SC\left(NH_2\right)_2 \right)^+ \rightarrow \left(Ag_2SO_4.SC\left(NH_2\right)_2 \right)^+ + 2Fe^{2+} \qquad (5.56)$$

$$2Ag + S \rightarrow Ag_2S \qquad (5.57)$$

Formation of metal–thiourea complexes can be attributed to the variations in the pH and redox potential (Eh) of the thiourea solutions with the addition of oxidant, as high redox potential and acidity of the solution led to an increase of Au and Pd leaching, in contrast to a decrease in the leaching of Ag. It appears that optimization of the oxidant concentration during the thiourea leaching process is the main challenge to avoid thiourea loss/oxidation, because the dissolution of precious metals was strongly dependent on the oxidant concentration.

5.3.2 Effect of Various Process Parameters

Thiourea is thought to be a low-toxicity reagent that exhibits a faster gold leaching rate, with apparently less interference from the base metals (Pb, Co, Ni, Zn); moreover, it is used in acidic conditions rather the alkaline conditions of cyanide and thiosulphate (Yannopoulos, 1991). The problems in gold leaching due to the occurrence of base metals in spent printed circuit boards and the sorption loss of gold from leach solution with carbonaceous matter coming from the detached hydrocarbon of the spent printed circuit board resins can be handled in thiourea leaching. However, there are several factors affecting thiourea leaching of precious metals from secondary sources.

5.3.2.1 Effect of Temperature

Temperature plays an important role in enhancement of leaching kinetics; hence plenty of work has been carried out in this area. A calcine powder sample of printed circuit board (3470 g/t Au) leached in a solution of 0.5 M thiourea + 0.05 M H_2SO_4 + 0.01 M Fe^{3+} ions at a pulp density 2.85 g L^{-1} with varying temperatures (30–60°C) did not show much enhancement in gold extraction up to 45°C (with ~80% leaching), rather it decreased remarkably (~75% leaching) at 60°C. Spent printed circuit boards without calcination showed a similar trend in results. The maximum of 90% gold extraction efficiency was obtained at 25°C for 2 h leaching of a pulverized sample of 430 g/t Au with 0.31 M thiourea solution (with 6% Fe^{3+} ions at pH 1). This gold leaching behavior as a function of temperature and gold concentration in the charged sample can be elaborated with the complex electrochemical mechanism involved in the system. The reason behind the suitability of higher temperatures (up to 45°C) for an Au-concentrated sample of calcined printed circuit board than that (25°C) for the direct pulverized sample of lesser gold can be explained by the increase in gold concentration reducing the stability zone of the $Au[SC(NH_2)_2]^{+2}$ complex. A decrease in gold extraction with a rise in temperature can be understood by thiourea decomposition, which results in the formation of colloidal sulphur in the presence of iron and the retardation of the reaction through passivation on the gold surfaces. The significant effect on gold leaching of increasing temperature can be corroborated by the chemically controlled reaction, also evidenced by the independence of the leaching rate from the stirring speed. This is found to be at variance with the reaction kinetics investigated using rotating discs by applying formamidine disulphide as an oxidant instead of ferric ions. The chemically controlled gold leaching from spent printed circuit boards is expected to be an electrochemical reaction (see Figure 5.11).The cathodic half-cell reaction for the reduction of formamidine disulphide (in Figure 5.11) make it seem as though the H^+ ion might participate in the rate-limiting reaction. But it has been found that the pH does not change with decomposition of thiourea, indicating that the formamidine disulphide exists in a protonated form (as reaction-b) instead of a neutral molecule (Schulze 1984; Groenewald, 1976; Habashi, 1969).

The presence of ferric ions in the bulk thiosulphate solution catalyzes the electrochemical reactions to facilitate the oxidation of metallic gold to aurous (Au^+) and silver to argentous (Ag^+) ions, (for Au^0 to Au^+).

5.3.2.2 Effect of Thiourea Concentration

Maintaining the appropriate dosage of thiourea in gold leaching is of prime importance. In general, for this kind of leaching system, 0.13M thiourea along with Fe^{3+} concentration up to 5 g L^{-1} at Eh and pH values nearly in the range of 400–450mV and 1–2, respectively, is optimal (Munoz and Miller, 2000). Some work has been reported with respect specifically to the leaching of gold from spent printed circuit boards. A pulverized sample of spent printed circuit board containing 430 g/t Au, 540 g/t Ag, 39.86% Cu, 0.457% Zn, and 0.396% Ni was leached in 0.26–0.36M thiourea solution along with 0.6% Fe^{3+} at pH 1.0 for 3 h duration (Li et al., 2012). At 0.26M thiourea, the leaching rate was the slowest, however it increased to the maximum (~90%) with 0.36M thiourea in solution in the initial 2 h of leaching and then decreased significantly (to ~60% after 3 h) with prolonged leaching. A concentration of 0.31 M thiourea in lixiviant solution was optimized in this case to yield 89.7% Au along with 48.3% Ag for 2 h leaching time. A quite similar leaching trend was observed, with maximum leaching efficacy with 0.31 M thiourea, while below and above that concentration, there was a remarkable decline in gold leaching (Camelino et al, 2015). This behavior strongly supports the occurrence of passivation phenomena in leaching with the degradation products of thiourea (see Equations 5.58–5.61). At variance with these results, the optimized dosage of thiourea increased to 0.5 M when the calcined powder (size, 53–75μm) of spent printed circuit board (containing high amount of Au = 3470 g/t) was subjected to leaching (Gurung et al., 2011). At a pulp density of 2.85 g L^{-1}, the extraction efficiency was nearly 90% after 24 h of leaching with 0.5 M thiourea in 0.05 M acidic solution. At concentrations lower than 0.5 M thiourea, gold extraction could not exceed 50%, even at a lower pulp density than 2.85 g L^{-1}. Going above 0.05M acid concentration did not improve the gold leaching yield.

Spent printed circuit board samples obtained after incineration and high-pressure oxidative leaching were examined by Batnasan et al. (2018) at various thiourea concentrations. The dissolution efficiency of the precious metals increased drastically with increase of the thiourea concentration from 1.25 g L^{-1} to 12.5 g L^{-1}, then remained nearly unchanged on further increase of the thiourea concentration up to 20 g L^{-1}. The maximum dissolution efficiency of 91%, 81%, and 11.9% for Au, Ag, and Pd was achieved at thiourea concentration of 12.5 g L^{-1} due to the appropriate thiourea/ $Fe_2(SO_4)_3$ molar ratio under this condition. Use of appropriate concentrations of thiourea and formamidine disulphide results in an increase in the leaching of precious metals, which can be expressed as follows:

$$2Au + 2SC(NH_2)_2 + (SCN_2H_3)_2 + 2H^+ \rightarrow 2Au\left[SC(NH_2)\right]_2^+ \qquad (5.58)$$

$$2Ag + 2SC(NH_2)_2 + 2(SCN_2H_3)_2 + 4H^+ \rightarrow 2Ag\left[SC(NH_2)\right]_3^+ \qquad (5.59)$$

$$2Pd + 4SC(NH_2)_2 + 2(SCN_2H_3)_2 + 4H^+ \rightarrow 2Pd\left[SC(NH_2)_2\right]_4^+ \qquad (5.60)$$

$$Ag_2S + 6SC(NH_2)_2 + 2H^+ \rightarrow 2Ag\left[SC(NH_2)_2\right]_3^+ + H_2S \qquad (5.61)$$

These results indicate that the formamidine disulphide $(SCN_2H_3)_2$ produced can be beneficial to the leaching efficiency of precious metals under precisely optimized leaching conditions. It is noteworthy that, with the addition of thiourea, the pH of the leaching medium does not change remarkably, whereas the redox potential in the medium falls from 0.67 V to 0.43 V. The variations of the redox potential with addition of thiourea and oxidant show completely opposite trends, probably related to oxidation of thiourea to form a ferric–thiourea complex and formamidine disulphide, respectively.

5.4 LIMITATIONS, CHALLENGES, AND ENVIRONMENTAL IMPACTS OF THIOUREA LEACHING

Although the toxicity of thiourea is far less than that of cyanide (a lethal dosage of thiourea is 10 g/kg), it is not an entirely environmentally friendly reagent. This is a subject of debate because thiourea is used in human thyroid treatments as a non-carcinogenic reagent (IARC, 1974; Shubik 1975). The discharge of various degradation products of thiourea, including urea, ammonia, formamidine disulphide, sulphur, cyanamide, carbon dioxide, sulphate and nitrate ions, is problematic and proper effluent treatment is needed (Gupta 1963; Preisler and Berger 1947; Hiskey and DeVries 1992). Cyanamide and formamidine disulphide are unstable and short-lived. The half-life of thiourea decomposition in surface water and soil is up to 168 h under aqueous aerobic biodegradation, and up to 336 h in groundwater without biodegradation (Howard 1991). There is some evidence of heavy metals dissolution in thiourea from minerals/soils causing soil and water pollution.

It must be noted that in the absence of any oxidizing agent, thiourea alone in lixiviant is less effective. $Fe_2(SO_4)_3$ is preferred as a cheaper reagent than H_2O_2, but it also increases thiourea consumption. An excess of $Fe_2(SO_4)_3$ suppresses the leaching of gold. An initial concentration of thiourea and $Fe_2(SO_4)_3$ along with the rate of oxidation of thiourea are the factors that most affect the leaching of gold. The formation of degradation products in successive oxidation stages of thiourea makes it difficult to control the leaching system. High consumption of reagents including $SC(NH_2)_2$, $Fe_2(SO_4)_3$ and H_2SO_4 makes the process more expensive than using cyanidation. Therefore, unless these complexities are handled carefully, thiourea leaching in gold extraction is quite difficult.

Commercial applications of thiourea in gold recovery processing have been hindered by the higher consumption of reagents and the complexity of the leaching system when treating various ores/concentrates and different recycled materials. At 154 µm, 90% Au and 50% Ag could be achieved. Further size reduction achieves full precious metal recovery. However, thiourea consumption is usually very high and it is more expensive than cyanide and thiosulfate lixiviants. There are still many challenges in the recovery of precious metal from electronic wastes, including low total recovery. In practice, <20% of the PMs from electronic wastes have been recovered and recycled. Precious metal loss during pre-treatment and multistep leaching should be minimized in electronic waste treatment.

ACKNOWLEDGEMENTS

This work was supported by the Brain Pool Programme through the National Research Foundation of Korea (NRF) funded by the Ministry of Science and ICT (Grant No. 2019H1D3A2A02101993) and the Basic Science Research Programme through the National Research Foundation of Korea (NRF) funded by the Ministry of Education (Project no. 2020R1I1A1A01074249).

REFERENCES

Abbruzzese, C., Fornari, P., Massidda, R., Veglio F., Ubaldini, S. (1995). Thiosulfate leaching for gold hydrometallurgy. *Hydrometallurgy.* 39(1): 265–276.

Anthony, E.Y., Williams, P.A. (1994). *Thiosulfate complexing of platinum group elements: Implications for supergene geochemistry. ACS Publications.*

Awadalla, F., Ritcey, G. (1991). Recovery of gold from thiourea, thiocyanate, or thiosulfate solutions by reduction-precipitation with a stabilized form of sodium borohydride. *Separation Science and Technology.* 26(9): 1207–1228.

Aylmore, M.G. (2001). Treatment of a refractory gold—copper sulfide concentrate by copper ammoniacal thiosulfate leaching. *Minerals Engineering.* 14(6): 615–637.

Aylmore, M.G., Muir, D.M. (2001). Thiosulfate leaching of gold—a review. *Minerals Engineering.* 14(2): 135–174.

Baláž, P., Ficeriová, J., Leon, C.V. (2003). Silver leaching from a mechanochemically pretreated complex sulfide concentrate. *Hydrometallurgy.* 70(1): 113–119.

Batnasan, A., Haga, K., Shibayama, A. (2018) Recovery of precious and base metals from waste printed circuit boards using a sequential leaching procedure. *JOM* 70(2):124. doi:10.1007/s11837-017-2694-y

Bean, S.L., (1997). Thiosulfates. In Kroschwitz, J.I. (ed.), *Kirk-Othmer Encyclopedia of Chemical Technology.* . New York: Wiley, pp. 51–68.

Benedetti, M., Boulëgue, J. (1991). Mechanism of gold transfer and deposition in a supergene environment. *Geochimica et Cosmochimica Acta.* 55(6): 1539–1547.

Briones, R., Lapidus, G. (1998). The leaching of silver sulfide with the thiosulfate–ammonia–cupric ion system. *Hydrometallurgy.* 50(3): 243–260.

Byerley, J. J., Fouda, S. A., and Rempel, G. L. (1973). Kinetics and mechanism of the oxidation of thiosulfate ions by copper (II) ions in aqueous ammonia solution. *Journal of the Chemical Society, Dalton Transactions*, (8), 889–893.

Byerley, J. J., Fouda, S. A., and Rempel, G. L. (1975). Activation of copper (II) ammine complexes by molecular oxygen for the oxidation of thiosulfate ions. *Journal of the Chemical Society, Dalton Transactions*, (13), 1329–1338.

Chen, J., Deng, T., Zhu G., Zhao, J. (1996). Leaching and recovery of cold in thiosulfate based system-a research summary at ICM.

Deschênes, G., Ghali, E. (1988). Leaching of gold from a chalcopyrite concentrate by thiourea. *Hydrometallurgy*. 20(2): 179–202.

Fleming C.A. (1998). The potential role of anion exchange resins in the gold industry. *EPD Congress 1998*. Warrendale, PA: The Minerals, Metals and Materials Society, pp. 95–117.

Flett, D., Derry, R., Wilson, J. (1983). Chemical study of thiosulfate leaching of silver sulfide. *Transactions of the Institution of Mining and Metallurgy Section C-Mineral Processing and Extractive Metallurgy*. 92(DEC): C216-C223.

Genik-Sas-Berezowsky, R. M., Sefton, V. B., and Gormely, L. S. (1978). *U.S. Patent No. 4,070,182*. Washington, DC: U.S. Patent and Trademark Office.

Gmelin, L.E. (1965). Copper thiosulfate complexes. In: *Gmelins Handbuch der AnorganischenChemie*. Berlin: VerlagChemie, pp. (B1) 591; (B593) 998–1003, 1414–1415.

Gmelin, L.E. (1969). Mercury thiosulfate complexes. In: *Gmelins Handbuch der AnorganischenChemie*. Berlin: VerlagChemie, pp. (B1) 52–55; (B53) 1030–1031; (B1034) 1406–1409.

Gmelin, L.E. (1972). Lead thiosulfate complexes. *In Gmelins Handbuch der AnorganischenChemie*. Weinheim: VerlagChemie, pp. (B1) 364–365; (C) 594–600.

Gmelin, L.E. (1973). Silver thiosulfate complexes. In *Gmelins Handbuch der AnorganischenChemie*. Weinheim/Bergstrasse: VerlagChemie, pp. (B3) 110–133.

Gong, Q., Hu, J., Cao, C. (1993). Kinetics of gold leaching from sulfide gold concentrates with thiosulfate solution. *Transactions of the Nonferrous Metals Society of China(China)*. 3(4): 30–36.

Gos, S., Rubo, A. (2000). Alternative lixiviants for gold leaching. A comparison. In: *Randol Gold & Silver Forum*. pp: 271–281.

Groenewald, T. (1976). The dissolution of gold in acidic solutions of thiourea. *Hydrometallurgy*. 1(3): 277–290.

Groudev, S. N., Spasova, I. I., and Ivanov, I. M. (1996). Two-stage microbial leaching of a refractory gold-bearing pyrite ore. *Minerals Engineering*, 9(7): 707–713.

Groves, W. D., and Blackman, L. (1995). *U.S. Patent No. 5,405,430*. Washington, DC: U.S. Patent and Trademark Office.

Guerra, E., and Dreisinger, D. B. (1999). A study of the factors affecting copper cementation of gold from ammoniacal thiosulfate solution. *Hydrometallurgy*, 51(2), 155–172.

Gupta, P.C. (1963). Analytical chemistry of thiocarbamides. *Fresenius' Journal of Analytical Chemistry*. 196(6): 412–431.

Gurung, M., Adhikari, B.B., Kawakita, H., Ohto, K., Inoue, K., Alam, S. (2011). Recovery of Au(III) by using low cost adsorbent prepared from persimmon tannin extract. *Chemical Engineering Journal*. 174: 556–563.

Habashi, F. (1969). *Extractive Metallurgy, vol. 1, General Principles*. New York: Gordon and Breach Science Publishers. Inc.

Hemmati, M., Hendrix, J., Nelson, J., Milosavljevic, E. (1989). *Extraction Metallurgy'89 symp*. London: Institute of Mining and Metallurgy, 665–678.

Hiskey, J., DeVries, F. (1992). Emerging process technol. In: *Cleaner Environ. Proc. Symp.* pp: 73–80.

Howard, P.H. (1991). *Handbook of environmental degradation rates*. Boca Raton: CRC Press.

Hu, J., Gong, Q. (1991). Substitute sulfate for sulfite during extraction of gold by thiosulfate solution. In: *Randol Gold Forum'91*. Cairns, pp 333–336.

Hubin, A., Vereecken, J. (1994). Electrochemical reduction of silver thiosulfate complexes part i: Thermodynamic aspects of solution composition. *Journal of applied electrochemistry*. 24(3): 239–244.

Huyhua, J., Zegarra, C., Gundiler, I. (1989). A comparative study of oxidants on gold and silver dissolution in acidic thiourea solutions. *Precious Metals* 89: 287–303.

Ilyas, S., Lee, J.C. (2014). Biometallurgical recovery of metals from waste electrical and electronic equipment: A review. *ChemBioEng Reviews*. 1(4): 148–169.

Jiang, T., Chen, J., Xu, S. (1993). A kinetic study of gold leaching with thiosulfate. *Hydrometallurgy. Fundamentals, Technology and Innovations*, 119–126.

Johnson, P. H., and Bhappu, R. B. (1969). *Chemical Mining: A Study of Leaching Agents*. State Bureau of Mines and Mineral Resources.

Johnson, J. A., and Davis, J. O. (1973). Effects of a specific competitive antagonist of angiotensin II on arterial pressure and adrenal steroid secretion in dogs. *Circulation Research*, 32(5): 1–159.

Langhans, J., Lei, K., Carnahan, T. (1992). Copper-catalyzed thiosulfate leaching of low-grade gold ores. *Hydrometallurgy*. 29(1-3): 191–203.

Lee, J.-C., Srivastava, R.R. (2016). Leaching of gold from the spent/end-of-life mobile phone-PCBs. In: *The Recovery of Gold from Secondary Resources*. Imperial College Press, pp. 7–56.

Li, J., Miller, J., Le-Vier M., Wan, R. (1995). The ammoniacal thiosulfate system for precious metal recovery. Society for Mining, Metallurgy, and Exploration, Inc., Littleton, CO, USA.

Livingstone, S.E. (1965). Metal complexes of ligands containing sulfur, selenium, or tellurium as donor atoms. *Quarterly Reviews, Chemical Society*. 19(4): 386–425.

Lulham, J., Lindsay, D., InternationalPatent WO 91/11539. (1991). *Separation process*. Davy McKee (Stockton) Limited, ClevelandTS18 3RE, UK.

Marchbank, A.R.,Thomas, K.G., Dreisinger, D., Fleming, C. (1996). Gold recovery from refractory carbonaceous ores by pressure oxidation and thiosulfate leaching. *Google Patents*.

Meng, X., Han, K.N. (1993). The dissolution behavior of gold in ammoniacal solutions. In J.B. Hiskey and G.W. Warren (eds), *Hydrometallurgy Fundamentals, Technology and Innovations*. Colorado: Society for Mining, Metallurgy and Exploration, Inc., 205–221.

Mountain, B.W., Wood, S.A. (1988). Solubility and transport of platinum-group elements in hydrothermal solutions: Thermodynamic and physical chemical constraints. In *Geoplatinum 87*. Dordrecht: Springer, pp. 57–82.

Muir, D.M., La Brooy, S.R., Deng, T., Singh, P. (1993). The mechanism of the ammonia-cyanide system for leaching copper-gold ores. In J.B. Hiskey and G.W. Warren (eds), *Hydrometallurgy: Fundamentals, Technology and Innovation*. Colorado: Society for Mining, Metallurgy and Exploration, Inc., 191–204.

Munoz, G., Miller, J. (2000). Noncyanide leaching of an auriferous pyrite ore from ecuador. *Minerals and Metallurgical Processing*. 17(3): 198–204.

Naito, K., Shieh, M.-C., Okabe, T. (1970). The chemical behavior of low valence sulfur compounds. V. Decomposition and oxidation of tetrathionate in aqueous ammonia solution. *Bulletin of the Chemical Society of Japan*. 43(5): 1372–1376.

Novakovskii, M.S., Ryazantseva, A.P. (1955) Cadmium complexes with thiosulfate.: *Trudy Khim. Fak.* 54 (12), 277–281 (In Russian).

O'Malley, G. (2001). The elution of gold from anion exchange resins. *Australian Patent*. WO, 123626.

Pedraza, A., Villegas, I., Freund, P., Chornik, B. (1988). Electro-oxidation of thiosulfate ion on gold: Study by means of cyclic voltammetry and auger electron spectroscopy. *Journal of electroanalytical chemistry and interfacial electrochemistry.* 250(2): 443–449.

Perez, A. E., and Galaviz, H. D. (1987). *U.S. Patent No. 4,654,078.* Washington, DC: U.S. Patent and Trademark Office.

Plaskin, I. N., M. Kozhukhova. (1960). Dissolution of gold and silver in solutions of thiourea. *Sbornik Nauchnyhk Trudov, Institut Tsvetnykh Metallov,* 33: 107–119.

Plimer, I.R., Williams, P.A. (1988). New mechanisms for the mobilization of the platinum-group elements in the supergene zone. *In: Geoplatinum 87.* Dordrecht: Springer, pp. 83–92.

Preisler, P.W., Berger, L. (1947). Oxidation-reduction potentials of thiol-dithio systems: Thiourea-formamidine disulfide1. *Journal of the American Chemical Society.* 69(2): 322–325.

Roy, A.B., Trudinger, P.A. (1970). *The biochemistry of inorganic compounds of sulfur.* Cambridge: Cambridge University Press.

Ryabchikov, D. I. (1943). On the structure of dithiosulphatoplatinite. In *CR (Doklady) Acad. Sci. URSS,* 41 (5): 208–209.

Schulze, R.G. (1984). New aspects in thiourea leaching of precious metals. *JOM.* 36(6): 62–65.

Shieh, M.-C., Otsubo, H., Okabe, T. (1965). The chemical behavior of low valence sulfur compounds. I. Oxidation of elemental sulfur with compressed oxygen in aqueous ammonia solution. *Bulletin of the Chemical Society of Japan.* 38(10): 1596–1600.

Shubik, P. (1975). Potential carcinogenicity of food additives and contaminants. *Cancer research.* 35(11 Part 2): 3475–3480.

Smith, R.M., Martell, A.E. (1976). Inorganic ligands. In *Critical Stability Constants.* New York: Springer, pp. 1–129.

Songina, O., Ospanov, K.K., Muldagalieva, I.K., Sal'nikov, S. (1971). Dissolution of gold with the use of thiourea in a hydrochloric acid medium. *Izvestiya Akademii Nauk Kazakhskoi SSR, Seriya Khimicheskaya.* 21: 9–11.

Ter-Arakelyan, K. (1984). On technological expediency of sodium thiosulfate usage for gold extraction from raw material. *Izv. V. U. Z. Tsvetn. Metall.* (5): 72–76.

Tozawa, K., Inui, Y., Umetsu, Y. (1981). Dissolution of gold in ammoniacal thiosulfate solution. *Metallurgical Society AIME. A81–25:* 1–12.

Tripathi, A., Kumar, M., Sau, D.C., Agrawal, A., Chakravarty, S., Mankhand, T.R. (2012). Leaching of gold from the waste mobile phone printed circuit boards (PCBs) with ammonium thiosulfate. *International Journal of Metallurgical Engineering,* 1(2): 17–21.

Tykodi, R. (1990). In praise of thiosulfate. *J. Chem. Educ.* 67(2): 146.

Tyurin, N.G., Kakowski, i.A. (1960). Behaviour of gold and silver in oxidising zine of sulfide depositIzu., *Buz. Tsyv. Metallurgy* 2: 6–13.(Russian).

Uri, N.(1947). 65. Thiosulfate complexes of the tervalent metals, iron, aluminium, and chromium. *Journal of the Chemical Society.* (Resumed) 65: 335–336.

Vasil'ev, A., Toropova, V.F., Busygina, A.A. (1953). The use of ion exchange for the separation of copper, cadmium and zinc from thiosulfate solutions.: *Uch. Zap. Kazausk. Un-ta.* 113(118): 91–102.

Vlassopoulos, D., Wood, S.A. (1990). Gold speciation in natural waters: I. Solubility and hydrolysis reactions of gold in aqueous solution. *Geochimica et Cosmochimica Acta.* 54(1): 3–12.

White, D. (1900). *The stratigraphic succession of the fossil floras of the Pottsville Formation in the Southern Anthracite Coal Field.* Pennsylvania: US Government Printing Office.

Wilkinson, G., Gillard, R.D. (1987). Comprehensive coordination chemistry: The synthesis, reactions, properties and applications of coordination compounds. In *Middle Transition Elements.* Pergamon.

Williamson, M.A., Rimstidt, J.D. (1993). The rate of decomposition of the ferric-thiosulfate complex in acidic aqueous solutions. *Geochimica et Cosmochimica Acta.* 57(15): 3555–3561.

Xu, Y., Schoonen, M.A. (1995). The stability of thiosulfate in the presence of pyrite in low-temperature aqueous solutions. *Geochimica et Cosmochimica Acta.* 59(22): 4605–4622.

Zhang, H., Dreisinger, D.B. (2002). The adsorption of gold and copper onto ion-exchange resins from ammoniacal thiosulfate solutions. *Hydrometallurgy.* 66(1): 67–76.

Zhao, D., Feng, J., Huo, Q., Melosh, N., Fredrickson, G. H., Chmelka, B. F., and Stucky, G. D. (1998). Triblock copolymer syntheses of mesoporous silica with periodic 50 to 300 angstrom pores. *Science*, 279(5350), 548–552.

Zipperian, D., Raghavan, S., & Wilson, J. P. (1988). Gold and silver extraction by ammoniacal thiosulfate leaching from a rhyolite ore. *Hydrometallurgy*, 19(3), 361–375.

6 Recovery of Precious Metals Using Precipitation, Adsorption, Electrowinning, Supercritical Fluids and Bio-mediated Approaches

Sadia Ilyas
Mineral Resources and Energy Engineering, Jeonbuk National University, Jeonju, Jeonbuk 54896, Republic of Korea

Muhammad Ahmad Muhsan
Mineral and Material Chemistry Lab, Department of Chemistry, University of Agriculture, Faisalabad 38040, Pakistan

Hyunjung Kim
Mineral Resources and Energy Engineering, Jeonbuk National University, Jeonju, Jeonbuk 54896, Republic of Korea

Department of Environment and Energy, Jeonbuk National University, Jeonju, Jeonbuk 54896, Republic of Korea

Rajiv Ranjan Srivastava
Center for Advanced Chemistry, Institute of Research and Development, Duy Tan University, Da Nang 550000, Vietnam

CONTENTS

6.1 RECOVERY OF PRECIOUS METALS BY PRECIPITATION, ADSORPTION, ELECTROWINNING AND BIOSORPTION/ BIOACCUMULATION: AN OVERVIEW

Extensive literature exists on the recovery of precious metals by cementation/precipitation, adsorption, agglomeration, bio-mediated approaches, solvent extraction, ion exchange, and so on, but there are limited studies dealing with real-time leach liquors from secondary sources and most of the work has been conducted with simulated/synthetic solutions that hinder the efficient implementation of the technologies at commercial scale.

To fulfil the sustainability targets and move towards a circular economy, the recovery of precious metals from processed urban mine liquors to production is an absolute necessity. Recovery processes are essentially employed to obtain metals of high purity for further applications, depending upon the concentration of leach liquors, availability of cheap electric power, and other economic considerations. This chapter reviews the feasibility of precious metal recovery from cyanide, halide, thio-sulphate, and thiourea-based leach liquors by precipitation, adsorption, nano-accu-mulation, and electrowinning. The fundamental principles and the effects of impurity metals on the recovery process are highlighted for each approach. Bio-metallurgical recovery of precious metals from various secondary liquors by biosorption are also discussed. The metal-binding ability of various biomaterials including algae, fungi, bacteria, and yeast, as well as certain biopolymers and bio-waste materials, is discussed with reference to precious metals.

6.2 RECOVERY OF PRECIOUS METALS BY PRECIPITATION/ CEMENTATION

Precipitation involves the conversion of soluble metal ions to insoluble form by chemical reaction with metal ions and precipitating agents. The choice of precipitant depends upon its selectivity and crystalline size (for easy filter and wash), and it should be possible to form quite stable and insoluble precipitates for quantitative recovery in later steps. Generally, precipitates are formed at a specific pH range; since most of them are re-dissolved outside this range, most are more insoluble in cold solutions and decompose at high temperature. The presence of a complexing ion can inhibit the precipitation process and oxidizing or reducing conditions are mostly necessary for efficient precipitation. Co-precipitation can occur if contaminants are soluble under the precipitation conditions. Metal ions in various leach liquors of secondary wastes/urban mine sources can be effectively precipitated as reduced metals, metal hydroxides, metal carbonates, metal sulphides, and metal oxalates, and cemented to attain selective recovery.

The direct precipitation of metals from an aqueous solution of their salt is of great interest. Thus gold is precipitated from chloride solution obtained by aqua regia leaching of gold bullions by ferrous ions or oxalic acid as follows:

$$Au^+ + Fe^{2+} \rightarrow Au + Fe^{3+} \tag{6.1}$$

$$2Au^{3+} + 3C_2H_2O_4 \rightarrow 2Au + 6H^+ + 6CO_2 \tag{6.2}$$

Palladium and platinum are precipitated by formate ions:

$$Pd^{2+} + HCOO^- \rightarrow Pd + H^+ + CO_2 \tag{6.3}$$

$$Pt^{4+} + 2HCOO^- \rightarrow Pt + 2H^+ + 2CO_2 \tag{6.4}$$

Based on these reactions, gold and the platinum metals are selectively separated from spent electrolytes during the electrolytic refining of gold on a commercial scale. Similarly from chloride-based liquors, platinum can be precipitated as the ammonium hexachloroplatinate and the metal is recovered by thermal decomposition of the precipitate (Habashi et al., 1987):

$$PtCl_4 + 2NH_4Cl \rightarrow (NH_4)_2 \left[PtCl_6 \right] \tag{6.5}$$

The precipitation of a metal from an aqueous solution of its salts by another metal is known as cementation, because the precipitated metal is cemented on the surface of the added metal. This phenomenon was first described by alchemists as transmutation. A piece of iron was dipped in copper sulphate solution and coated with a layer of metallic copper. The cementation process can be predicted in terms of electrode potentials. TA metal with more positive potential, in the electromotive series, will displace a metal with a less positive potential.

The electrochemical order of metals in a KCN solution indicates the sequence (from positive to negative) as:

$$Mg > Al > Zn > Cu > Au > Ag > Hg > Pb > Fe > Pt$$

Each metal dissolves more readily than the metals on its right, and will precipitate those metals from the solution. According to this sequence, aluminium will displace gold and silver more readily than will zinc.

In the case of halide leach liquors, cementation is one of the simple ways to recover precious metals, especially from commonly used chloride leaching. Reductive precipitation of gold is performed by contacting the leach liquor with a metal having a potential above that of the precious metal in the electrochemical series. In the case of Au^{3+}, the metals (M generally stands for iron and aluminium) which can form trivalent ions in chloride solution are usually employed due to their half-cell reactions as follows:

$$Au^{3+} + 3e^- \rightarrow Au^0 \; E^0 = 1.40\,V \tag{6.6}$$

$$Fe^{3+} + 3e^- \rightarrow Fe^0 \; E^0 = -1.21\,V \tag{6.7}$$

$$Al^{3+} + 3e^- \rightarrow Al^0 \; E^0 = -1.66 \, V \tag{6.8}$$

The precipitation reaction of gold can be commonly written as:

$$Au^{3+} + M^0 \rightarrow Au^0 + M^{3+} \tag{6.9}$$

In principle, the metal M should be dissolved to precipitate the gold from leach liquor, hence the pH is always maintained in the acidic range.

Based on the above reactions, gold and platinum metals can be separated on a commercial scale from spent electrolytes during the electrolytic refining of gold (Habashi et al., 1987). Further studies were performed by Yousif (2019) on selective precipitation of Pt, Pd, and Rh from spent catalytic converters. Prior to precipitation, the distillation of HCl was conducted by evaporation at 190°C, which also leads to hydrolysis of palladium and rhodium species after dilution. The individual precipitation of Pt in the presence of Pd and Rh was performed by adding NH_4Cl (290 g/L) at 40°C with continuous stirring. A yellowish Pt precipitate of $(NH_4)_2[PtCl_6]$ was obtained, which was filtered, washed with ammonium chloride solution (140g/L), calcined at 800°C, and dried to obtain a fine Pt powder of more than 99.5% purity. To selectively precipitate palladium in the presence of rhodium, the filtrate from the platinum stage was evaporated and sodium chlorate was added slowly (3g) with constant stirring until a bright red precipitate of $(NH_4)_2[PdCl_6]$ was formed, which was calcined at 900°C. Finally, rhodium from the filtrate was precipitated with KOH as lemon-yellow rhodium hydroxide $(Rh(OH)_3)$, filtered, water washed, air-dried (decomposed to Rh_2O_3) and ignited at 1150°C to produce a grey Rh metal powder of 95.4% purity.

Recovery of precious metals by cementation from cyanide leach liquors were first practised on an industrial scale by MacArthur with zinc shavings in the 1890s. In 1900, C. W. Merrill introduced zinc dust to achieve more efficient recovery of gold (Habashi et al., 1987). The addition of zinc also evolved hydrogen gas that can contribute to gold precipitation; however, gold is not precipitated by hydrogen at atmospheric pressure. The following reactions take place:

$$2Au(CN)_2^- + Zn^0 \rightarrow 2Au^0 + Zn(CN)_4^{2-} \tag{6.10}$$

$$2Au(CN)_2^- + Zn^0 + 3OH^- \rightarrow 2Au^0 + HZnO_2^- + 4CN^- + H_2O \tag{6.11}$$

$$Zn^0 + 4CN^- + 2H_2O \rightarrow Zn(CN)_4^{2-} + 2OH^- + H_2 \tag{6.12}$$

$$Au(CN)_2^- + H_2 \rightarrow Au^0 + 2CN^- + 2H^+ \tag{6.13}$$

Barin et al. (1980) proposed an overall chemical reaction by considering the hydrogen evolution in gold cementation by zinc, as below:

$$Au(CN)_2^- + Zn^0 + H_2O + 2CN^- \rightarrow Au^0 + Zn(CN)_4^{2-} + OH^- + \frac{1}{2}H_2 \tag{6.14}$$

Cementation is a heterogeneous redox reaction controlled by the rate at which aurocyanide and cyanide ions are transferred to the zinc surface (Nicol, 1979; Finkelstein, 1972; Fleming, 1992). The reductive precipitation of precious metals by zinc on an industrial scale was further improved by introducing oxygen instead of air to the leach liquor.

A minimum of 0.1 g/L to 1.7 g/L NaCN concentration is critical for cementation of precious metals like gold (Nicol, 1979; Barin et al., 1980). The concentration of metal itself has a direct influence on the cementation rate, which is essentially a first-order reaction controlled by the transfer rate of metal-cyanide ions. Although a change in solution pH (in the range of 9 to 12) has no appreciable effect on cementation, a higher pH may lead to formation of intermediate hydroxides, which can retard or sometimes stop the cementation process. Finkelstein (1972) reported that anions such as sulphate, sulphide, thiosulphate, and ferrocyanide might reduce gold precipitation yield by 1–2% from 10^{-3} M cyanide solutions. The free sulphates may precipitate as gypsum to reduce reactivity in the cementation process. Nicol (1979) found that sulphide ions can passivate the zinc surface even at lower concentrations of 1×10^{-4} M. For efficient cementation recovery of gold, the leach liquor should not contain > 5 ppm suspended particles and > 1 ppm dissolved oxygen, with a free cyanide concentration > 0.035 M at pH in the range of 9 to 11.

Reductive precipitation of precious metals from the impregnated (thiosulphate-based) leach liquor using inorganic zinc metal (Merrill–Crowe process) or organic acid (predominantly oxalic acid) is a common process in gold recovery; however it is not very effective in the thiosulphate-ammonia system. The metal precipitants often have a deleterious effect on thiosulphate ions, producing unwanted cations and thus complicating the lixiviant recycling process. The contamination of solid products is often a result of either undissolved (excess) precipitant or co-precipitation with other metal ions, necessitating further purification. Copper is a reasonable choice, as gold-depleted copper solution can be directly recycled to the leaching stage. Precipitation by the addition of sulphide salts or by chemical reduction with sodium borohydride, hydrogen or sulfphr dioxide has also been investigated (Awadalla and Ritcey, 1991; Deschênes and Ritcey, 1990; Johnson and Bhappu, 1969). These techniques are not much favoured, as they are less selective and tend to precipitate most metals from solution as well as hindering the recycling of the leach liquor. The electro-reduction of aurothiosulphate ions to deposit on the cathode is especially problematic in the presence of a great excess of unwanted cations of copper, which get co-deposited on the cathode product. This results in a devalued product requiring further purification. Side reactions involving the oxidation or reduction of thiosulphate may also interfere (Aylmore, 2001). This lowers the efficiency of electrowinning by increasing the energy input required to recover the desired metals from solution, making it an unviable option for recovering the precious metal.

Reduction precipitation from thiourea leach liquor is one of the main ways of recovering precious metal. It is mostly aluminium, iron, and lead that are used for this purpose. However, reports reveal that using Al as the precipitant metal does not yield complete recovery, leaving a 2% gold ion in the solution (van Lierde et al., 1982). The US Bureau of Mines has reported ~99% recovery of precious metals from thiourea leach liquor at the cost of 6.4 kg consumption of Al for each kg of the precious metals (gold and silver). In principle, thiourea leach liquor contains iron, hence, iron is preferred for cementing gold by the following reaction (Groenewald, 1976; Zouboulis et al., 1993):

$$2Au\left[SC\left(NH_2\right)_2\right]_2^+ + Fe^0 \rightarrow 2Au^0 + Fe^{2+} + 4SC\left(NH_2\right)_2 \qquad (6.15)$$

In comparison to Fe, using Pb powder for gold cementation yielded quite significant results from HCl-thiourea solution (Wen, 1982). The cementation reaction with lead powder can be written as (Tataru 1968):

$$\frac{n}{2}Au\left[SC(NH_2)_2\right]_2^+.Cl^- + Pb^0 \rightarrow \frac{n}{2}Au^0 + Pb\left[SC(NH_2)_2\right]_n Cl_2 + \left(\frac{n}{2}-1\right)Cl_2 \quad (6.16)$$

A comparatively lower recovery using Fe is described in the study by Wang et al. (2011), finding that the presence of oxidants in leach liquor negatively affects the gold cementation reaction. The ferric ion significantly hinders the cementation process because of the increased redox potential of the solutions, which signifies the presence of a suitable electron acceptor. It may cause the Fe powder to be consumed by ferric ions, as follows:

$$Fe^{3+} + Fe^0 \rightarrow 3Fe^{2+} \quad (6.17)$$

The removal of iron powder lowers the availability of this reductant for the cementation of gold, resulting in a negative effect on gold cementation. The addition of tri-sodium citrate to the system can potentially control the redox potential of the solution by forming a ferric–citrate complex. useful for enhancing gold recovery by controlling the ratio of Fe^{3+}/Fe^{2+}.

6.3 RECOVERY OF PRECIOUS METALS BY ADSORPTION

Adsorption is a surface phenomenon and involves the adhesion of metal ions on the solid surface from the gas or liquid phase, creating a film of the adsorbate on the surface of the adsorbent. For prospective metal recovery, adsorption consists of two steps: loading of the adsorbent, and recovery of metal ions from the adsorbent. Three mechanistic theories have generally been suggested for the adsorption phenomenon. They are thought to operate at the same time but to varying degrees. All adsorption processes are thought to take place due to van der Waal forces, further limited to the adsorption of inorganic acids. The primary adsorption of a proton (H+ ions) by physical forces was followed by secondary adsorption of anions. These anions of an adsorbed acid were able to be displaced by different anions added to charcoal. The chemical complex theory indicates that adsorption could be due to neutralization of the acid groups on the surface, while the electrochemical mechanism suggests that oxygen in contact with an aqueous suspension of charcoal is reduced to hydroxyl groups and hydrogen peroxide according to the following equation:

$$O_2 + 2H_2O + 2e^- \rightarrow H_2O_2 + 2OH^- \quad (6.18)$$

Since charcoal tends to have a positive charge at the surface, anions are attracted towards the surface to maintain electrical neutrality and are thus adsorbed (Habashi et al., 1987; McQuiston and Chapman, 1951).

McQuiston and Chapman (1951) first patented the adsorption of a gold–cyanide complex on activated carbon. Resulting new developments introduced since that time, carbon in pulp (CIP) and carbon in leach (CIL), are considered commercially viable processes for gold recovery. It has been observed that the rate of gold adsorption increased with gold concentration, shaking speed/agitation, and process temperature, but was insignificantly affected by thiourea concentration or the presence of ferrous ions. Silver and copper ions decreased the rate via competition for the surface sites. A high concentration of ferric ions (5g/L) also substantially reduced the rate, probably due to changes in solution chemistry. Partial decomposition of the complex to metallic gold has also been observed under certain conditions. Gross and Scott (1927) also studied the adsorption of gold and silver from cyanide-based solution on pine charcoal and it was concluded that 0.04g of gold and 0.02g of silver can be adsorbed per gram of charcoal within 50 hours of equilibrium time. Both gold and silver can inhibit each other's adsorption if they coexist or have free cyanide and caustic soda in solution. The adsorption capacity of charcoal also decreases with increasing free cyanide, caustic soda, chlorides, nitrates, sulphates, and sulphides due to competition for the available exchange sites and with the precipitation of gold and silver as aurous and argentous cyanides due to the increased acidity of the solution. Charcoal with adsorbed gold and silver is usually burned to recover the metals. The use of sodium sulphide solution to recover gold selectively from silver has also been investigated, while mercurous nitrate solution was found to be efficient for silver dissolution.

Lam et al. (2008) observed that aminopropyl- and thiolpropyl-grafted mesoporous silica adsorbed gold selectively from mining and electroplating discharges. The aminopropyl- and thiolpropyl-grafted mesoporous silica exhibited high affinity for gold from both discharges and also exhibited 100% selectivity for the gold from gold–copper and gold–nickel binary solutions. Studies by Zalupski et al. (2014) investigated the adsorption behavior of mesoporous carbon and sulphur-impregnated mesoporous carbon for precious metals (Au, Pd, Pt). Adsorption isotherms for Au^{3+}, $Pd^{2+,}$ and Pt^{4+} indicated that sulphur-impregnated mesoporous carbon can enhance the adsorption of these metal ions at pH3 with synthetic chloride solution. It was also found that the adsorption of metal ions by mesoporous carbon-based adsorbents from the dilute acidic leach liquor of urban mined sources such as electronic scrap is feasible.

Precious metals recovery from thiourea leach liquor was principally studied by Soviet scientists (Lodeishchikov et al., 1968) and has been practiced at the New England Antimony Mines located in Hillgrove, New South Wales. High carbon loading (6–8 kg/t carbon) with a satisfactory efficiency of 90% gold from leach liquor of 27 mg/L Au by charging 20 g/L of carbon in pulp has been achieved, but with a high co-adsorption loss (up to 30%) of thiourea (Schulze, 1984). Thiourea can be partially recovered back by hot water back-washing of the adsorbed carbon. The adsorption process follows the Langmuir monolayer isotherm over a wide range of gold concentrations (Zhang et al., 2004). The equilibrium loading of gold decreases with increasing thiourea concentration, pH, and temperature. The presence of Fe^{3+} and Fe^{2+} ions at low level (up to 700 mg/L) does not affect the equilibrium loading; however, Cu^{2+} ion significantly reduces it, presumably by competitive adsorption. In the initial stage, the rate of gold adsorption approximates first-order kinetics and is controlled by the diffusion of the gold–thiourea complex to the carbon surface. A change in thiourea concentration does not affect the initial rate of adsorption, nor does the presence of 5 g/L Fe^{2+} ions, but an increase in the initial gold concentration, agitation,

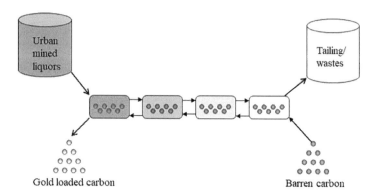

FIGURE 6.1 Recovery of precious metal by carbon adsorption.

and temperature greatly affect the adsorption rate. A high concentration of Fe^{3+} ion substantially suppresses the adsorption rate constant, probably due to the deleterious oxidation products of thiourea. Ag^+ and Cu^{2+} ions also strongly reduce the rate by competitive adsorption.

Recovery of precious metals, particularly gold, from cyanide-based leach liquors by carbon adsorption is a well-practised process (Figure 6.1) that had a strong impact on the economics of gold metallurgy during deregulation of the gold price in the mid-1970s.

The adsorption mechanism of gold onto the carbon surface can be explained as follows: 1) adsorption of the anionic gold–cyanide complex is maintained by electro-static attraction orVan der Waal forces; and 2) the gold–cyanide complex is altered to other forms and precipitated in reduced form onto the carbon surface.

By replacing the Merrill–Crowe process, the carbon-in-pulp (CIP), carbon-in-leach (CIL), and carbon-in-column (CIC) processes allowed the treatment of low-grade (high-clay) ores at lower capital and operating costs and with a higher yield. The Merrill–Crowe and carbon adsorption processesI are compared in Table 6.1.

TABLE 6.1

A comparison between the Merrill–Crowe and carbon adsorption processes

Merrill–Crowe Process

Advantages	- capex, labour and maintenance cost are lower
	- can handle large Ag-to-Au ratio in leach liquor
Disadvantages	- pre-treatment of leach liquor is needed prior to cementation
	- sensitive to interfering ions in the leach liquor

Carbon Adsorption Process

Advantages	- pre-treatment of leach liquor is not needed
	- efficient recovery handling the carbonaceous ores
	- up to 99.9% recovery of all the soluble gold in cyanide solution
Disadvantages	- loss of gold with fine carbon, CIP needs more cyanide in system

---

CIP is a sequential leach and adsorption technique for gold recovery from the cyanide solution of liberated gold. During leaching, pulp flows through cyanidation agitation tanks, then the (impregnated) leach liquor flows through agitation tanks for adsorption of gold onto activated carbon. Due to the difference in particle size, screening is carried out to separate the barren pulp from gold-loaded carbon. In practice, a series of tanks (usually 5 or 6) is used to contact the carbon and leach slurry.

The CIL is a simultaneous process of gold leaching (by cyanidation) and adsorption onto activated carbon, mainly applicable to processing carbonaceous gold ores but equally viable for cyanide-based recovery of gold from urban-mined liquors. A simultaneous leaching-adsorption process helps to minimize the problem of preg-robbing.

The CIC consists of a series of fluidized bed carbon columns, up through which solution flows, and is mostly used for gold recovery from the heap-leach solution. The ability to process solutions containing 2–3 wt % solids is advantageous for CIC.

Although CIP did not become popular until the late 1970s, Davis (1880) and Johnson (1894) had obtained patents almost a century before for using wood charcoal from chlorine and cyanide leach solutions, respectively. Gross and Scott (1927) published an extensive report in 1927 on recovering gold and silver from cyanide solutions including parametric investigation on elution. Sodium sulphide, sodium cyanide, and sodium hydroxide were identified as aiding elution, but efficient elution remained a serious impediment to wider acceptance of this process. In 1952, Carlton Mill in Colorado introduced the first CIP flowsheet (Fast, 1988), employing ammonia as the complexation agent for gold elution. The use of sodium sulphide and caustic cyanide in elution became the first successful commercial elution practices, known as the Zadra process (Zadra, 1950; Zadra et al., 1952). The Zadra elution process in CIP at the Homestake Mine in South Dakota (Fast, 1988) was the first-known modern CIP process to be put in place. By the year 2000, several hundred plants were operating it.

In modern CIP, the majority of the activated carbon used to recover the gold from cyanide solution is either granular coconut-shell carbon or peat-based extruded carbon. Gold-loading kinetics (activity) and loading capacity, elution kinetics, level of gold elution, strength and abrasion resistance, particle-size distribution, and wet density are the criteria on which the CIP operation depends. Due consideration of the physico-chemical properties of virgin carbon is therefore required if it is to be selection for use in CIP. Under the American Society for Testing and Materials (ASTM International) standards, most activated carbon manufacturers have their own in-house testing procedures.

Activated carbon is a heterogeneous material. The softer carbon has higher activity; hence, the softer carbon lost due to attrition is the most active portion. Numerous methodologies to monitor the adsorption rate of gold onto carbon from alkaline cyanide solution have been proposed (Avraamides, 1989). Although these vary in terms of equipment used, solution composition, carbon dosage in pulp and the particle size of carbon, all involve attaching a known mass of carbon to the solution of a known gold concentration, solution analysis at regular intervals, and hence determination of the activity of carbon using gold loading/adsorption data. One of the common phenomena observed for sorption kinetics is that the data are often a good match with the rate equation for the initial stage of adsorption, but later, when carbon loading becomes excessive, the rate constant fails to match the rate equation (La Brooy et al., 1986). A sample of virgin carbon is often used as control with a relative activity monitor of industrial carbon in use. McArthur et al. (1887) suggested that the activity of carbon should be calculated after a period of attrition. Since the loss of more active components occurs with attrition, dropping the activity of the carbon, the data collected would be more representative of industrial operations. Follis (1992) advocated determining carbon activity by volume instead of measuring the mass. To obtain reliable results, activity tests should be carried out in industrial process water instead of using distilled water. Approximately 30–50% slower kinetics has been found in hypersaline solutions than in distilled water (La Brooy et al., 1986). The loading capacity of activated carbon is determined by an adsorption isotherm that can be defined as the equilibrium loading on carbon in contact with 1 mg/L of gold solution. In most cases (Parker Centre method, Mintek method, Norit method, Anglo American Research Laboratories method), the varying masses of pulverized carbon are contacted with gold cyanide solution for over 20 h (AMIRA,1987; Shipman, 1994; Osei-Agyemang et al., 2015). In a different approach, carbon is contacted for 1 h with 1 L of 10 mg/L gold solution. On analysis of the residual gold in solution, gold adsorbed onto carbon is calculated as G1. The recovered carbon is then placed in a new batch of 10 mg/L gold solution for a further hour to give the calculation of G2. Cumulative gold loading is plotted after at least 11 repetitions, and shows an increase in gold loading on the carbon with the increase in the number of solution contacts. Higher loading on the carbon is advantageous for decreasing the plant size required for the elution regeneration operation (Bailey, 1987). Various factors affecting the gold adsorption have been studied, including cyanide ion concentration, co-existing ions, pH, and particle size.

A higher concentration of free cyanide has a detrimental effect on gold adsorption with carbon. However, as free cyanide in solution prevents the co-adsorption of copper, free cyanide solution is recommended in carbon adsorption of gold from copper-bearing leach liquors.

The effect of co-existing metals and the ionic strength of the solution on carbon loading is significant. The degree of gold adsorption from the cyanide solution depends on the presence of cations in the solution (Davidson, 1974). In the presence of other metal ions, aurocyanide is adsorbed onto carbon following the series:

$$Ca^{2+} > Mg^{2+} > H^+ > Li^+ > Na^+ > K^+$$

Loading of gold in carbon from de-ionized water is low. Depending on the solution pH, the zeta potential values of carbon change from positive to negative, hence the behavior of carbon in adsorbing the protons and hydroxyl ions change as well with respect to the pH. It has been found that the equilibrium loading of gold onto carbon increases with lower pH. The influences of Ca^{2+} and OH^- ions are antithetic in practice. A high concentration of Ca^{2+} enhances gold adsorption, while a high pH decreases the adsorption loading of gold.

The adsorption rate is significantly affected by the carbon particle size. Woollacott and Erasmus (1992) suggested that the gold loading is distributed among the carbon particles. The smaller the particle size, the higher the adsorption rate, due to a larger surface area for adsorption. Although the size range of particles is relatively small in a circuit, it is nevertheless significant. For the same contact time, smaller particles load higher gold than larger particles, hence, the loading of gold on the individual particle will be distributed.

6.4 RECOVERY OF PRECIOUS METALS BY ELECTROWINNING

Enriched solutions of precious metals (Au, Pt, Ag), including Cu after elution, can be transferred to electro-win the metal deposition on the cathode. The cathode is subsequently treated with H_2SO_4 for removal of metal impurities prior to melting and collection of the doré. The cast doré then undergoes electro-refining to obtain pure gold, separating it from the Ag and Pt. The electrochemical reaction for electrowinning of gold can be understood as:

$$4OH^- \rightarrow O_2 + 2H_2O + 4e^- \qquad (6.19)$$

$$2e^- + 2H_2O \rightarrow H_2 + 2OH^- \qquad (6.20)$$

$$KAu(CN)_2 \rightarrow K^+ + Au(CN)_2^- \qquad (6.21)$$

$$Au(CN)_2^- \rightarrow Au^+ + CN^- \qquad (6.22)$$

$$e^- + Au^+ \rightarrow Au^0 \qquad (6.23)$$

The cathode attracts positive ions to its surface, forming the Helmholtz double layer (Wilkinson, 1986). When the negatively charged $Au(CN)_2^-$ approaches this layer, it becomes polarized in the electric field of the cathode. Thus, the ligand distribution around the metal is distorted and diffusion of the metal complex into the Helmholtz layer breaks the complex, releasing the positively charged metal cation to be deposited onto the cathode. The stability constant of the aurocyanide complex can be given as (Wilkinson, 1986):

$$\frac{\left[Au(CN)_2^-\right]}{\left[Au^+\right]\left[CN^-\right]^2} = 10^{38.3} \qquad (6.24)$$

Hence, the extremely low concentration of $[Au^+]$ can be considered as:

$$\left[Au^+\right] = \frac{\left[Au(CN)_2^-\right]}{\left[CN^-\right]^2}.10^{-38.3} \qquad (6.25)$$

Therefore, the rate of gold deposition from the aurocyanide solution is driven by the polarization of $Au(CN)_2^-$ ions, which approach the cathode surfaces and are distorted as described above. Although the system can be operated under alkaline or neutral conditions, the concentration of [Au⁺] increases in acidic pH (3.1 to 7.0), as the equilibrium of the reaction is affected by the formation of HCN (Wilkinson, 1986). It is known that the aurocyanide solution is stable without the evolution of HCN down to a pH of 3.1 (Fisher and Weimer, 1964). As the current density and cathode current efficiency increase with gold concentration, a high gold-containing solution is recommended for electrowinning.

The electrolytic recovery of gold from impregnated cyanide solutions was firstly applied in the Siemens–Halske electrolytic method (Adamson, 1972). In this process, gold was electrolytically deposited onto lead foil cathodes, which were removed periodically, melted into ingots of lead, and processed for gold recovery. Gold electrowinning from impregnated cyanide solutions has two major inherent advantages over the chemical reduction (precipitation) of gold: (i) no addition of chemical reagents leads to the recycling of the cyanide solution in the extraction process; and (ii) high-purity gold is yielded. But a low gold- impregnated solution is a poor electrolyte, causing low current density with a slow deposition rate of gold. The ideal current density and current efficiency for gold electrowinning from cyanide solutions are proportional to the amount of gold in the electrolyte. The electrowinning of gold from impregnated mill solutions therefore has to cope with a low current density. In some cases, the direct electrowinning of gold from heap-leach (impregnated solution) liquor has also been proposed. However, the low gold content (0.75 to 2.0 ppm Au) is not attractive for achieving ideal current density and efficiency of gold deposition.

The electrolytic reduction of gold from $Au[SC(NH_2)_2]_2^+$ complex solution can be achieved by the following reaction:

$$Au\left[SC(NH_2)_2\right]_2^+ + e^- \rightarrow Au + 2SC(NH_2)_2.\ E = -0.38\ V \tag{6.26}$$

With a cathodic potential range of –0.15 V to –0.38 V, it follows a diffusion-controlled reaction (Groenewald, 1977). However, cathodic reduction of gold is not attributable to thiourea as such; it is formamidine disulphide, an oxidation product of thiourea, that is thought to reduce on the cathodic surface. Notably, separate anodic and cathodic compartments are needed to prevent the formation of decomposition products of thiourea in the anodic compartment which may re-dissolve the deposited gold from the cathode surface. The use of a Pb-anode minimizes the oxidation decomposition of thiourea, and applying low current density with a high catholyte circulation rate yields a better current efficacy for gold deposition.

6.5 RECOVERY OF PRECIOUS METALS BY AGGLOMERATION

The coal–oil gold agglomeration (CGA) process is used for oleophilic/hydrophobic free gold particles (1 to 100 μm) from various primary and secondary slurry sources. In the CGA process, oil (either vegetable, diesel, or kerosene) act as a bridge between the coal and gold particles, and coal as a carrier enables significant separation of gold-containing agglomerates. The CGA process is regarded as efficient for liberated or free gold (Akcil et al., 2009, Calvez et al., 1998, Kotze, 2000). Under optimum conditions, gold recoveries of 95% can be achieved with a batch mode and 62–75% on a pilot scale (Bonney, 1992).

6.6 RECOVERY OF PRECIOUS METALS BY SUPERCRITICAL FLUIDS EXTRACTION

Supercritical fluid extraction is a simple process, with good selectivity and low energy consumption. Supercritical fluids have low surface tension, are less toxic than other solvents, and are easily recycled. They are used in wide variety of reactions (Laintz et al., 1992; Eckert et al., 1996; Phelps et al., 1996). At controlled temperature and pressure, metal ions can be easily leached and efficiently extracted from supercritical fluids according to their size, boiling point, polarity, and molecular weight.

Faisal et al. (2008) investigated the recovery of Pd, Pt, and Rh from spent automobile catalytic converters using supercritical carbon dioxide ($SCCO_2$) containing tributyl phosphate (TBP) as additional chelating agents. They found that the addition of a chelating ligand was essential to extract precious metals, because insignificant extractions (less then 3%) were observed with pure $SCCO_2$. Iwao et al. (2007) compared the effect of different chelating agents (Cyanex 302, $TBP/HNO_3/H_2O$, or acetyl-acetone) on Pd extraction by using $SCCO_2$. Of those chelating agents, Cyanex 302 obtained the maximum extraction efficiency of more than 99%. Under optimal conditions, the highest extraction rates of Pd for acetyl-acetone and $TBP/HNO_3/H_2O$ were around 80% and 60%, respectively. The difference was owing to a reduced ability to form a complex of acetyl-acetone and $TBP/HNO_3/H_2O$ with palladium.

6.7 BIO-MEDIATED RECOVERY OF PRECIOUS METALS

Bio-mediated processing can play a vital role in metal recovery from various urban-mined leached liquors. In general, bio-mediated metal recovery from leach liquors of secondary waste like waste electrical and electronic equipment and spent catalysts can be achieved by the following routes:1) interaction of cationic metal species with microbial cell via biosorption; 2) metal cations can bio-accumulate within the cell wall; 3) translocation of metal ions within the cells via metal-binding proteins; 4) Bio-precipitation after interaction with extracellular polymeric substances or microbially mediated anions; and 5) enzymatically mediated metal volatilizations.

Generally, biosorption is regarded as a complex process influenced by various factors such as the nature of metal-accessible bio-ligands, the nature of the biosorbent (alive, dead), the chemical, stereo-chemical, and coordination characteristics of the targeted metals, and the characteristics of the metal solution, such as pH and the competing ions (Tsezos et al. 2011; Deng and Wang 2012; Wang and Chen 2009).

Biosorption can be either metabolically dependent or an independent process and can be regarded as extracellular accumulation/precipitation, cell surface sorption/precipitation, and intracellular accumulation, depending on the metal sorption location. Similarly, physico-chemical mechanisms (including ion exchange, complexation/chelation, and metal coordination) depend on the specific properties of the biomass such as live, dead, or derived material. Additionally, metabolism-dependent bio-mediated processes also include bio-precipitation (S^{2-} or PO_4^{3-}), bio-sequestration by metal-binding proteins like peptides or siderophores, bio-assisted transport, and internal compartmentalization (Gadd, 2010) as shown in Figure 6.2.

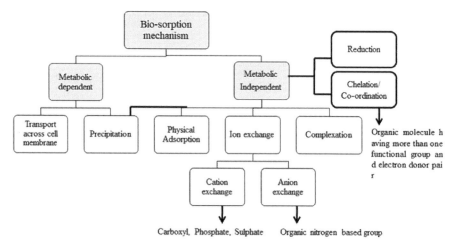

FIGURE 6.2   Biosorption mechanisms.

Source: Modified from Ilyas and Lee (2014).

Investigations by Kratochvil and Volesky (1998) suggested that metal biosorption can be both physisorption and chemisorption. Physisorption occurs either by electro-static interactions or ion exchange, while chemisorption involves complexation/che-lation, bio-precipitation, and bio-reduction. Generally, the cell wall of a bio-based system (bacteria, fungi, algae, bio-derived material, etc.) is the first to interact with metal ions for deposition on the surface or within the cell wall structure (Vijayaraghavan and Yun 2008; Wang and Chen, 2009). Carboxyl-, phosphonate-, amine-, and hydroxyl-based functional groups on the microbial cell wall facilitate biosorption of metal ions. Differences in the metal uptake rate can be attributed to a difference in the properties of micro-organisms such as cell wall structure, nature of functional groups, and surface area.

Vijayaraghavan and Yun (2008) showed that bacterial cells act as efficient bio-sorbents due to the high surface area available per unit volume and poten-tially active chemisorption sites. Golab et al. (1995) observed that the carboxyl groups of the peptidoglycan-containing cell wall of *Streptomyces pilosus* facili-tate the binding of divalent metal ions. Amine-based functional groups are also considered efficient for chelating cationic metal ions and adsorbing anionic metal species via electrostatic interactions or hydrogen bonding. Bio-mediated recovery of precious metals from the leach liquor of secondary wastes by algal, fungal, bacterial, agriculture or food waste-based biomasses has also been investigated.

6.7.1   Agro-waste-/Food Waste-based Bio-mediated Recovery of Precious Metals

Ishikawa et al. (2002) investigated the adsorption behavior of gold from cya-nide-based electroplating wastes with an eggshell membrane as potential adsorbent and proposed a physical sorption mechanism, while Pethkar and Paknikar (1998) found that bio-sorption of Au^{3+} by eggshell membranes follows a chemisorption mechanism.

The adsorption mechanisms of gold and palladium with condensed tannin gel were reported by Kim and Nakano (2005). They observed metallic palladium on the tannin-gel particles formed after the reduction of Pd^{2+} ions to zero-valent Pd, while the hydroxyl groups of tannin gel were noticed to be oxidized during adsorption. Soleimani and Kaghazchi (2008) investigated the adsorption behavior of gold from industrial wastewater by activated carbon of the hard shell of apricot stones. The results indicated that 98% of gold was adsorbed after 3 h of contact at ambient temperature.

The adsorption pattern of gold on rice husk and barley straw was also investigated using gold-containing solutions. The maximum adsorption capacity of a rice husk for gold was 0.76 mol /kg and of barley straw was 1.47 mol/kg. The efficiency of barley straw for adsorption of gold from the industrial spent solution was also found to be highly significant and selective in the presence of base metals (Chand et al., 2009).

Carbonaceous adsorbents prepared from flax shive adsorbed gold from gold-bearing spent solution (Cox et al., 2005). Lemon peel adsorbs gold selectively, showing an insignificant affinity for other precious metals and base metal ions from chloride-based solution (Parajuli et al., 2008). Table 6.2 lists the recovery of precious metals by various agriculture/food wastes as efficient biosorbents.

6.7.2 BACTERIA-, FUNGI-, AND ALGAE-BASED BIO-MEDIATED RECOVERY OF PRECIOUS METALS

Creamer et al. (2006) investigated bio-mediated recovery of precious metals from urban-mined leach liquors (electronic waste) by *Desulfovibrio desulfuricans* in a columnar electro-bioreactor (2L) supplied with nitrogen/hydrogen. They observed that adding H_2 gas along with *Desulfovibrio desulfuricans* biomass in leach liquor (2mM of Pd^{2+}) has an insignificant effect on biosorption of palladium. The study was extended to investigate the effect of Cu^{2+} ions on the removal of Pd^{2+} and Au^{3+} from synthetic solutions and leach liquors and it was concluded that Cu^{2+} inhibited the recovery of Pd^{2+}, but not of Au^{3+}, which can be selectively recovered from other metal ions (Table 6.3).

The binding mechanism of gold and silver with *Cladosporium cladosporioides* by X-ray photoelectron spectroscopy and Fourier transform infra-red spectroscopy was also elucidated. No chemical changes to the bio-sorbent were observed after metal loading with spectroscopic analysis, indicating that the acidic conditions merely favoured electrostatic interaction between $AuCl^{4-}$ (gold anionic species) and protonated biomass. Table 6.4 shows some fungal-based biomasses as potential candidates for precious metal recovery.

Comprehensive work on gold biosorption mechanism by algal biomass was carried out by Watkins et al. (1987) and Greene et al. (1986). It was suggested that interaction of $AuCl^{4-}$ with *Chlorella Vulgaris* involved consecutive steps of the rapid reduction of Au^{3+} to Au^+ followed by a slow reduction from Au^+ to Au by functional

TABLE 6.2

Bio-mediated recovery of precious metals by agriculture/food waste-based biomasses

Bio-sorbent	Bio-mediated metal	Process pH	q_{max} [mmol g^{-1}]	References
Agro-waste/food wastes as bio-sorbents for precious metals				
Hen eggshell membrane	Au$^+$	3	0.67	Schiewer and Volesky, 1996
Hen eggshell membrane	Au^{3+}	3	3.1	Schiewer and Volesky, 1996
Lysozyme	Au^{3+}, Pd^{2+}, Pt^{4+}	-	-	Maruyama et al., 2007
Bovine serum albumin	Au^{3+}, Pd^{2+}, Pt^{4+}	-	-	Maruyama et al., 2007
Alfalfa	Au^{3+}	5.0	0.18	Gamez et al., 2003
Condensed-tannin gel	Au^{3+}	2.0	1.0	Kim and Nakano, 2005
Condensed-tannin gel	Pd^{2+}	2.0	40	Volesky, 1992
Bayberry tannin immobilized collagen fibre membrane	Au^{3+}	3.0	0.23	Ma et al., 2006
Bayberry tannin immobilized collagen fibre membrane	Pt^{4+}	4.0	0.32	Ma et al., 2006
Acid-washed *Ucides cordatus* (waste crab shells)	Pd^{2+}	3.4	0.17	Niu and Volesky, 2003
Glutaraldehyde crosslinked chitosan	Au$^+$	1.6	2.9	Arrascue et al., 2003
Sulphur derivative of chitosan	Au^{3+}	3.2	3.2	Arrascue et al., 2003
Glutaraldehyde crosslinked chitosan	Au^{3+}	2.0	2.44	Guibal et al., 2002
Thiourea derivative of chitosan	Pd^{2+}	2.0	2.54	Guibal et al., 2002
Rubeanic acid derivative of chitosan	Pd^{2+}	2.0	3.24	Guibal et al., 2002
Thiourea derivative of chitosan	Pd^{2+}	2.0	2.0	Guibal et al., 1999
Glutaraldehyde crosslinked chitosan	Pt^{4+}	2.0	1.6	Guibal et al., 1999
Chitosan derivatives	Pt^{4+}	2.0	3.5	Chassary et al., 2005
Chitosan derivatives	Pd^{2+}	2.0	3.2	Chassary et al., 2005

group-mediated ligand exchange reactions. Spectroscopic investigations of the bio-sorption of Au^{3+} by de-alginate seaweed wastes carried out by Romero-González et al. (2003) indicated colloidal Au on the surface of de-alginate seaweed formed by consecutive reductions of Au^{3+} to Au. Table 6.5 describes algal-mediated recovery of precious metals with process pH.

TABLE 6.3
Bio-mediated recovery of precious metals by bacterial biomasses

Bio-sorbent	Bio-mediated metal	Process pH	q_{max} [mmol g^{-1}]	References
Bacteria as bio-sorbents for precious metals				
Streptomyces erythraeus	Au^{3+}	4.0	0.03	Ishikawa et al., 2002
Spirulina platensis	Au^{3+}	4.0	0.026	Ishikawa et al., 2002
Desulfovibrio desulfuricans	Pd^{2+}	2.0	1.2	Vargas et al., 2004
Desulfovibrio fructosivorans	Pd^{2+}	2.0	1.2	Vargas et al., 2004
Desulfovibrio vulgaris	Pd^{2+}	2.0	1.0	Vargas et al., 2004
Desulfovibrio desulfuricans	Pt^{4+}	2.0	0.23	Vargas et al., 2004
Desulfovibrio fructosivorans	Pt^{4+}	2.0	0.17	Vargas et al., 2004
Desulfovibrio vulgaris	Pt^{4+}	2.0	0.17	Vargas et al., 2004
Bacillus subtilis	Au^{+}	2.0	0.008	Niu and Volesky 1999

TABLE 6.4
Bio-mediated recovery of precious metals by fungal-based biomasses

Bio-sorbent	Bio-mediated metal	Process pH	q_{max} [mmol g^{-1}]	References
Fungi as bio-sorbents for precious metals				
Saccharomyces cerevisiae	Au^{3+}	5.0	0.026	Savvaidis 1998
Cladosporium cladosporioides	Au^{3+}	4.0	0.5	Pethkar and Paknikar 1998
Cladosporium cladosporioides	Au, waste	4.0	0.18	Pethkar and Paknikar 1998
Cladosporium cladosporioides-1	Au^{3+}	4.0	0.4	Søbjerg et al., 2011
Cladosporium cladosporioides-2	Au^{3+}	4.0	0.5	Søbjerg et al., 2011
Cladosporium cladosporioides-1	Ag^{+}	4.0	0.4	Søbjerg et al., 2011
Cladosporium cladosporioides-2	Ag+	4.0	0.12	Søbjerg et al., 2011
Aspergillus niger	Au^{3+}	2.5	1.0	Kuyucak and Volesky 1988
Rhizopus arrhizus	Au^{3+}	2.5	0.8	Kuyucak and Volesky 1988
PVA-immobilized biomass (*Fomitopsis carnea*)	Au^{3+}	1–13	0.48	Khoo and Ting 2001
A. niger	Ag^{+}	5–7	0.9	Akthar et al., 1995
Neurospora crassa	Ag^{+}	5–7	0.6	Akthar et al., 1995
Fusarium oxysporum	Ag^{+}	5–7	0.5	Akthar et al., 1995

TABLE 6.5

Bio-mediated recovery of precious metals by algal-based biomasses

Bio-sorbent	Bio-mediated metal	Process pH	q_{max} [mmol g^{-1}]	References
Algae as bio-sorbents for precious metals				
Chlorella vulgaris	Ag$^+$	6.7	0.5	Cordery et al., 1994
Chlorella vulgaris	Au^{3+}	2	0.5	Darnall et al., 1986
Sargassum natans	Au^{3+}	2.5	2.1	Kuyucak and Volesky 1988
Ascophyllum nodosum	Au^{3+}	2.5	0.15	Kuyucak and Volesky 1988
Sargassum fluitans	Au$^+$	2 2.0	0.0032	Niu and Volesky 1999
Alginate cross-linked with CaCl$_2$	Au^{3+}	2.0	1.47	Torres et al., 2005
De-alginated seaweed	Au^{3+}	3	0.4	Romero-Gonzalez et al., 2003

6.8 BIO-REDUCTION/BIO-NANO ENCAPSULATION OF PRECIOUS METALS INTO METALLIC NANOPARTICLES

The bio-reduction of precious metals as a recent addition to the portfolio of metal bio-mediated processes is still in its infancy, with multiple electronic transfers involved. However, it is widely accepted that direct contact with the cell surface and extracellular electron shuttle are the main driving forces for metal bio-reduction (Gaspard et al., 1998; Lloyd 2003; Deplanche et al., 2011). It is also believed that bio-reduction can be facilitated by enzymatic systems under favourable conditions, independently of cell metabolism (Yong et al., 2010). In some cases, metal reduction to lower valence states directly involves electron transport reactions to give crystals of metal oxide or base metal coated on the cell surface.

Bio-reduction and bio-nano-encapsulation studies were conducted to recover precious metals from spent automotive catalyst leachates of (acidic) *Desulfovibrio desulfuricans* cells. Precious metals were observed to deposit in reduced form on the bacterial cell surface as metallic nanoparticles, and to remain tightly bound. Similar to *Desulfovibrio desulfuricans*, *Escherichia coli* were also able to reduce precious metals enzymatically on the cell surface through hydrogenase activity (Yong et al., 2010). These bio-assisted metallic nanoparticles were capable of being used as catalysts in fuel cells, as metallic support sheets, for clean-up of groundwater affected by chlorinated aromatic pollutants, for decontamination of pesticides, treatment of oils to remove toxic contaminants and in catalytic oil upgrading (Bennett et al., 2013; Mabbett et al., 2006; Murray et al., 2017; Omajali et al., 2017; Yong et al., 2015).

For precious metal-containing leach liquor with relevant high concentrations of acidic leaching lixiviant, where the potential for enzymatic bio-nanoparticle synthesis is more limited, a two-step approach was developed by Mabbett et al., (2006). In this integrated process, bacterial cell tools were utilized to reduce small amounts of precious metals enzymatically as biological seeds; the bio-seeds were then used for catalytic functions in the subsequent metal-reduction and recovery processes from various wastes including industrial waste, electronic waste, automotive catalytic waste, and refractory brick furnace linings as well as road dust (Mabbett et al., 2006; Creamer et al., 2006; Murray et al., 2017). Slow process kinetics, the decrease in loading capacity at a high concentration of precious metals in liquor, and poor selectivity when dealing with leachers of multi-metal ions are major obstacles to commercial implementation that need to be addressed carefully (Skibar et al., 2005; Ek et al., 2004; Omajali et al., 2017).

ACKNOWLEDGEMENTS

This work was supported by the Brain Pool Programme through the National Research Foundation of Korea (NRF) funded by the Ministry of Science and ICT (Grant No. 2019H1D3A2A02101993) and the Basic Science Research Programme through the National Research Foundation of Korea (NRF) funded by the Ministry of Education (Project no. 2020R1I1A1A01074249).

REFERENCES

Adamson, R.J. (1972). *Gold metallurgy in South Africa. Chamber of Mines of South Africa*, pp. 203–255.

Akcil, A., Wu, X. Q., and Aksay, E. K. (2009). Coal-Gold Agglomeration: An alternative separation process in gold recovery. *Separation & Purification Reviews*, 38(2): 173–201.

Akthar, M. N., Sastry, K. S., and Mohan, P. M. (1995). Bio-sorption of silver ions by processed Aspergillus niger biomass. *Biotechnology Letters*, 17(5): 551–556.

AMIRA, P.P.A. (1987). Carbon-in-pulp gold technology. Progress report no. 4.

Arrascue, M. L., Garcia, H. M., Horna, O., and Guibal, E. (2003). Gold sorption on chitosan derivatives. *Hydrometallurgy*, 71(1-2): 191–200.

Avraamides, J. (1989). CIP carbons — selection, testing and plant operations. In: Bhappu, B. and Harden, R.J. (Eds.), *Gold Forum on Technology and Practices – World Gold 89*, Chapter 34, Littleton, CO: SME, 288–292.

Awadalla, F., Ritcey, G. 1991. Recovery of gold from thiourea, thiocyanate, or thiosulfate solutions by reduction-precipitation with a stabilized form of sodium borohydride. *Separation Science and Technology*. 26(9): 1207–1228.

Aylmore, M.G. (2001). Treatment of a refractory gold–copper sulfide concentrate by copper ammoniacal thiosulfate leaching. *Minerals Engineering*. 14(6): 615–637.

Bailey, P. (1987). Application of activated carbon to gold recovery. (retroactive coverage). *The Extractive Metallurgy of Gold in South Africa, South African Institute of Mining and Metallurgy*. 1: 379–614.

Barin, I., Barth, H., Yaman, A. (1980). Electrochemical investigations of the kinetics of gold cementation by zinc from cyanide solutions. *Erzmetall*. 33: 399–403.

Bennett, J. A., Mikheenko, I. P., Deplanche, K., Shannon, I. J., Wood, J., and Macaskie, L. E. (2013). Nanoparticles of palladium supported on bacterial biomass: new re-usable heterogeneous catalyst with comparable activity to homogeneous colloidal Pd in the Heck reaction. *Applied Catalysis B: Environmental*, 140, 700–707.

Bonney, C. F. (1992). Coal-gold agglomeration–a novel approach to gold recovery. *Innovations in Gold and Silver Recovery*, 2301–2308.

Calvez, J. P. S., Kim, M. J., Wong, P. L. M., and Tran, T. (1998) Use of coal-oil agglomerates for particulate gold recovery. *Minerals Engineering*, 11(9): 803–812.

Chand, R., Watari, T., Inoue, K., Kawakita, H., Luitel, H. N., Parajuli, D. and Yada, M. (2009). Selective adsorption of precious metals from hydrochloric acid solutions using porous carbon prepared from barley straw and rice husk. *Minerals Engineering*, 22(15): 1277–1282.

Chassary, P., Vincent, T., Marcano, J. S., Macaskie, L. E., and Guibal, E. (2005). Palladium and platinum recovery from bicomponent mixtures using chitosan derivatives. *Hydrometallurgy*, 76(1-2): 131–147.

Cordery, J., Wills, A. J., Atkinson, K., and Wills, B. A. (1994). Extraction and recovery of silver from low-grade liquors using microalgae. *Minerals Engineering*, 7(8), 1003–1015.

Cox, M., Pichugin, A. A., El-Shafey, E. I., and Appleton, Q. (2005). Sorption of precious metals onto chemically prepared carbon from flax shive. *Hydrometallurgy*, 78(1-2): 137–144.

Creamer, N. J., Baxter-Plant, V. S., Henderson, J., Potter, M., and Macaskie, L. E. (2006). Palladium and gold removal and recovery from precious metal solutions and electronic scrap leachates by Desulfovibrio desulfuricans. *Biotechnology Letters*, 28(18): 1475–1484.

Darnall, D. W., Greene, B., Henzl, M. T., Hosea, J. M., McPherson, R. A., Sneddon, J., and Alexander, M. D. (1986) Selective recovery of gold and other metal ions from an algal biomass. *Environmental Science & Technology*, 20(2): 206–208.

Davidson, R. (1974). The mechanism of gold adsorption on activated charcoal. *Journal of the Southern African Institute of Mining and Metallurgy*. 75: 67–76.

Davis, W.M. 1880. Depositing gold from its solutions. *U.S. Patent*. 227:963.

De Vargas, I., Macaskie, L. E., and Guibal, E. (2004). Bio-sorption of palladium and platinum by sulfate-reducing bacteria. *Journal of Chemical Technology & Biotechnology: International Research in Process, Environmental & Clean Technology*, 79(1): 49–56.

Deng, X., and Wang, P. (2012). Isolation of marine bacteria highly resistant to mercury and their bioaccumulation process. *Bioresource Technology*, 121: 342–347.

Deplanche, K., Murray, A. J., Mennan, C., Taylor, S., and Macaskie, L. E. (2011). Biorecycling of precious metals and rare earth elements. *Nanomaterials*, 2011: 279–314.

Deschênes, G., Ritcey, G.M. (1990). Recovery of gold from aqueous solutions. *Google Patents*.

Eckert, C. A., Knutson, B. L. and Debenedetti, P. G. (1996). Supercritical fluids as solvents for chemical and materials processing. *Nature*, 383(6598): 313–318.

Ek, K. H., Morrison, G. M., and Rauch, S. (2004). Environmental routes for platinum group elements to biological materials—a review. *Science of the Total Environment*, 334, 21–38.

Faisal, M., Atsuta, Y., Daimon, H. and Fujie, K. (2008). Recovery of precious metals from spent automobile catalytic converters using supercritical carbon dioxide. *Asia-Pacific Journal of Chemical Engineering*, 3(4): 364–367.

Fast, J.L. (1988). Carbon-in-pulp pioneering at the Carlton Mill - how CIP processing blossomed as a routine at Golden Cycle in the 1950s. *E&MJ-Engineering and Mining Journal* 189(6): 56–57.

Finkelstein, N. (1972). *Gold Metallurgy on the Witwatersrand*. (Ed. R. J. Adamson). Cape Town: Cape and Transvaal Printers, 295.

Fisher, J., Weimer, D. (1964). *Precious metals plating*. Teddington: R. Draper Ltd.

Fleming, C. A. (1992). Hydrometallurgy of precious metals recovery. *Hydrometallurgy*, 30(1-3): 127–162.

Follis, R. (1992). Assessing activated carbon quality in hydrometallurgical circuits: Analysis and presentation of data. *In: Proceedings of Randol Gold Forum*, 469–476.

Gadd, G. M. (2010). Metals, minerals and microbes: geomicrobiology and bioremediation. *Microbiology*, 156(3): 609–643.

Gamez, G., Gardea-Torresdey, J. L., Tiemann, K. J., Parsons, J., Dokken, K., and Yacaman, M. J. (2003). Recovery of gold (III) from multi-elemental solutions by alfalfa biomass. *Advances in Environmental Research*, 7(2): 563–571.

Gaspard, S., Vazquez, F., and Holliger, C. (1998). Localization and solubilization of the iron (III) reductase of Geobacter sulfurreducens. *Applied and Environmental Microbiology*, 64(9): 3188–3194.

Golab, Z., Breitenbach, M., and Jezierski, A. (1995). Sites of copper binding in Streptomyces pilosus. *Water, Air, and Soil Pollution*, 82(3-4): 713–721.

Greene, B., Hosea, M., McPherson, R., Henzl, M., Alexander, M. D., and Darnall, D. W. (1986). Interaction of gold (I) and gold (III) complexes with algal biomass. *Environmental Science & Technology*, 20(6): 627–632.

Groenewald, T. (1976). The dissolution of gold in acidic solutions of thiourea. *Hydrometallurgy*, 1(3): 277–290.

Groenewald, T. (1977). Potential applications of thiourea in the processing of gold. *Journal of the Southern African Institute of Mining and Metallurgy*, 77(11): 217–223.

Gross, J., Scott, J.W. (1927). Precipitation of gold and silver from cyanide solution on charcoal. USGPO

Guibal, E., Sweeney, N. V. O., Vincent, T., and Tobin, J. M. (2002). Sulfur derivatives of chitosan for palladium sorption. *Reactive and Functional Polymers*, 50(2): 149–163.

Guibal, E., Vincent, T., and Mendoza, R. N. (1999). Synthesis and characterization of a thiourea derivative of chitosan for platinum recovery. *Journal of Applied Polymer Science*, 75(1): 119–134.

Habashi, F., Awadalla, F.T., Yao, X. B. (1987). The hydrochloric-acid route for phosphate rock. *Journal of Chemical Technology and Biotechnology*, 38:115–126.

Ilyas, S., Lee. J.C. (2014). Biometallurgical recovery of metals from waste electrical and electronic equipments: A review. *ChemBioEng Reviews*, 1(4): 148–169.

Ishikawa, S. I., Suyama, K., Arihara, K., and Itoh, M. (2002). Uptake and recovery of gold ions from electroplating wastes using eggshell membrane. *Bioresource Technology*, 81(3): 201–206.

Iwao, S., El-Fatah, S. A., Furukawa, K., Seki, T., Sasaki, M. and Goto, M. (2007). Recovery of palladium from spent catalyst with supercritical CO_2 and chelating agent. *The Journal of supercritical fluids*, 42(2): 200–204.

Johnson, W. (1894). Method of abstracting gold and silver from their solutions in potassium cyanides. *US Patent*. 522: 260.

Johnson, P. H., and Bhappu, R. B. (1969). *Chemical mining: A study of leaching agents*. State Bureau of Mines and Mineral Resources.

Khoo, K. M., and Ting, Y. P. (2001). Bio-sorption of gold by immobilized fungal biomass. *Biochemical Engineering Journal*, 8(1): 51–59.

Kim, Y. H., and Nakano, Y. (2005). Adsorption mechanism of palladium by redox within condensed-tannin gel. *Water Research*, 39(7): 1324–1330.

Kotze, F. W. (2000). Free gold recovery by coal-oil agglomeration. *Journal of the Southern African Institute of Mining and Metallurgy*, 100(1): 57–62.

Kratochvil, D., and Volesky, B. (1998). Advances in the bio-sorption of heavy metals. *Trends in Biotechnology*, 16(7): 291–300.

Kuyucak, N., and Volesky, B. (1988). Biosorbents for recovery of metals from industrial solutions. *Biotechnology Letters*, 10(2): 137–142.

La Brooy, S., Bax, A., Muir, D., Hosking, J., Hughes, H., Parentich, A. (1986). Fouling of activated carbon by circuit organics. *Gold*, 123–132.

Laintz, K. E., Wai, C. M., Yonker, C. R. and Smith, R. D. (1992). Extraction of metal ions from liquid and solid materials by supercritical carbon dioxide. *Analytical Chemistry*, 64(22): 2875–2878.

Lam, K. F., Fong, C. M., Yeung, K. L., and Mckay, G. (2008). Selective adsorption of gold from complex mixtures using mesoporous adsorbents. *Chemical Engineering Journal*, 145(2): 185–195.

Lloyd, J. R. (2003). Microbial reduction of metals and radionuclides. *FEMS Microbiology Reviews*, 27(2-3): 411–425.

Lodeishchikov, V., Panchenkov, A., Briantseva, L. (1968). Use of thiourea as a solvent in the extraction of gold from an ore. *Nauoh. Tr., Irkutsk. Gos. Nauoh.-Issled. Inst. Redk. Tsvet. Metal*. 19: 72–84.

Ma, H. W., Liao, X. P., Liu, X., and Shi, B. (2006). Recovery of platinum (IV) and palladium (II) by bayberry tannin immobilized collagen fiber membrane from water solution. *Journal of Membrane Science*, 278(1-2): 373–380.

Mabbett, A. N., Sanyahumbi, D., Yong, P., and Macaskie, L. E. (2006). Biorecovered precious metals from industrial wastes: single-step conversion of a mixed metal liquid waste to a bioinorganic catalyst with environmental application. *Environmental Science & Technology*, 40(3): 1015–1021.

Maruyama, T., Matsushita, H., Shimada, Y., Kamata, I., Hanaki, M., Sonokawa, S. and Goto, M. (2007). Proteins and protein-rich biomass as environmentally friendly adsorbents selective for precious metal ions. *Environmental Science & Technology*, 41(4): 1359–1364.

McArthur, J., Forrest, R., Forrest, W. (1887). Process obtaining gold and silver from ores. *British patent. Patent No.* 14,174.

Mcquiston, J. F. W., and Chapman, T. G. (1951) *U.S. Patent No. 2,545,239*. Washington, DC: U.S. Patent and Trademark Office.

Murray, A. J., Zhu, J., Wood, J., and Macaskie, L. E. (2017). A novel biorefinery: biorecovery of precious metals from spent automotive catalyst leachates into new catalysts effective in metal reduction and in the hydrogenation of 2-pentyne. *Minerals Engineering*, 113: 102–108.

Nicol, H. (1979). A modern study of the kinetics and mechanism of the cementation of gold. *Journal of the Southern African Institute of Mining and Metallurgy*, 79: 191–198.

Niu, H., and Volesky, B. (1999). Characteristics of gold bio-sorption from cyanide solution. *Journal of Chemical Technology & Biotechnology: International Research in Process, Environmental & Clean Technology*, 74(8): 778–784.

Niu, H., and Volesky, B. (2003). Characteristics of anionic metal species bio-sorption with waste crab shells. *Hydrometallurgy*, 71(1-2): 209–215.

Omajali, J. B., Hart, A., Walker, M., Wood, J., and Macaskie, L. E. (2017). In-situ catalytic upgrading of heavy oil using dispersed bionanoparticles supported on gram-positive and gram-negative bacteria. *Applied Catalysis B: Environmental*, 203: 807–819.

Osei-Agyemang, E., Paul, J.F., Lucas, R., Foucaud, S., Cristol, S. (2015). Stability, equilibrium morphology and hydration of zrc (111) and (110) surfaces with h 2 o: A combined periodic dft and atomistic thermodynamic study. *Physical Chemistry Chemical Physics*. 17(33): 21401–21413.

Parajuli, D., Kawakita, H., Kajiyama, K., Ohto, K., Harada, H., and Inoue, K. (2008). Recovery of gold from hydrochloric acid by using lemon peel gel. *Separation Science and Technology*, 43(9-10): 2363–2374.

Pethkar, A. V. and Paknikar, K. M. (1998). Recovery of gold from solutions using Cladosporium cladosporioides biomass beads. *Journal of Biotechnology*, 63(2): 121–136.

Phelps, C. L., Smart, N. G. and Wai, C. M. (1996). Past, present, and possible future applications of supercritical fluid extraction technology. *Journal of Chemical Education*, 73(12): 1163–1168.

Romero-González, M. E., Williams, C. J., Gardiner, P. H., Gurman, S. J., and Habesh, S. (2003). Spectroscopic studies of the bio-sorption of gold (III) by dealginated seaweed waste. *Environmental Science & Technology*, 37(18): 4163–4169.

Savvaidis, I. (1998). Recovery of gold from thiourea solutions using microorganisms. *Biometals*, 11(2): 145–151.

Schiewer, S., and Volesky, B. (1996). Modeling multi-metal ion exchange in bio-sorption. *Environmental Science & Technology*, 30(10): 2921–2927.

Schulze, R.G. (1984). New aspects in thiourea leaching of precious metals. *JOM*. 36(6): 62–65.

Shipman, A. (1994). Laboratory methods for the testing of activated carbon for use in carbon-in-pulp plants for the recovery of gold. Mintek.

Skibar, W., Macaskie, L. E., Pompe, W., Rousset, M., and Selenska-Pobell, S. (2005). Novel precious metal-based bionanocatalysts from scrap. Final Report EU Contract GRD1-2001-40424. The European Commission, Brussels.

Søbjerg, L. S., Lindhardt, A. T., Skrydstrup, T., Finster, K., and Meyer, R. L. (2011). Size control and catalytic activity of bio-supported palladium nanoparticles. *Colloids and Surfaces B: Biointerfaces*, 85(2): 373–378.

Soleimani, M. and Kaghazchi, T. (2008). Adsorption of gold ions from industrial wastewater using activated carbon derived from hard shell of apricot stones–An agricultural waste. *Bioresource Technology*, 99(13): 5374–5383.

Tataru, S. (1968). Precipitation par cementation de l'or en solutions acid. *Rev. Roum. Chim*: 1043–1049.

Torres, E., Mata, Y. N., Blazquez, M. L., Munoz, J. A., Gonzalez, F., and Ballester, A. (2005). Gold and silver uptake and nanoprecipitation on calcium alginate beads. *Langmuir*, 21(17): 7951–7958.

Tsezos, M., Remoundaki, E. and Hatzikioseyian, A. (2011). Workshop on clean production and nanotechnologies, Seoul.

Van Lierde, A., Olli, I., Ler, P., Leosille, M. (1982). Développement du nouveau procedé de traitment pour le mineraux de salsigne. *Ind. Min. Les tech. la*: 399–410.

Vijayaraghavan, K. and Yun, Y. S. (2008). Bacterial biosorbents and bio-sorption. *Biotechnology Advances*, 26(3): 266–291.

Volesky, B. (1992). In *Harnessing Biotechnology for the 21st Century* (Eds M. R. Ladisch), Washington, DC: American Chemical Society.

Wang, Z., Chen, D., and Chen, L. (2007). Gold cementation from thiocyanate solutions by iron powder. *Minerals Engineering*, 20(6): 581–590.

Wang, Z., Li, Y., Ye, C. (2011). The effect of tri-sodium citrate on the cementation of gold from ferric/thiourea solutions. *Hydrometallurgy*. 110(1): 128–132.

Watkins, J. W., Elder, R. C., Greene, B., and Darnall, D. W. (1987). Determination of gold binding in an algal biomass using EXAFS and XANES spectroscopies. *Inorganic Chemistry*, 26(7): 1147–1151.

Wen, C.D. (1982). Proceedings XIV international mineral processing congress. Toronto, Canada, 17–23 October.

Wilkinson, P. (1986). Understanding gold plating. *Gold Bulletin*. 19: 75–81.

Woollacott, L., Erasmus, C. (1992). The distribution of gold on loaded carbon. *Journal of the South African Institute of Mining and Metallurgy*. 92(7): 177–182.

Yong, P., Liu, W., Zhang, Z., Beauregard, D., Johns, M. L., and Macaskie, L. E. (2015). One step bioconversion of waste precious metals into Serratia biofilm-immobilized catalyst for Cr (VI) reduction. *Biotechnology Letters*, 37(11): 2181–2191.

Yong, P., Mikheenko, I. P., Deplanche, K., Redwood, M. D., and Macaskie, L. E. (2010). Biorefining of precious metals from wastes: An answer to manufacturing of cheap nano-catalysts for fuel cells and power generation via an integrated biorefinery. *Biotechnology Letters*, 32(12): 1821–1828.

Yousif, A. M. (2019). Recovery and then individual separation of platinum, palladium, and rhodium from spent car catalytic converters using hydrometallurgical technique followed by successive precipitation methods. *Journal of Chemistry*., 2019:1–7.

Zadra, J. (1950). A process for the recovery of gold from activated carbon by leaching and electrolysis. US Dept. of the Interior, Bureau of Mines.

Zadra, J., Engel, A.L., Heinen, H.J. (1952). Process for recovering gold and silver from activated carbon by leaching and electrolysis. US Dept. of the Interior, Bureau of Mines.

Zalupski, P. R., McDowell, R., and Dutech, G. (2014). The adsorption of gold, palladium, and platinum from acidic chloride solutions on mesoporous carbons. *Solvent Extraction and Ion Exchange*, 32(7): 737–748.

Zhang, H., Ritchie, I. M., and La Brooy, S. R. (2004). The adsorption of gold thiourea complex onto activated carbon. *Hydrometallurgy*, 72(3-4): 291–301.

Zouboulis, A., Kydros, K., Matis, K. (1993). Recovery of gold from thiourea solutions by flotation. *Hydrometallurgy*, 34(1): 79–90.

7 Recovery of Precious Metals by Solvent Extraction

Sadia Ilyas
Mineral Resources and Energy Engineering, Jeonbuk National University, Jeonju, Jeonbuk 54896, Republic of Korea

Hyunjung Kim
Mineral Resources and Energy Engineering, Jeonbuk National University, Jeonju, Jeonbuk 54896, Republic of Korea

Department of Environment and Energy, Jeonbuk National University, Jeonju, Jeonbuk 54896, Republic of Korea

Rajiv Ranjan Srivastava
Center for Advanced Chemistry, Institute of Research and Development, Duy Tan University, Da Nang 550000, Vietnam

CONTENTS

7.1 RECOVERY OF PRECIOUS METALS BY SOLVENT EXTRACTION: AN OVERVIEW

The solvent extraction process consists of two steps: extraction and stripping. During extraction, soluble metal ions/species in aqueous phase are loaded by agitation with immiscible organic solvent to the organic phase. The loaded metal ion/species from the organic phase are then stripped by agitation with appropriate stripping solutions. In this way organic solvents are regenerated and/or recycled, while the metal species are enriched in stripped solution (Figure. 7.1). An ideal extractant should offer selectivity, have high loading capacity, should be sufficiently immiscible with the aqueous

173

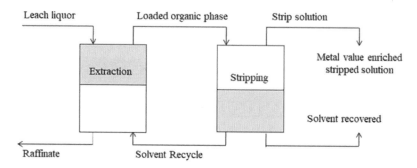

FIGURE 7.1   Simplified sketch of solvent extraction process.

phase (based on density, viscosity, surface tension), should be safe to handle, offer easy stripping, should be safe during storage and should not hydrolyze easily during extraction and stripping. In practical terms, a compromise is usually made for extractants to fulfil the maximum criteria (Habashi, 1997).

7.2 GENERAL CLASSIFICATION AND MECHANISM OF SOLVENT EXTRACTION

When a metal containing aqueous phase is agitated with an immiscible organic phase, it is distributed between two phases and is measured by distribution coefficient K_D

$$K_D = \frac{Concentration\ of\ metal\ value\ in\ organic\ phase}{Concentration\ of\ metal\ value\ in\ aqueous\ phase} \tag{7.1}$$

A high value of the distribution coefficient is indicative of the high extractability of that particular extractant. Distribution may be physical or chemical in nature, depending upon the system. Physical interactions mostly validate the Nernst distribution law, which does not necessarily hold in chemical interactions. Extraction systems are classified into seven classes for general consideration. However, there are gradual transitions from one mode of behavior to another (Habashi, 1997; Marcus, 1963).

Class 1: Distribution of neutral covalent molecules (e.g., ruthenium tetroxide, iodine, or mercury halides) between an aqueous phase and organic phase, mostly inert solvents such as aliphatic and aromatic hydrocarbons occurred without strong solvation via physical interaction based on relative solubility. Compounds like $AlCl_3$ and Ge show this kind of behavior, in addition to extracting as halo-acids.

Class II: Halo-metallic acid extractions involve halide-based anionic complexes of metals with ligands. These are extracted as acids, the protons of which are solvated by solvating solvents, containing mainly oxygen as donor atoms. Generally, it is not possible to assign a definite solvation number to oxonium ion (proton). For example, the extraction of indium bromide by ether or of protactinium chloride by hexone. Some compounds exhibit this behavior, along with direct solvation of the metal, e.g., MoO_2Cl_2 (Mo^{6+}).

Class III: An important class of extraction systems where solvating solvents directly solvate the metallic cation. It is generally plausible to assign a definite solvation number that is the difference between the number of anionic ligands needed to make the complex neutral and the coordination number of the metal. Often, secondary solvation occurs as well. The solvents of systems belonging to Class II are also in this class, but in addition, there are also very strongly solvating solvents like tri-n-butyl phosphate (TBP), which are more strongly basic than ethers or ketones. These will be considered separately below. Examples of these extraction systems are the extraction of cobalt perchlorate by octanol, and of uranyl nitrate by TBP.

Class IV: Liquid cation exchangers, which are organic acids, mainly acidic phosphorus esters, dissolved in diluents, are another important class. They extract metals by forming complexes with them and are usually further solvated by additional molecules of ester, as for example the extraction of lanthanides by di-butyl-phosphoric acid-forming $Ln(Bu_2PO_4, HBu_2PO_4)_8$. At high acidities, acid dissociation of the esters is repressed, and they may then act as solvating solvents, like TBP (Class III). In many, but not all cases, the acid phosphorus esters behave like chelating agents when a metal displaces the acid hydrogen and forms a chelate ring with two oxygen atoms connected to the phosphorus.

Class V; The class of chelate extraction, where metals are complexed by reagents satisfying simultaneously the charge neutralization and coordination number requirements, yielding compounds much more soluble in inert organic solvents than in water, are outside the scope of this review. These chelates usually do not require further solvation, although in some cases, such as with 2-thenoyltrifluoroacetone (TTA), this can bring about much higher distribution coefficients.

Class VI: In extraction by strongly basic reagents, the solvent, usually diluted by an inert diluent, is attached so strongly to protons that stable onium species are formed, like tri-alkyl-ammonium cations. These extract anionic metal complexes by ion-pair formation rather than by direct solvation. Since the anion attached to the ammonium cation may be exchanged for others, or for complex metal anions, these solvents are often called liquid anion exchangers, resembling the resin exchangers in many of their properties. An example is an extraction of uranyl sulphate by tri-isooctylamine (TIOA) from sulphuric acid-forming $(iOc_3\text{-}NH)_4UO_2(SO_4)_2$. Quaternary amines extract by a similar mechanism but are effective also in non-acid solutions.

Class VII: The final extraction system class includes ion pairs formed by large cations and anions, which as with the chelates do not require further solvation, and behave in an inert solvent as if they were covalent molecules, bringing us back to Class I. Examples are tetraphenylarsonium perrhenate and caesium tetra-phenylborate. A similarity to extraction by amines is also evident, particularly to the behavior of quaternary amines, although they belong to Class VI (Marcus, 1963).

In the case of precious metals (PMs), organic solvents extract metal complexes either through outer-sphere mechanisms (non-coordinating) with ionic and/or ionic dipole interactions between solvent and metal complex or through an inner-sphere mechanism (coordination), where solvent active species displace ligand from the metal complex while acting as a nucleophile.

Organic extractants such as quaternary ammonium salts (R_4N^+), tertiary amines (R_3N), and also solvents such as alcohols, ethers, and ketones extract by solvating the outer sphere of a metal complex. The solvation involves dipole attraction/binding. The equilibrium mostly depends on the basicity (nucleophilicity) of R. In solvation processes the basicity of S is low and the equilibrium lies more to the left.

$$MCl_x^{n-} + nR^+Y^- \rightleftarrows \left(R^+\right)^n \left[MCl_x^{n-}\right] + Y^- \tag{7.2}$$

$$MCl_x^{n-} + yS \rightleftarrows \left(R^+\right)^{-n} \left[MCl_x^{n-}\right].yS \tag{7.3}$$

Overall, the extraction of metal anions relates to various factors including charge, stoichiometry, and the size of the ion pair. For example, $[AuCl_4]^-$ ion is easily extracted by a wide variety of anion-exchange solvents including solvating systems such as methyl-iso-butyl-ketone (MIBK) and di-butyl-carbitol (Butex), while platinum-group metals are not extracted significantly by these solvating systems and thus provide selectively separation of gold from other platinum-group metals (Hidehiro and Kakita, 1959; Specker and Doll, 1956; Morris and Khan, 1968; Seeley and Crouse, 1966).

7.3 COMPLEXATION CHEMISTRY OF PRECIOUS METALS RELEVANT TO SOLVENT EXTRACTION

Precious metals (PMs) do not form hydrated cations to an appreciable extent like base metals (such as $[Ni(H_2O)_6]^{2+}$), but prefer coordination complexation with various types of ligands (nucleophilic). PM coordination complexes are bond more effectively with nucleophilic ligands due to orbital overlap of 4d and 5d orbitals, which are larger than the 3d-orbitals of transition metals. From a thermodynamic perspective, PMs in their common oxidation states tend to form most stable complexes with heavier donor atoms containing ligands (soft/class-b centres). Thus, the stability of complex varies with the approximate order:

$$S \sim C > I > Br > N > O > F \tag{7.4}$$

This is predominantly applicable to Pt^{2+}, Pt^{4+} and Pd^{2+}. The above order indicates that those in a lower position will not replace higher ones when two ligand concentrations are approximately equal. Variances in ligand substitution (exchange) kinetics are particularly marked for PMs and light transition metals. Inertness to ligand substitution for transition metal complexes varies according to the position in the periodic table and mostly follows the order:

$$3^{rd} \text{ row} > 2^{rd} \text{ row} > 1^{st} \text{ row} \tag{7.5}$$

The actual rate varies with electronic configuration (Table 7.1). For example, Co^{3+}, Rh^{3+} and Ir^{3+} with d^6 configuration is inert but Ni^{2+}, Pd^{2+} and Pt^{2+} with d^8 configuration is labile. Compared to base metals, where equilibria are established rapidly, PM equilibria may take hours or months to establish at room temperature (Basolo and Pearson, 1958; Ahrland et al., 1958; Marcus and Kertes, 1969).

$$Cu\left(H_2O\right)_6^{2+} + 4Cl^- \rightleftarrows CuCl_4^{2-} + 6H_2O \tag{7.6}$$

Table 7.2 lists the commonly observed chloro-complexes of PMs that are particularly important for leaching and recovery. Although these chloro-complexes tend to undergo stepwise aquation/hydrolysis (to varying extents in water), this reaction is greatly inhibited in strong chloride media. The ability of various PM species to form ion pairs with large organic cations is of prime importance if ion

TABLE 7.1
Variation in substitution kinetics of transition metals with position in the periodic table

Electronic Configuration of d orbital	Oxidation State of Metal	Row	Metal Complex	Reaction	Rate k (s^{-1})
d^6	Co^{3+}	1st	$Co(NH_3)_5Br^{2+}$	Acid hydrolysis [a]	6.3×10^{-6}
d^6	Rh^{3+}	2nd	$Rh(NH_3)_5Br^{2+}$	Acid hydrolysis [a]	$\sim 1 \times 10^{-8}$
d^6	Ir^{3+}	3rd	$Ir(NH_3)_5Br^{2+}$	Acid hydrolysis [a]	$\sim 2 \times 10^{-10}$
d^8	Ni^{2+}	1st	Trans-$[Ni(PEt_3)_2(o$-tolyl)Cl]$	With pyridine [a],[b]	3.3×10
d^8	Pd^{2+}	2nd	Trans-$[Pd(PEt_3)_2(o$-tolyl)Cl]$	With pyridine [a],[b]	5.8×10^{-1}
d^8	Pt^{2+}	3rd	Trans-$[Pt(PEt_3)_2(o$-tolyl)Cl]$	With pyridine [a],[b]	6.7×10^{-6}

Source: Modified from Basolo and Pearson (1958); Basolo et al. (1961).

TABLE 7.2
Commonly observed chloro-complexes of PMs with various d-systems

Precious Metals	Chloro-complexes	Electronic Configuration	Oxidation State
Gold	$[Au(Cl)_4]^-$	d^8	Au^{3+}
Platinum	$[Pt(Cl)_4]^{2-}$	d^8	Pt^{2+}
	$[Pt(Cl)_6]^{2-}$	d^6	Pt^{4+}
Palladium	$[Pd(Cl)_4]^{2-}$	d^8	Pd^{2+}
	$[Pd(Cl)_6]^{2-}$	d^6	Pd^{4+}
Iridium	$[Ir(Cl)_6]^{2-}$	d^5	Ir^{4+}
	$[Ir(Cl)_6]^{3-}$	d^6	Ir^{3+}
Rhodium	$[Rh(Cl)_6]^{3-}$	d^6	Rh^{3+}
Ruthenium	$[Ru(Cl)_6]^-$	d^4	Ru^{4+}
	$[Ru_2(O)(Cl)_{10}]^{4-}$	d^4	Ru^{4+}
	$[Ru(Cl)_6]^{3-}$	d^5	Ru^{3+}
	$[Ru(Cl)_5(H_2O)]^{2-}$	d^5	Ru^{3+}
Osmium	$[Os(Cl)_6]^{2-}$	d^4	Os^{4+}

exchange is employed. In general, the size, polarizability, and charge of the ion being absorbed are the predominant factors but in the case of anionic metal complexes, the nature and stoichiometry of the resulting ion pair (complex anion/organic cation) are also very important.

Stoichiometry affects the packing of the ion pair; for example, it is harder to pack $3[MCl_6]^{3-}$ around singly positive organic cation sites than to pack $2[MCl_6]^{2-}$ or $[MCl_4]^-$ around the complex anion. This reverses the normal charge effect and leads to the following observed order of extractability for PM chloro-complexes:

$$MCl_4^- > MCl_4^{2-} > MCl_6^{2-} > MCl_6^{3-} \qquad (7.7)$$

Similarly, the effect of the stoichiometry of the ion pair is also observed in complex chemistry; for example, large organic cations such as $AsPh_4^+$ (tetraphenylarsonium) can precipitate species of different stoichiometry from those obtained with a simple inorganic cation (e.g., Cs^+) from the same solution due to packing effects. .Addition of $AsPh_4Cl$ to aqueous solutions of PdX_4^{2-} and PtX_4^{2-} leads to the precipitation of PdX_6^{2-} and $Pt_2X_6^{2-}$ (X= CI, Br, I), the ion pair having a metal/organic cation ratio of 1. Therefore, species such as $AuCl_4^-$, $PtCl_4^{2-}$, $PtCl_6^{2-}$ and $IrCl_6^{2-}$ are efficiently extracted with the exception of $RhCl_6^{3-}$ and $IrCl_6^{3-}$ (i.e., ions of charge 3-) (Marcus and Kertes, 1969).

7.4 OXIDATION STATES/CHARGES OF TRANSITION METALS

Generally, heavier transition metals (HTMs) exhibit a wider variety of stable oxidation states than the lighter transition metals (LTMs), including PMs. The corresponding oxidation states for 3rd-row transition metals (e.g., Ir, Os, Pt) are more stable than 2nd-row transition metals (e.g., Rh, Ru, Pd). Thus: $Os^{8+} > Ru^{8+}$, $Os^{4+} > Ru^{4+}$, $Ir^{4+} > Rh^{4+}$ (only stable with π donor ligands e.g., F-), $Pt^{4+} > Pd^{4+}$.

This wide variation in oxidation states providing various charges, differing stoichiometries, varied stereochemistry and rates of reaction all further facilitate selective separation (Table 7.3). Although Pt^{4+} reactions can be catalyzed by Pt^{2+} (if present), the significant difference in substitution rate for Pd^{2+} compared to Pt^{2+} or Pt^{4+} can be used to separate Pd from Pt using a ligand exchange mechanism (Robb and Harris, 1965; Poulsen and Garner, 1962).

TABLE 7.3

Common oxidation state pairs and their mode of separation

Oxidation State Pair	Metal Complex	Comments
Ir^{4+}/Ir^{3+}	$[Ir(Cl)_6]^{2-}$ $Ir(Cl)_6]^{3-}$	High distribution in ion exchange Low distribution in ion exchange
Pt^{4+}/Pt^{2+}	$[Pt(Cl)_6]^{2-}$ $[Pt(Cl)_4]^{2-}$	Very inert to substitution More labile
Ru^{4+}/Ru^{8+}	$[Ru(Cl)_6]^{2-}$ RuO_4	Difficult to separate due to complex equilibria Volatile and can be distilled

TABLE 7.4

Ligand substitution behavior of some chloro-complexes of PMs

PMs	Chloro-complex	Behavior toward Substitution
Os^{4+}	$[Os(Cl)_6]^{2-}$	Inert to substitution
Pt^{4+}	$[Pt(Cl)_6]^{2-}$	Inert to substitution
Ir^{3+}	$[Ir(Cl)_6]^{3-}$	Inert to substitution
Pt^{2+}	$[Pt(Cl)_4]^{2-}$	Moderately inert
Rh^{3+}	$[Rh(Cl)_6]^{3-}$	Moderately inert
Ir^{4+}	$[Ir(Cl)_6]^{2-}$	Moderately inert
Ru^{3+}	$[Ru(Cl)_6]^{3-}$	Moderately labile
Ru^{4+}	$[Ru(Cl)_6]^{-}$	Moderately labile
Pd^{2+}	$[Pd(Cl)_4]^{2-}$	Labile
Au^{3+}	$[Au(Cl)_4]^{-}$	Labile

Source: Modified from Basolo et al. (1961).

A change in electronic configuration and oxidation states changes the kinetics of substitution reactions. For example, species with d^6 electronic configuration tend to show slow substitution kinetics, while others are more labile. Inertness to substitution increases for HTMs within a row and reaction rates tend to decrease in the order $d^5 > d^4 > d^3 > d^6$ for octahedral complexes. The kinetics of square planar complexes with d^8 configuration vary as $Pd^{2+} > Au^{3+} \gg Pt^{2+}$. Because process kinetics change with oxidation state, which is correlated with electronic configuration, Ir^{4+} (d^5) $\rightarrow$ Ir^{3+} (d^6) can be accomplished more quickly than Pt^{4+} (d^6) $\rightarrow$ Pt^{2+} (d^8) due to the labile and inert effect of the d^5 and d^6 electron system. Further, the redox potentials of these two couples are quite close [Ir^{4+}/Ir^{3+} -0.87 V; Pt^{4+}/Pt^{2+} -0.77 V], while the rate of change is very different. Table shows rate-constant data for some PM chloro-species (Basolo et al., 1961; Connick, 1961; Rund et al., 1964; Robb and Harris, 1965; Poulsen and Garner, 1962; Tucker et al., 1964; Miano and Garner, 1965).

7.5 SOLVENT EXTRACTION REFINING APPROACHES FOR VARIOUS PRECIOUS METALS

Various approaches can be used to extract and separate PMs according to the degree of purity required and the content of the starting material and its reaction kinetics. Gold can be selectively recovered from solution containing other PMs due to its fast reduction kinetics and favourable reduction potential. A small amount of platinum co-extracted with gold can be efficiently removed by scrubbing with dilute acid or water. Impurities of Fe, Te, and As can be removed either by MIBK-based extractants or more recently by treatment with iron powder along with HCl (precipitation) . The solvent can be recycled by steam or conventional distillation (based on boiling point). Figure 7.2 shows the distribution of gold with other elements.

Gold can be extracted from ammoniacal thiosulphate solutions by solvent extraction using a number of potential organic extractants diluted in various hydrocarbons (e.g., benzene, kerosene, and octanols). In several cases, the presence of ammonia in

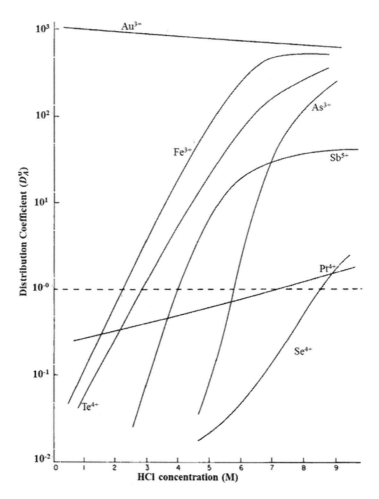

FIGURE 7.2   Distribution of gold and other elements in MIBK.
Source: Modified from Cleare et al. (1979).

solvent extraction gold has been found to improve extraction efficiency (Zhao et al., 1998). The amines alone are effective extractants, with efficacy increasing in the order of 1j > 2j > 3j alkylamines. Aromatic diluents or kerosene performed better than *n*-octanol and chloroform, apparently due to the inductive electron acceptor effects of the latter solvents on amines (Chen et al., 1996; Zhao et al., 1998). A solution of NaOH (> 10 pH) efficiently stripped the gold from the loaded organic within 10 min contact time (Zhao et al., 1998). Phosphorus-based organic compounds performed better in the presence of the primary amine than alone, suggesting synergistic electron-donating effects (Zhao et al., 1998). Electron-donating synergism also accounted for a significant improvement in the performance of the amine extractants in the presence of a trialkylamine oxide (TRAO). The gold complex is partitioned into the organic phase, whereas the other metals ideally remain in the aqueous phase.

The organic phase may then be separated, stripped of gold, and returned to the extraction circuit.

Gold dissolves in chloride complex by forming anionic species; hence, the extraction of gold can be achieved by amine base organic solvents. During gold–chloride complex extraction, free acid may be co-extracted into amine solvents, which adversely affects the loading capacity for gold. Using Hostarex A327 in n-decane, the extraction equilibria are found to be dependent on the ionic strength and of exothermic nature. The extraction reaction can be written as (Martinez et al., 1999):

$$\left(R_3NH^+Cl^-\right)_{org} + \left(AuCl_4^-\right)_{aq} = \left(R_3NH^+AuCl_4^-\right)_{org} + \left(Cl^-\right)_{aq} \qquad (7.8)$$

Gold–chloride complex extraction can also be performed using phosphine oxide extractants by following the solvation mechanism (Martinez et al., 1996; Mironov and Natorkhina, 2012). The extraction reaction can be written as:

$$H_{aq}^+ + \left(AuCl_4^-\right)_{aq} + nH_2O_{aq} + mTBP_{org} = H^+AuCl_4^-.mTBP.nH_2O \qquad (7.9)$$

In both cases, the gold extracted from the loaded organic can easily be stripped in a thiourea-HCl solution at mole ratio 1:1 (Narita et al., 2006).

An anion-exchange mechanism can be involved in the co-extraction of Pt and Pd as chloro-anions by an amine-based solvent. The Rh^{3+} and Ir^{3+} as $[MCl_6]^{3-}$ ions are weakly extracted and are unable to compete with Cl^- for the anionic sites under highly acid conditions. Thus, if Ir is kept as Ir^{3+} and Ru and Os are removed by oxidative distillation as RuO_4 and OsO_4, then Pt and Pd can be separated from Ir and Rh. Subsequent oxidation of Ir^{3+} to Ir^{4+} enables Ir to be removed by the same approach. With the current approach, differential stripping of Pt and Pd from the amine system is feasible only at a low concentration of both metals. Pd^{2+} can be stripped by strong acid (12M HCl) readily than Pt^{4+}. Certain additives (primarily organic acids) can modify the distribution curves for Pt^{4+}, lowering the distribution coefficient of extraction (from 100 to around 10) but improving the strip at high acid ($D\sim0.5$). Thus, both palladium and platinum can be stripped by concentrated HCl and separated by chemical means.

An alternative route to ion exchange is to keep Ir in oxidized form (Ir^{4+}) and extract Pt, Pd, and Ir in one step with an amine-based extractant. Iridium can be separated by reduction, with Ir^{3+} returning to the aqueous phase while Pd and Pt are dealt with as before (Figure 7.3). The problem in this route is the tendency for the organic extractant to reduce Ir^{4+} to Ir^{3+} over a certain period of time. Differential stripping of these metals (Pt, Pd, and Ir) from the organic phase is also a complex process and high purity is difficult to obtain (Khan and Morris, 1967; Ginzburg, 1975).

The kinetic difference between $[PdCl_4]^{2-}$ and $[PtCl_6]^{2-}$ chloro-complexes (Pd and Pt) can be exploited and both can be selectively separated in terms of ligand substitution. Various commercial organic extractants have been assessed and those with high efficiency for Pd are of the hydroxyl-oxime type, classified into α and β-hydroxyoximes (Figure 7.4). Both types of oxime can be considered for selective extraction of Pd from a mixture of other PMs, excluding gold. LIX 63 and XI-8A are common

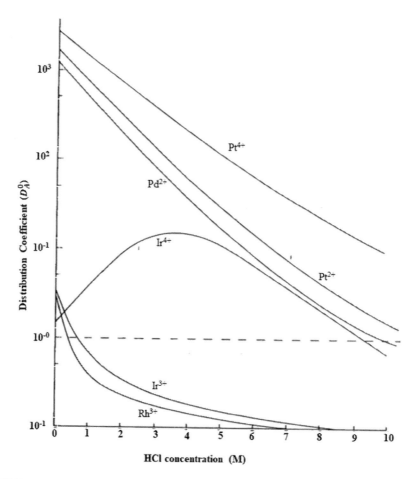

FIGURE 7.3   Distribution data for the extraction of PM chloro-anions by tri-n-octylamine.
Source: Modified from Cleare et al. (1979).

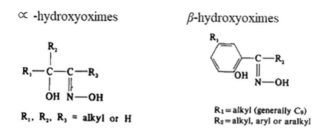

FIGURE 7.4   General structures of ∝ and β-hydroxyoximes.

examples of α-hydroxyoximes while LIX 65N, LIX 70, P.17, P, 5000, and SME529 belong to the β-hydroxyoxime class.

7.5.1 α-Hydroxyoximes

LIX63 is a typical example of α-hydroxyoximes, which can selectively recover Pt^{2+} over Pd^{4+} from chloride media with a separation factor of >100 (on plant liquor). At 10% oxime concentration, the α-hydroxyoximes have the advantage of a high distribution coefficient for Pd with an equilibrium time of 30 minutes. Loaded Pd can be stripped in a multistage process at high acid concentration with only a few parts 10^{-6} of Pd remaining in the raffinate due to relatively high solubility in concentrated acid (1800–2000 parts 10^{-6} in 6M-HCl compared to <20 parts 10^{-6} in 0.1M-HCl), which complicates the recycling of the solvent and acid. Investigations on α-hydroxyoximes show that one mole of H^+ is released for every mole of Pd taken up. This suggests a reaction of 1:1 stoichiometry (Equations 7.8–7.9).

$$\left[PdCl_4\right]^{2-} + \alpha-oxH \rightleftarrows \left[\left(ClPd\left(\alpha-ox\right)\right)\right] + H^+ + 3Cl^- \qquad (7.10)$$

$$2\left[PdCl_4\right]^{2-} + 2\,\alpha-oxH \rightleftarrows \left[\left(ClPd\left(\alpha-ox\right)_2\right)\right] + 2H^+ + 6Cl^- \qquad (7.11)$$

Excess chloride tends to alter the equilibrium and inhibit the forward reaction, while other anions tend to compete with the oxime ligand (α-ox$^-$) for the Pd centre. Formation of a chloro- bridged complex ([(ClPd ($\alpha - ox)_2$]) is expected, as the anion $[Pd_2Cl_6]^{2-}$ is known to be present in weak HCl solutions and can be precipitated by large organic cations. Figure 7.5 gives distribution data for the extraction of palladium by hydroxyoximes.

7.5.2 β-Hydroxyoximes

The β-hydroxyoximes seem to have a higher selectivity against Pt than α-systems (up to an order of magnitude better). Most β-hydroxyoximes (LIX70) have good distribution coefficients for Pd at low acidity and better strip compared to α at high acidity. Additionally, solubility in strong acid is much lower than for α-hydroxyoximes, being 100–150 parts 10^{-6} in 6M-HCl. A major drawback of β-hydroxyoxime-based extractants are long equilibration time (3h) with a 10% oxime concentration that ultimately slows down the rate of reaction. Working at elevated temperatures can improve the kinetics noticeably but is associated with increased process cost in terms of energy consumption, and the possibility of solvent degradation.

In particular, the rate of the extraction reaction becomes important where various liquors are concerned, as competing ligands such as excess sulphate or chloride can significantly slow the rate of reaction (extraction). This effect can be critical in cases where the rate is already slow.

Unlike α-hydroxyoximes, β-hydroxyoximes tend to extract with a stoichiometric ratio of 2:1 with two protons released per Pd taken up. Deviation from this at the

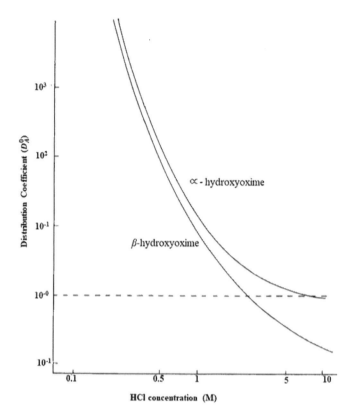

FIGURE 7.5 Distribution data for the extraction of palladium by hydroxyoximes.
Source: Modified from Cleare et al. (1979).

beginning of the extraction can be attributed to the initial formation of a 1:1 complex. Probably in this case, either the 1:1 complex proceeds quickly to the 2:1 stage, or the β-hydroxy group sterically hinders the bridged species. Excess chloride tends to suppress forward reaction while other anions (in sufficient concentration) tend to compete.

$$\left[PdCl_4 \right]^{2-} + 2\,\beta - oxH \; \rightleftarrows \; [Pd\,(\beta - ox)_2 + 2H^+ + 4Cl^- \qquad (7.12)$$

Copper, if present in liquor, can be easily stripped by strong hydrochloric acid which is used to remove palladium from the organic phase, but it can also be removed in a separate dilute acid wash stage. Chloro-anionic complexes of ruthenium (Ru) tend to be extracted (to some extent) by anion-exchange solvents and ideally should be removed prior to recovery of Pd and Pt, or Pt alone, by amine-based extractant.

If palladium is removed by an oxime and Ru/Os as tetraoxides by steam/ distillation, platinum can be recovered on its own by anion exchange. A wide variety of amine-based solvents can be used to extract $[PtCl_6]^{2-}$, although secondary, tertiary and quaternary amine-based solvents have superior distribution characteristics to extract $[Pt(Cl)_6]^{2-}$. The equilibrium lies strongly to the right and stripping can constitute a problem (Eq. 7.13).

$$\left[Pt_6 \right]^{2-} + 2amH^+ \rightleftarrows \left(amH \right)_2 \left[Pt\,Cl_6 \right] \tag{7.13}$$

The selection of stripping reagent/media depends on the amine used for extraction. Strong coordinating ligands such as thiourea (soft ligands, S-donor) that can be effectively used for stripping cause difficulties for further removal of platinum from strip liquor. Formation of inner-sphere complexes can be a prime concern, as this can lead to establishing non-extractable platinum in the organic solvent by the following reaction (Khan and Morris, 1967; Ginzburg, 1975):

$$\left[PdCl_6 \right]^{2-} + n\left(am \right) \rightleftarrows \left(amH \right)_2 \left[Pt\,Cl_{6-n}\left(am \right)_n \right]^{(2-n)} + nCl^- \tag{7.14}$$

Complex formation decreases in the order: primary > secondary > tertiary. Quaternary salts are unable to form inner-sphere complexes (unless degraded) due to non-availability of nitrogen electrons for donation to the metal centre. Conversely, associated disadvantages of these systems are the formation of very strong ion pairs that are difficult to strip except with strong oxidizing acids or complexing agents, and deprotonation cannot be considered as an option in the quaternary salts case. If amine rather than quaternary salt systems is used, some loss of solvent capacity and lock-up of Pt must be tolerated. As is usually the case, there are options to be weighed up (Ginzburg, 1975).

ACKNOWLEDGEMENTS

This work was supported by the Brain Pool Programme through the National Research Foundation of Korea (NRF) funded by the Ministry of Science and ICT (Grant No. 2019H1D3A2A02101993), and the Basic Science Research Programme through the National Research Foundation of Korea (NRF) funded by the Ministry of Education (Project no. 2020R1I1A1A01074249).

REFERENCES

Ahrland, S., Chatt, J., Davies, N. R. (1958). The relative affinities of ligand atoms for acceptor molecules and ions. *Quarterly Reviews, Chemical Society*. 12(3): 265–276.

Basolo, F., Chatt, J., Gray, H. B., Pearson, R. G., Shaw, B. L. (1961).Kinetics of the reaction of alkyl and aryl compounds of the nickel group with pyridine. *Journal of the Chemical Society*. 2207–2215.

Basolo, F., Pearson, R. G. (1958). *Mechanisms of inorganic reactions: a study of metal complexes in solution*. 2nd ed. New York: Wiley, p. 164.

Chen, J., Deng, T., Zhu, G., Zhao, J. (1996). Leaching and recovery of cold in thiosulfate based system - a research summary at ICM.

Cleare, M. J., Charlesworth, P., Bryson, D. J. (1979). Solvent extraction in platinum group metal processing. *Journal of Chemical Technology and Biotechnology*. 29: 210–214.

Connick, R. E. (1961). *Advances in the chemistry of coordination complexes*.Ed. S. Kirschner. New York: Macmillan Co., p. 15

Ginzburg, S. I. (1975). *Analytical chemistry of platinum metals*. New York: Wiley, p.454.

Habashi, F. (1997). *Handbook of extractive metallurgy, Volume 2*. Heidelberg, Germany.

Hidehiro, G. O. T. O., Kakita, Y. (1959). Studies on the Extraction and Determination of Metal Salts with Methyl Isobutyl Ketone. In Extraction from Acid Solution. *Science Reports of the Research Institutes, Tohoku University. Ser. A, Physics, Chemistry and Metallurgy.* 11: 1–20.

Khan, M. A., Morris, D. F. C. (1967). Application of Solvent Extraction to the Refining of Precious Metals. *II. Purification of Ruthenium. Separation Science*, 2(5):635–644.

Marcus, Y., Kertes, A. S. (1969). *Ion exchange and solvent extraction of metal complexes*. New York: Wiley.

Marcus, Y. (1963). Solvent extraction of inorganic species. *Chemical Review*, 63(2): 139–170.

Martinez, S., Sastre, A.M., Alguacil, F.J. (1999). Solvent extraction of gold(III) by the chloride salt of the tertiary amine Hostarex A327. Estimation of the interaction coefficient between $AuCl_4^-$ and H^+. *Hydrometallurgy*. 52(1): 63–70.

Martinez, S., Sastre, A., Miralles, N., Alguacil, F.J. (1996). Gold(III) extraction equilibrium in the system Cyanex 923-HCl-Au(III). *Hydrometallurgy*. 40(1–2): 77–88.

Miano, R. R., Garner, C. S. (1965). Kinetics of aquation of hexachloroosmate (IV) and chloride anation of aquopentachloroosmate (IV) anions. *Inorganic Chemistry*, 4(3): 337–342.

Mironov, I.V., Natorkhina, K.I. (2012). On the selection of extractant for the precipitation of high-purity gold. *Russian Journal of Inorganic Chemistry*, 57(4): 610–615.

Morris, D. F. C., Khan, M. A. (1968). Application of solvent extraction to the refining of precious metals—III: Purification of gold. *Talanta*. 15(11): 1301–1305.

Narita, H., Tanaka, M., Morisaku, K., Abe, T. (2006). Extraction of gold(III) in hydrochloric acid solution using monoamide compounds. *Hydrometallurgy*, 81(3–4): 153–158.

Poulsen, I. A., Garner, C. S. (1962). A thermodynamic and kinetic study of hexachloro and aquopentachloro complexes of iridium (III) in aqueous solutions. *Journal of the American Chemical Society*. 84(11): 2032–2037.

Robb, W., Harris, G. M. (1965). Some exchange and substitution reactions of hexachlororhodium (III) and pentachloroaquorhodium (III) ions in aqueous acid solutions. *Journal of the American Chemical Society*. 87(20): 4472–4476.

Rund, J. V., Basolo, F., Pearson, R. G. (1964). Catalysis of substitution reactions of rhodium (III) complexes. The reaction of aquopentachlororhodate (III) ion with pyridine. *Inorganic Chemistry*, 3(5): 658–661.

Seeley, F. G., Crouse, D. J. (1966). Extraction of Metals from Chloride Solutions and Amines. *Journal of Chemical and Engineering Data*, 11(3):424–429.

Specker, H., Doll, W. (1956). Photometric determination of iron in pure metals, alloys and non-ferrous ores after separation by distribution between two solvents. *Fresenius' Journal of Analytical Chemistry*. 152 (1-3): 178–185.

Tucker, M. A., Colvin, C. B., Martin Jr, D. S. (1964). Substitution reactions of trichloroammineplatinate (II) ion and the trans effect. *Inorganic Chemistry*, 3(10): 1373–1383.

Zhao, D., Feng, J., Huo, Q., Melosh, N., Fredrickson, G. H., Chmelka, B. F., and Stucky, G. D. (1998). Triblock copolymer syntheses of mesoporous silica with periodic 50 to 300 angstrom pores. *Science*, 279(5350): 548–552.

8 Recovery of Precious Metals Using Ion-Exchange Chromatographic Approaches

Sadia Ilyas
Mineral Resources and Energy Engineering, Jeonbuk National University, Jeonju, Jeonbuk 54896, Republic of Korea

Hyunjung Kim
Mineral Resources and Energy Engineering, Jeonbuk National University, Jeonju, Jeonbuk 54896, Republic of Korea

Department of Environment and Energy, Jeonbuk National University, Jeonju, Jeonbuk 54896, Republic of Korea

Rajiv Ranjan Srivastava
Center for Advanced Chemistry, Institute of Research and Development, Duy Tan University, Da Nang 550000, Vietnam

CONTENTS

8.1 ION-EXCHANGE CHROMATOGRAPHY

All chromatographic techniques work on the principle of distribution of solute (containing components to be separated) between the stationary phase (solid, liquid-impregnated

TABLE 8.1

Chromatographic techniques and their mode of separation

Chromatographic Techniques	Property
Ion-exchange chromatography	Charge
Chromatofocusing	Charge
Gel filtration	Size
Hydrophobic interaction chromatography	Hydrophobicity
Reversed-phase chromatography	Hydrophobicity
Affinity chromatography	ligand specificity

Source: Modified from GE Healthcare (2010).

solid, gel) and the mobile phase (liquid, gas). The distribution coefficient (partition coefficient) for each component to be separated can be represented as:

$$K_D = \frac{\text{Concentration of metal value in stationary phase}}{\text{Concentration of metal value in mobile phase}} \tag{8.1}$$

Each separated component may have discrete values of K_D, reflecting their relative affinities with the stationary phase. Table 8.1 lists various chromatographic techniques with their mode of separation.

Ion-exchange chromatography (IEC) is one of the most frequently used chromatographic techniques for purification, with high loading capacity and high resolution, commercially available in spherical particles of 0.5–2 mm in diameter.

8.2 MECHANISMS AND CLASSIFICATION OF ION-EXCHANGE CHROMATOGRAPHY

In ion-exchange chromatography (IEC), a reversible exchange of ions takes place between a mobile and a stationary phase, the latter being a matrix of ion exchangers. Sorption/metal loading is the extraction process in which the targeted metal ions from the liquids are exchanged with mobile ions from the ion exchangers.

In elution, the adsorbed metal ions on the exchanger (anion or cation) are eluted with small volumes of buffers/solutes of different ionic strengths. In this way, the exchangers are regenerated and metal ion-enriched solutions are processed for further metal recovery.

An ion-exchange medium is a solid matrix that contains attached anionic or cationic groups. Ions of opposite charge in solution can exchange onto the corresponding attached groups..

According to their matrix charge, ion exchangers can be classed as anion exchangers, with a positively charged (i.e. cationic) matrix, and cation exchangers, with a negatively charged (i.e.anionic) matrix. Exchange reactions for both exchangers can be represented as:

$$R - M^{n-}C^{n+} + B^{n+} \leftrightarrow R - XM^{n-}B^{n+} + C^{n+} \left(\text{Cation exchanger}\right) \tag{8.2}$$

$$R - M^{n+}A^{n-} + C^{n-} \leftrightarrow R - M^{n+}C^{n-} + A^{n-} \left(\text{Anion exchanger}\right) \tag{8.3}$$

Ion exchanger material (either cation or anion) can be of inorganic or organic nature and derived from synthetic or natural sources. Among inorganic exchangers, analite, chabazite, and montmorillonite are common examples of natural cation exchangers, while kaolinite, fluoroapatite, hydroxyapatite, etc. are commonly used natural anion exchangers. Similarly, polymerized products of an aromatic amine/aldehyde are commercially available as a synthetic, organic, anion exchanger, while sulphonated phenol from aldehyde exchangers are commercially available as synthetic, organic, cation exchangers. Beside these types, synthetic organic exchangers have been prepared in form of sheets corresponding to an ideal semipermeable membrane. Similarly, solvent-impregnated exchangers/chelating exchangers with a specific affinity for particular metals have been prepared.

Chelating/complexing ion exchangers are mostly polymeric with polydentate ligands (chelate/complex-forming functional groups) containing various donor atoms of nitrogen (e.g., azo groups, nitriles, amides, amines), oxygen (ether, carboxylic, carbonyl, hydroxyl), sulphur (thiocarbamates, thioether, thiol), and phosphorus (phosphoryl groups). Chelating/complexing exchangers can directly coordinate with metal ions either via covalent bond formation or via integrated ion-exchange and solvent extraction approaches. Among chelating exchangers, the fundamental concept of solvent-impregnated exchangers is based on impregnation/immobilization of an appropriate solvent on porous polymer matrices by a physical impregnation process (Cortina et al., 1998). In particular, manufacturers have synthesized these un-functionalized exchangers with various copolymers such as Amberlite XAD 1180 (St-DVB polyaromatic), Amberlite XAD2 (macroporous St-DVB), Amberlite XAD7 (acrylic), DowexOptipore L-493 (macroporous St-DVB), Amberlite IRA-400 (gel St-DVB), etc. The complexation chemistry of precious metals is described in Chapter 3 (see p. xx).

8.3 RECOVERY OF PRECIOUS METALS BY ION-EXCHANGE CHROMATOGRAPHY FROM CHLORIDE-BASED LIQUORS

Recovery of PMs by IEC is a well-documented process. Several varieties of ion-exchange exchangers/resins are available commercially. They are stable in several solvents, highly recyclable, in and are capable of selective binding with certain metal ions at low concentration (Barbaro and Liguori, 2009; Marinho et al., 2011) as detailed in Table 8.2.

Previous literature exists on recovery of precious metals (Pt, Pd and Rh) by many commercial IERs including SuperLig® 2, 133, 182 and 190 (Izatt et al., 2015), Amberlite exchangers (IRA-93, IRA-63, IRA-400 and IRA-420) (Gaita and Al-Bazi, 1995), Amberlyst exchangers (A29 and A21) (Hubicki et al., 2008), Lewatit exchangers (Monoplus MP600 and TP214) (Nikoloski et al., 2015), Purolite reins (A400 TL, S985 and S940) (Wołowicz and Hubicki, 2014), and Dowex exchangers (MSA-1 and MSA-2) (Wołowicz and Hubicki, 2014).

8.3.1 RECOVERY OF PRECIOUS METALS BY ANION EXCHANGERS

Hussay (1949) observed that gold recovery from cyanide leach liquor using an anion exchanger was feasible. However, along with gold, other metals like iron, copper, nickel, zinc, and cobalt were co-sorbed as impurity metals. It was also

TABLE 8.2

Concentration of precious metals and impurity elements in urban-mined liquors

Urban Mine	Nature of Urban-mined Liquor	Precious Metals (mg/L)			Accompanying Metals (mg/L)	References
		Pt	Pd	Rh		
Spent automotive catalyst	Chloride	25.6–150	13.25–550	3.37–8.9	Al (265.7–2700), Cr (53.9–(88.27–1500), Ni (377–1000), Cu (20.4), Zn (2 4 2)	Nguyen et al., 2016; Trinh et al., 2017; Sun and Lee 2011
Spent petroleum reforming catalyst	Chloride	129	54.0	–	Al (3539–4917), Fe (268.8), Cr (1.0)	Paiva et al., 2017; Sun and Lee 2015
Liquid crystal display	Chloride	364	–	62	Al (13880), Mg (6980), Fe (1308)	Truong and Lee, 2018
Spent catalytic converter	Cyanide	130–405	0.066–0.65	23.51–45.6	Cu (0.728), Fe (9.1), Ni (0.414)	Aguilar et al., 1997

TABLE 8.3

Selective recovery of gold from other impurity metals

Leach Liquor	Exchanger (sorption)	Selective Eluent	Eluted Metals	Reference
Cyanide leach liquor	Anion exchanger	0.2 N HCl	Zn, Ni	Hussey, 1949
Cyanide leach liquor	Anion exchanger	1-2 N NaCN	Cu, Fe	Hussey, 1949
Cyanide leach liquor	Anion exchanger	Acetone+ HCl (5%)	Au	Hussey, 1949
Cyanide leach liquor	Anion exchanger	2 N NaSCN	Co	Hussey, 1949

found that selective elution of gold from other impurity metals was possible (see Table 8.3).

For separation of Pt^{4+}, Pd^{2+}, and Rh^{3+} in chloride-based media, anion exchange is the predominant mechanism because these metals are present as anionic complexes. Many anion exchangers can be used for selective recovery (see Table 8.4).

As Table 8.4 shows, a strong anion exchanger has higher exchangeability than a weak anion exchanger, due to the high strength of the quaternary ammonium groups for complexing with precious metal ions (Silva et al., 2018).

The selectivity of strong anion exchangers depends on the characteristics of the targeted metal ions. For example, the binding ability (sorption) of an anion exchanger for Rh^{3+} ions is poor compared to Pt^{4+} (>90%) and Pd^{2+} (>80%). These results, however, indicate the easy elution of Rh^{3+} and difficulties in the separation of Pt^{4+} and Pd^{2+}. This behavior can be explained by the difference in geometrical configurations

TABLE 8.4

Characteristics of anion exchangers used for precious metal recovery from chloride leach liquors

Trade Name	Functional Groups	Matrix/ copolymer	Structure	Type	Precious Metal Recovery (%)			References
					Pt	**Pd**	**Rh**	
Lewatit MonoPlus *MP 600*	quaternary ammonia base	St-DVB	Macro-porous	Strong base	97	84	37	(Nikolosk et al., 2015)
Diaion SA10A	tertiary amine group	St-DVB	Gel	Strong base	100	–	20	(Sun et al., 2015)
Diaion SA20A	dimethyl ethanol amine	St-DVB	Gel	Strong base	100	–	20	
Diaion PA308	tertiary amine group	St-DVB	Porous	Strong base	100	–	20	
Diaion WA-21 J	tertiary amine group	St-DVB	Macro-porous	Weak base	90	85	75	Tanaka et al., 2012
AM-2B	quaternary ammonia base/ secondary amine group	St-DVB	Macro-porous	Strong base + Weak base	89	–	51	Kononova et al., 2011
AN-251	tertiary amine group	VP-DVB	Macro-porous	Weak base	88	–	61	
AN-82-10P	hexamethylene amine	St-DVB	Porous	Weak base	88	–	48	
AV-17–8	quaternary ammonia base	St-DVB	Gel	Strong base	88	–	54	
Purolite A 500	quaternary ammonia base	St-DVB	Macro-porous	Strong base	89	–	55	
Purolite A 530	quaternary ammonia base	St-DVB	Macro-porous	Strong base	88	–	49	
Purolite S 985	polyamine	PAc-DVB	Macro-porous	Weak base	89	–	94	
AG 1-X8	quaternary ammonia base	St-DVB	Macro-porous	Strong base	99	–	4	Sun et al., 2012
AG 1-X2	quaternary ammonia base	St-DVB	Macro-porous	Strong base	96	–	0	
AGMP-1	quaternary ammonia base	St-DVB	Macro-porous	Strong base	99	–	**0**	
Dowex 1X8	quaternary ammonia base	St-DVB	Gel	Strong base	–	95	15	Lee and Chung, 2003
Isolute SAX	quaternary ammonia base	Silica	Macro-porous	Strong base	95	95	–	Fontas et al., 2009
Oasis Max	quaternary ammonia base	DVB	Macro-porous	Strong base	100	99	0	Hidalgo et al., 2006

Note: St–styrene; DVB–divinylebenzene; VP–vinylpyridine; PAc–polyacrylic.

and charge densities of metal ions, which are strongly affected by the acidic strength of media. On the other hand, weak anion exchangers collectively adsorb Pt^{4+}, Pd^{2+}, and Rh^{3+}. This can be attributed to chelation interaction rather than conventional ion-association processes (Silva et al., 2018). Additionally, an anion exchanger containing both strong and weak ion-exchanging functional groups (AM-2B exchanger) has also been used for the separation of Pt^{4+} and Rh^{3+} (Kononova et al., 2011). The exchanger possesses higher ion-exchange efficiencies for both Pt^{4+} and Rh^{3+}, but poses difficulties for selective metal elution.

8.3.2 Recovery of Precious Metals by Chelating Exchangers

Selective recovery of PMs with chelating exchangers obeys Pearson's hard and soft acid base rule (HSAB), by which soft metal ions (Pd^{2+}) preferably coordinate with soft bases (S > N > O) and hard metal ions (Cu^{2+}) coordinate with hard bases (O > N > S).

An extensive literature exists for separation of PMs (Pt^{4+}, Pd^{2+}, and Rh^{3+}) by chelating exchangers with diverse functional groups. The majority of studies conducted dealt with either immobilization of non-functionalized exchangers with organic extractants or improvement of the polymeric-extractant system via modification of available polymeric matrices followed by solvent impregnation which offers high loading capacity and hydrophobicity. Table 8.5 shows the structure and synthesis protocol of chelating exchangers for Pt^{4+}, Pd^{2+}, and Rh^{3+}.

8.3.3 Recovery of Precious Metals by Solvent-Impregnated Chelating Exchanger

A comprehensive list of solvent-impregnated exchanger matrices, impregnated solvents, donor ligands, metal selectivity and loading capacity is given in Table 8.6. These types of exchangers (Amberlite IRA-400, −411 and XAD7 (S-donor)) offer higher selectivity for Pd^{2+}ions than $Pt^{4+}$and Rh^{3+} ions due to the HSAB concept (Gandhi et al., 2015). The organometallic complexes of palladium chloride with two thio-carbamoyl compounds has been suggested by Silva et al. (2018) as a thio-carbamyl-Amberlite XAD-7 exchanger for Pd^2.

During a mechanistic study by slope analysis it was observed that Pd^{2+} either complexed with two monomeric ligands of impregnated extractant 4-t-butyl(dimethylthiorbamoyloxy) benzene (MTCA/monomer), or one dimeric ligand 1,1′-bis[(dimethylthiocarbamoyl)oxy]-2,2-thiobis[4-t-butylbenzene] (DTCA/dimer) (DTCA/dimer) (Figure 8.1). A similar type of interaction was reported while using thiacalix[4]aniline, thiacalix[4]arene, poly(styrene sulfonic acid), N,N,N,N -tetra-(2-ethylhexyl) dithiodiglycolamide and dihexylsulphide as the complexing agents.

Kancharla and Sasaki (2019) impregnated an anion exchanger with the S-donor extractant 2-methylthiophene (Thp) and observed selectivity for $[Pd(Thp)_2(NO_3)_2]$ complex compared to platinum. Similarly, P-donor-containing extractants such as Cyanex 301 and DEHTPA have also been impregnated into ion exchangers to enhance Pd^{2+} selectivity over Pt^{4+} and Rh^{3+} (Table 8.6). Investigations of precious metal recovery by Cyanex 301 have been reported by Kakoi et al., (1994), Truong

TABLE 8.5
Synthetic description of chelating exchangers for precious metal recovery

Chelating Exchanger	Synthetic Description	References
Polyacrylonitrile (PAN)	5 g of PAN was put into 100 mL of thiourea solution (15%) and stirred at $110°C$ for 24 h. Then, 10 mL of glutaraldehyde was added and resulting exchanger was called PAN	Morcali and Zeytuncu 2015
1,3,5-Triazine-Pentaethylenehezamine (Tapeha)	Synthesized by mixing 150.62 mmol pentaethylenehexamine (peha) with 72.36 mmol K_2CO_3 in a tetrahydrofuran (THF) solution. Then, 40.76 mmol cyanuric chloride and 150.62 mmol PEHA (both dissolved in THF) were slowly added to the mixture for 24 h. The THF was later evaporated.	Sayın et al., 2015; Sayın et al., 2017)
Modified magnetic exchanger (MMR)	10 g of magnetic particles (Fe_2O_3) was put into 30 mL ethanol solution containing 2% 3-(2',3'-epoxypropoxy) propyl trimethoxy silane and stirred for 4 h.	Zhang et al., 2001
Cross-linked lignophenol	Dried wood powder was first pre-treated in a solution of ethanol and benzene. 5 g of pre-treated powder was mixed with 50 mL of phenol and 100 mL of 72% sulphuric acid solution; the mixture was stirred for 1 h. Further, the mixture was centrifuged to separate the organic and aqueous phases. 300 mL of diethyl ether was added to the organic phase after discarding of aqueous phase; the lignophenol precipitate was obtained. Cross-linking was carried out using paraformaldehyde through the following steps: 5 g of lignophenol, 50 mL of sulphuric acid (72%) and 6.5 g of paraformaldehyde were mixed at $100°C$ for 24 h. The mixture was cooled and 5% sodium hydrogen carbonate solution was added.	Zhou et al. 2010

(Continued)

TABLE 8.5 (Continued)
Synthetic description of chelating exchangers for precious metal recovery

Chelating Exchanger	Synthetic Description	References
Gallic acid exchanger (GAR)	0.5 mol of GA was dissolved in 500 mL of deionized water. Subsequently, 372.5 mL of solution containing 27% formaldehyde was added. pH of the mixture was adjusted to 8 by adding 13.3 N NH_3. The mixture was stirred at temperature of 85°C for 3 h. The remaining formaldehyde was washed by HNO_3.	Can et al., 2012
Polyacrolein-St-DVB	55 mL of acrolein, 13 mL of DVB, 11 mL of styrene, 94 mL of TL and 3.4 g of benzoyl peroxide were added into 520 mL of water containing 100 g of NaCl and 2.6 g of polyvinyl alcohol. The mixture was stirred at 40–75°C for total 12.5 h.	Zhang et al., 1994
Valonea tannin exchanger (TAR)	23.5 g of valonea extract powder was dissolved in 124 mL of solution containing 1.33 mol ammonia. 130 mL of solution containing 37% formaldehyde was added to the resulting solution and stirred at elevated temperature for 5 min.	Can et al., 2013
Polystyrene-2-amino-1,3,4-thiadiazole (PS-ATD)	1.0 g of chloromethyl polystyrene beads (PS-Cl) which cross-linked with 8% DVB was mixed with 175 mL of toluene (TL) in a 500 mL flask under inert condition. A certain amount of ATD and metallic sodium was added to the flask. The exchanger produced was subsequently washed with TL, deionized water, acetone and ether, followed by drying in a vacuum at 50°C	Xiong et al., 2014

Chelating Exchanger	Synthetic Description	References
Poly(vinylbenzylchloride) (PVBC) 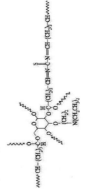	10 mL of 4-vinylbenzylchloride, 0.05 g of 2,2-azo-bis(isobutyronitrile) and 20 mL of TL were mixed under inert atmosphere at 70°C for 9 h. The product was further dissolved in tetrahydrofuran and the polymer was precipitated with methanol.	Fayemi et al., 2013
Poly (4-Vinylpyridine-Divynlbenzene)	An amount of hydroxyethyl cellulose, gelatin, sodium chloride, and sodium nitrite were dissolved in hot water. After complete dissolution, monomer phase of 4-vinylpyridine, divinylbenzene and benzoylperoxide were poured at 85°C for total 14 h.	Kumaresan et al., 2008
Persimmon powder formaldehyde (PPF)	Prepared by immobilization of persimmon powder with formaldehyde. The gel obtained was ground to 125–250 μm and washed with distilled water to remove impurities.	Nakano et al., 2001; Yi et al., 2016
Diethylaminoethyl (DEAE)-cellulose-thiourea-glutaraldehyde	Mixing thiourea (39 mmol) and glutaraldehyde (2 mL of 50% v/v) in 20 mL distilled water for 3 h. After that, DEAE was added to the mixture and vigorously stirred overnight.	Guibal et al., 2000; Morcali et al., 2016

(Continued)

TABLE 8.5 (Continued)

Synthetic description of chelating exchangers for precious metal recovery

Chelating Exchanger	Synthetic Description	References
Imidazol exchanger	An amount of vinylbenzyl chloride and divinylbenzene were reacted with diethyl malonate in dry THF. The product was further reacted with 3-aminopropyl imidazole.	Parodi et al., 2008
Bis(3-aminopropyl)amine bonded silica gel (BAPA-SG)	Silica gel was activated in conc. HCl for 4 h, followed by reacting the activated silica gel with 3-chloropropyltrimethoxysilane in anhydrous toluene under inert atmosphere. The product was washed with toluene, ethanol and diethyl ether.	Sivrikaya et al., 2011
Poly[N-(4-bromophenyl)-2-methacrylamide-co-2-acrylamido-2- methyl-1-propanesulfonic acid-co-DVB]	BrPMAAm monomer, DVB and azobisisobutyronitrile were mixed in dimethylformamide solution at $70°C$ for 3 h under inert atmosphere. The exchanger obtained was filtered and washed with diethylether.	Tokalıoğlu et al., 2009

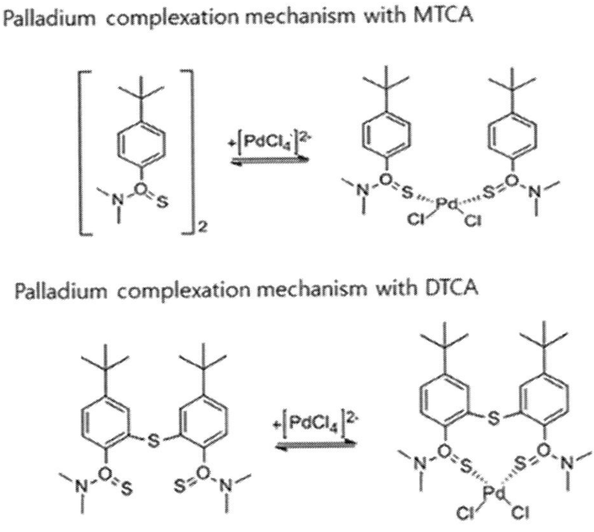

Palladium complexation mechanism with MTCA

Palladium complexation mechanism with DTCA

FIGURE 8.1 Palladium complexation mechanism with MTCA and DTCA.
Source: Modified from Silva et al. (2018); Gandhi et al. (2015)

and Lee (2018), and Vincent et al. (2007). These investigations indicate a significant difference in Pd^{2+} extractability compared to Pt^{4+} and Rh^{3+} owing to the strong interaction between Pd^{2+} and the $P = S$ bond in Cyanex 301. Dowex Optipore L493 exchanger impregnated with Cyanex 301 showed similar behavior (Navarro et al., 2017). Unlike conventional amine-based exchangers, the loading capacity of this impregnated exchanger for Pd^{2+} is independent of HCl concentration. Similar results were observed with the Amberlite XAD2/DEHTPA exchanger (Rovira et al., 1998), indicating their application in high HCl-containing leach liquors. This can be explained as follows: Cyanex 301 and DEHTPA, as acid extractants, provide H^+ as the counterion which, however, is not suitable for the ion-exchange reaction with excess Cl^- concentration. In this case, the strong coordination involved between Pd^{2+} ion and the active extractants (Equations 8.4–8.5) can facilitate metal extraction (Rovira et al., 1998; Vincent et al., 2007).

$$PdCl_4^{2-} + nC301 \rightarrow (C301)^n PdCl_2 + 2Cl^- \ (C301 = Cyanex\ 301) \qquad (8.4)$$

$$PdCl_4^{2-} + 4HL \rightarrow PdL_2(HL)_2 + 4Cl^- + 2H^+ \ (HL = DEHTPA) \qquad (8.5)$$

Cyphos IL101 ($R_3R'P^+Cl^-$), a phosphorus-based extractant, impregnated into Amberlite XAD-7 and −1180 exchangers, has been examined for the selective separation of Pd^{2+} over Pt^{4+} from chloride-based media (Nguyen et al., 2016; Gandhi et al., 2015; Nourmoradi et al., 2012; Navarro et al., 2012a, b) that load palladium according to Equations 8.6–8.7:

TABLE 8.6
Salient characteristics of solvent impregnated chelating exchangers employed for precious metal recovery

Solvent impregnated matrix	Organic Extractant	Types	Selectivity	Loading capcity (mg/g)	References
Amberlite XAD2	4-t-butyl (dimethylthicarbamoyl)	S-donor	Pd	7.9	Haga et al., 2018
	1,1'-bis dimethylthicarbamoyloxy]-2,2-thiobis [4-t-butyl benzene](DTCA/Dimer)	S-donor	Pd	6.2	Haga et al., 2018
	Tri-octyl/docylamine (Alamine 336)	N-donor	Pd	NA	Rovira et al., 1998
	Di-(2-ethylhexyl) thiophosphoric acid (DEHTPA)	P-donor	Pd	NA	Rovira et al., 1999
Amberlite IRA-400, -411 & XAD7	p-sulfonatothiacalix[6]arene	S-donor	Pd	279 (IRA400), 265 (IRA-411), 135 (XAD7)	Rovira et al., 1999
Amberlite XAD-1180	Trihexyl(tetradecyl) phosphonium (Cyphos IL101)	P-donor	Pd	79	Navarro et al., 2017
Dowex Optipore L493	Bis(2,4,4-trimethylpentyl) dithiophosphinic acid (Cyanex 301)	P-donor	Pd	NA	Wójcik et al., 2011
Silica gel DavisilTM	Guanidinium	N-donor	Pd	NA	Kramer et al., 2005
PS-DVB	Guanidinium	N-donor	Pd	NA	Gulko et al., 1972
DVB	Guanidinium	N-donor	Pd	280	Jermakowicz-Bartkowiak, and Kolarz 2011
TAPEHA exchanger		N-donor	Pd	517	Sayin et al., 2015; Sayin et al., 2017
PAN exchanger	Thiourea	N & S donor	Pd	7.78	Morcali and Zeytuncu 2015
Magnetic chitosan exchanger (MCN)	Ethylenediamine	N-donor	Pt and Pd	171 (Pt) 138 (Pd)	Zhou et al., 2010

Solvent impregnated matrix	Organic Extractant	Types	Selectivity	Loading capcity (mg/g)	References
Cross-linked lignophenol	Ethylenediamine	N-donor	Pt and Pd	43 (Pt) 40 (Pd)	Parajuli et al., 2006
Poly(2,2′m-phenylene-5,5′dibenzimidazole) (PBI)	Dithiooxamide (DTOX)	N & S donor	Pd	NA	Parajuli et al., 2006
Chitosan exchanger	L-lysine	N-donor	Pd and Pt	129.3(Pt) 109.5 (Pd)	Fujiwara et al., 2007
Chitosan + epichlorohydrin (PEI)	Thiourea	N & S donor	Pd	155	Chassary et al., 2005
Chitosan + gluraldehyde	Thiocarbamoyl (thiocyanate + thiourea)	N & S donor	Pd	310	Butewicz, et al., 2010
Chitosan + ethyleneglycol diglycidyl ether	Glycine	N-donor	Pt and Pd	122.5 (Pt), 120.4 (Pd)	Ramesh et al., 2008
Chloromethylated polysterene beads	5-aminoimidazole-4- carboxamide (AMIN)	N-donor	Pd, Pt	285 (Pd) 283 (Pt)	Xu et al., 2019
St-DVB (Amberlite IRC-78)	Iminodiacetic acid	N-donor	Pt, Pd	66 (Pt) 58.5 (Pd)	Park et al., 2000
Polyacrolein-St-DVB	Hydrazine (P-HZ)	N-donor	Pt, Pd	171.6 (Pt) 145.9 (Pd)	Park et al., 2000
Polyacrolein-St-DVB	Phenylhydrazine (P-PHZ)	N-donor	Pd	64.4 (Pt) 52 (Pd)	Siddhanta and Das 1985
St-DVB	Thiosemicarbazide	N & S donor	Pt, Pd	138.5 (Pt) 82.7 (Pd)	Siddhanta and Das 1985
Magnetic exchanger	Nonylthiourea (NTH)	N & S donor	Pd	10.9	Uheida et al., 2006
Modified magnetic exchanger (MMR)	) 2-Chloroethoxymethyl thiirane (CEMT) + diamine	N & S donor	Pd, Pt	290.6 (Pt) 258.6 (Pd)	Zhang et al., 2001

$$PdCl_4^{2-} + R_3R'P^+Cl^- \rightarrow \left(R_3R'P^+\right)PdCl_3^- + 2Cl^- \qquad (8.6)$$

$$PdCl_4^{2-} + 2R_3R'P^+Cl^- \rightarrow \left(R_3R'P^+\right)2PdCl_4^- + 2Cl^- \qquad (8.7)$$

However, the co-loading of Pt^{4+} was also reported (Table 8.6), indicating non-selective separation behavior. Some N-donor extractants such as tri-octyl/decyl amine (Alamine 336), tri-n-octylamine (TOA), N-(2-(2-Pyridyl)ethyl), picolylamine, and 2,6-diaminopyridine have also been used as impregnated extractants (Haga et al., 2018; Wołowicz and Hubicki, 2012; Wójcik et al., 2011; Gulko et al., 1972; Kramer et al., 2005; Gulko et al., 1972) with various types of exchanger but there were selectivity constraints on the commercial implementation of these. Separation of Pt^{4+}, Pd^{2+}, and Rh^{3+} with solvent-impregnated chelating exchangers based on these two approaches is summarized in Table 8.6.

Exchangers with N- and S-based active groups can offer better selectivity for Pd^{2+} via ion-association and chelation mechanisms (Sayın et al., 2017; Uheida et al., 2006; Fujiwara et al., 2007; Chassary et al., 2005; Uheida et al., 2006).

$$R.NH_2^+Cl^- + \left[PdCl_4\right]^{2-} \rightarrow R.NH_2^+.\left[PdCl_4\right]^- + Cl^- \qquad (8.8)$$

$$R.NH_2^+Cl^- + \left[PdCl_4\right]^{2-} \rightarrow R.NH^-\left[PdCl_3\right]^- + H^+ + 2Cl^- \qquad (8.9)$$

$$R.C = S^+\left[PdCl_4\right]^{2-} \rightarrow R.C = S^-\left[PdCl_3\right]^- + Cl^- \qquad (8.10)$$

Various factors affect adoption efficiency and the concomitant metal recovery, including the ionic state of the metal, and the co-existence of preciousand base metals. Ionic states of precious metal species significantly affect the adsorption capacity of the exchanger (Nikoloski et al., 2015; Wołowicz and Hubicki 2014; Mel'nikov et al., 2012). Pt^{4+} with $[PtCl_6]^{2-}$ is strongly exchanged at a wide concentration range of chloride ions with amine-based exchangers, while Pd^{2+} exchanged at low chloride concentrations (Sun et al., 2012; Wołowicz and Hubicki 2012) due to the difference in charge density of the two metals. This is advantageous for their selective recovery. Rh^{3+} as $[MCl_6]^{3-}$ is less well exchanged due to its hydrolysis into various anionic, neutral, and cationic species such as $[RhCl_5(H_2O)]^{2-}$, $[RhCl_4(H_2O)_2]^{2-}$, $[Rh(H_2O)_3Cl_3]$, and $[Rh(H_2O)_5Cl]^{2+}$. Issues still to be addressed for an efficient and selective recovery process include establishing control over metal species during separation, the problem of high acid consumption in prior leaching before separation, difficulties in acid handling, water treatment issues caused by dilution of leach liquor for enhanced recovery of palladium, exchanger poisoning at high temperature, and acid concentration (Nikoloski and Ang, 2014; Buslaeva et al., 1990 ; Ginzburg et al., 1972; Sinitsyn and Buslaeva, 1992; Buslaeva et al., 1990; Zagorodni, 2006).

Osmium (Os), iridium (Ir), and ruthenium (Ru) mostly exist as the tetraoxide in aqueous chloride media and behave similarly to Pt, Pd and Rh with changes in acid concentration, contact time, and temperature (Bernardis et al., 2005; Lee and Chung,

2003; MacNevin and Crummett, 1953; Majavu and Tshentu, 2017; Trautmann and Holdt, 2015; Yi-Yong and Xing-Zhong, 1994).

Studies have been conducted on the use of various reducing agents (ascorbic acid, hydrogen peroxide, hydroxylamine-hydrochloric acid) to reduce Ir^{4+} to Ir^{3+} for lower sorbtion of iridium and selective recovery of platinum and palladium. MacNevin and Crummett (1953) converted anionic Pd- and Rh-chloride to cationic Pd- and Rh-amines by ammonium hydroxide treatment. As ammonia does not affect Ir^{4+}, quantitative separation of Pd^{4+} and Rh^{3+} from Ir^{4+} by cation exchange was suggested. Topp and Grote (1996) found a stronger affinity of 1, 2, 4, 5-tetrazine-modified ion exchanger towards Pd^{2+} compared with other PMs.

Similarly, the use of anion exchangers (N-donor) for the recovery of Pt^{4+}, Pd^{2+}, and Rh^{3+}, in the presence of Au^{3+} and Ag^{1+}, established the following separation order: $Ag^{1+} > Au^{3+} > Pt^{4+} > Pd^{2+} \gg Rh^{3+}$ (Butewicz et al., 2010; Els et al. 2000a & b; Peng et al., 2009).

Base metals are leached along with PMs in various leaching processes as impurity elements. Base metals are mostly cationic species and are not exchanged much with counter-anions in the exchanger during recovery process and do not affect PM recovery (Sun and Lee, 2011; Hubicki and Wójcik, 2006; Leung and Hudson, 1992; Hubicki et al., 2008; Parodi et al., 2008; Hubicki et al., 2006). Parodi et al., 2008; Moriyama et al., 1981; Susoyeva et al., 2016).

However, it was observed that Pd^{2+} uptake onto imizadol exchanger decreased from 60% to 40% with 5 g/L of Zn in HCl (0.25 M) having 100 mg/L of Pd^{2+}. It was also observed that the rhodium-loading capacity of some anion exchangers (Purolite exchangers; S920, S985 and A500) increased in the presence of Sn. This is attributed to the reduction of Rh^{3+} to the Rh^{1+} state by the oxidation of Sn^{2+} to Sn^{4+}, which further forms a Rh-Sn-Cl complex as in the following equations:

$$\left[RhCl_6\right]^{3-} + 6\left[SnCl_3\right]^{-} \rightarrow \left[Rh\left(SnCl_3\right)_5\right]^{4-} + \left[SnCl_6\right]^{2-} + 3Cl^{-} \quad (8.11)$$

$$\left[RhCl_5 H_2O\right]^{2-} + 6\left[SnCl_3\right]^{-} \rightarrow \left[Rh\left(SnCl_3\right)_5\right]^{4-} + \left[SnCl_6\right]^{2-} + 2Cl^{-} + H_2O \quad (8.12)$$

8.4 RECOVERY OF PRECIOUS METALS FROM THIOSULPHATE-, CYANIDE-, IODIDE-, AND BROMIDE- BASED MEDIA

The ion-exchange process has been widely proposed for the recovery of precious metals, particularly gold from thiosulphate leach liquors. The adsorption process can be presented as:

$$3\left(-^{+}NR_3\right)_2 SO_4^{2-} + 2Au\left(S_2O_3\right)_3^{2-} = 2\left(-^{+}NR_3\right)_3 Au\left(S_2O_3\right)_3^{2-} + 3SO_4^{2-} \quad (8.13)$$

Despite its suitability for adsorbing the gold–thiosulfate complex, the recovery is complicated by the presence of various sulphur species (polythionate, tetrathionate, trithionate, etc.) generated by the oxidation of thiosulphate. These species are adsorbed onto the strong-base resins and reduce the gold loading by competing with gold-complex ions (Fagan, 2000; O'Malley, 2001). A typical concentration of 350 mg/L trithionate and 420 mg/L tetrathionate can suppress gold adsorption from 26 to 2 kg/t of the strong-base resin from a solution of 0.3 mg/L Au. An addition of 0.5 g/L Na_2SO_3 to the leach liquor in an inert atmosphere can control this detrimental effect by converting the tetrathionate back to thiosulphate. Trithionate can also be eliminated by the addition of sulphide, but the undesirable precipitation of gold sulphide is problematic.

Introducing resin in pulp (RIP) can also minimize the degradation of thiosulphate leach liquor, although a relatively dilute leach liquor would be required (containing 0.03–0.05 mol/L thiosulphate, 0.5–1.6 mmol/L Cu^{2+}, and 7–100 mmol/L NH_3 at pH 7–9). RIP can co-adsorb the complexes of both gold and copper which subsequently goes to selective elution. Copper can be eluted first in ammoniacal thiosulphate (100–200 g/L). Alternatively and preferably, the use of an oxygenated buffer solution of NH_4OH-$(NH_4)_2SO_4$ can facilitate the recycling of eluent solution in leaching. Gold from the Cu-depleted leach solution can be eluted in a subsequent step in a thiocyanate solution. The high cost of thiocyanate counter-ions and their toxicity on the resins make them undesirable (Marchbank et al., 1996), and they can be replaced by a cheaper and less toxic reagent, trithionate, or tetrathionate (dosage 40–200 g/L). The polythionate eluents cause less deviation in pH levels, thus minimizing osmotic shock and consequent resin attrition. The effects of trithionate and tetrathionate on gold elution are shown in Table 4.1. Further, the resin can be regenerated by flushing with a (~2 g/L) solution of sodium hydrogen sulphide, recycling both tetrathionate and trithionate into thiosulphate ions, as below:

$$S_3O_6^{2-} + S^{2-} = 2S_2O_3^{2-} \tag{8.14}$$

$$4S_4O_6^{2-} + 2S^{2-} + 6OH^- = 9S_2O_3^{2-} + 3H_2O \tag{8.15}$$

A series of Russian ion-exchange polymers adsorbing 9.5–17.9 mg/L gold from an ammonia-thiosulphate leach liquor revealed higher adsorption at the lower pH values (Kononova et al., 2001). AV-17-10P, a trimethyl ammonium (strong-base) functionalized resin could achieve 94% adsorption efficiency at pH 6 and 85% at pH 11. However, a fair recovery of gold was also observed at pH 6 by resins with both strong-base and weak-base groups (polyfunctional resins), resins with weak-base groups, and with amphoteric phosphonic acid–pyridine copolymers (Table 8.7).

Subsequently, the elution of gold by thiourea in aqueous sulphuric acid (0.5 mol/L each) could yield > 93% efficiency after 1 h operation at ambient temperature. The larger capacity of strong-base resins should also make them more tolerant to low levels of competing anions. However, Minix, a strong-base resin with excellent selectivity for aurocyanide, performed as poorly as the weak-base/polyamine resins (at pH 8). It has been noted that copper concentration in the pulp increases as the gold displaces it from the resin; hence, due to a gradual formation of the competing ions trithionate and tetrathionate in the liquor, the resin contact time must be minimized (O'Malley, 2001). In addition to gold, the thiosulphate complexes of other metals such as lead, copper, zinc, and silver are adsorbed onto strong-base resins

TABLE 8.7

Characteristics of selected polymeric adsorbents for gold recovery

Polymeric Adsorbent (Resin)	Functional Group Affixed to Polymer	Percent Gold Recovery at pH = 10.8-11.0	Percent Gold Recovery at pH = 5.8-6.1	Strong Base Capacity (SBC) (meq/g)	Total Exchange Capacity (meq/g)
ANFK-5 (No pores)	$®$-$PO(ONa)_2$+$\{N(CH_3)_2\}_n$+Poly(vinylpyridine)	54.2	87.5	-	Unknown
AP-2-12P	$®$-$(CH_3)_2N^+CH_2N(CH_3)_2$	65.8	90.4	1.1	3.7
AV-17-10P	$®$-$N^+(CH_3)_3$	85.4	94.2	4.1	4.4
AN-106-7P	$®$-$NH(CH_3)_2NH(CH_2)_2NH_2$	39.0	88.1	-	8.9
AN-85-10P	$®$-$NHCH_2CH_2NH_2$	51.0	86.5	-	6.2
	$®$-$N(CH_2CH_2CH_2CH_3)_2$&				
AP-24-10P		47.9	86.5	1.3	4.1
AP-100	-$(CH_3)_2N^+Ph$ 1°&2°-amines + $®$-N^+R_3	72.9	91.3	0.7	3.9

(Conditions: Five-hour contact time, 0.5 M $Na_2S_2O_3^{2-}$, 0.5 M NH_3, Ambient temperature, Gold 9.5–17.9ppm, $®$- resin backbone).

from the leach liquors (Fagan, 2000; O'Malley, 2001). This reduces the loading capacity for gold adsorption and unless these can be separately eluted, these metals will contaminate the final gold eluate. The proposed affinity order for adsorption of thiosulphate complexes onto strong-base resins, based on mixed-metal adsorption tests, was reported to be: Au > Pb >> Ag > Cu >> Zn. Although they are kinetically slower to adsorb, the presence of these anions in leach liquors restricts the maximal gold recovery that can be achieved. This may become a major problem for more aggressive leaching operations where considerable thiosulphate is consumed during leaching and hence polythionates are abundant in the liquor. The application of guanidine for functionalized polystyrene resin (Aurix) to the recovery of gold from liquors containing thiosulphate (25–200 mM) and ammonia (> 50 mM) at pH 8–10 permits the protonated form of resin due to a high pK_a value, 13.5 (Virnig and Sierakoski, 2001). The proponents claim that gold can be stripped from the sorbent using aqueous NaOH (pH > 11), with the optional additives of NaCN and/or a carboxylic acid such as sodium benzoate to facilitate more efficient elution. Gold adsorption by a strong-base resin followed by various elution options is schematically presented in Figure 8.2.

For adsorbing the cationic gold complex, $Au[SC(NH_2)_2]_2^+$, strong cation-exchanger resins are as effective as activated carbon or charcoal (Groenewald, 1977). As the cationic gold speciation in thiourea predominantly exists in the acidic range (< 4 pH), the cation-exchange capacity of resins significantly changes with respect to

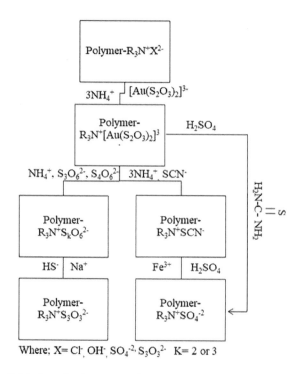

Where: X= Cl⁻, OH⁻, SO₄⁻², S₃O₃²⁻ K= 2 or 3

FIGURE 8.2   Gold adsorption by a strong-base resin followed by various systematic elutions

the pH and gold concentration in the solution. An alkaline sodium thiosulphate solution and a solution of bromine in hydrochloric acid have been reported as the most promising eluent solutions; however, the former is preferable.

Schoeman et al. (2017) observed the potential of an anion exchanger with a trimethylammonium-based functional group like Ambersep 900Cl, Dowex 21 K XLT, Purolite A500, Amberlite IRA 478RF Cl, Puropack PPA 400, Amberlite PWA5, Amberjet 4600Cl, Ambersep 920U and thiouronium, Minix based as Purolite S920, and polyamine based as Purolite S 985 to recover precious metals and gold from a synthetic cyanide leach solution. The results indicated that the Purolite S 920 (chelating exchanger) and Purolite S 985 weak-base anion exchanger showed poor recovery of Pt^{4+} and Pd^{2+}, due to the conversion of functional groups to free base form at high pH values. The Minix exchanger was capable of showing high selectivity for gold, moderate selectivity for platinum and palladium, and poor selectivity for base metals. This was due to the lower charge density of $[Au(CN)_2]^{2-}$ which had a more favourable reaction with the tri-butyl functional group. The Dowex 21 K XLT, Amberjet 4600, and Amberlite PWA-5 exchangers showed high recoveries $[Pt(CN)_4]^{2-}$ and $[Pd(CN)_4]^{2-}$(92–96%). Dybczyński and Maleszewska (1974) converted Dowex exchangers (anion exchangers) to their bromide form by washing with 2 M HBr solutions. The pre-treated exchanger was then contacted with synthetic bromide solutions of Pt^{4+} (20 mg/mL), Pd^{2+} (20 mg/mL), and Rh^{3+} (5 mg/mL) and a similar selectivity order was obtained as that with chloride-based leach liquor. Similerly, Makishima et al. (2001) pre-treated TEVA, an ammonium-based anion exchanger, by injecting bromine gas and washing with HBr solution (0.1 M). They successfully adsorbed >97% of platinum and palladium bromo-complexes which were separated selectively in the following elution step. Hoshi et al. (1997) observed the behavior of dimethylglyoxalbis (4-phenyl-3-thiosemicarbazone) (DMBS)-impregnated Amberlite XAD-7 for separation of platinum and palladium from synthetic iodide solution. It was noticed that both metals were chelated with DMBS at a stoichiometric ratio of 1:1. The chelation rate of palladium was higher than that of platinum at room temperature.

8.5 SELECTIVE ELUTION OF PRECIOUS METALS FROM ANION EXCHANGER

Extensive literature exists on the use of HCl/chloride salts, perchlorate, ammonia solutions and a combination of HCl/thiourea for selective elution of platinum, palladium, rhodium, iridium, etc. from metal ion-loaded anion exchangers (Gaita and Al-Bazi 1995; Nikoloski et al., 2015; Fontàs et al., 2009; Wójcik et al., 2011; Gaita and Al-Bazi, 1995; Fayemi et al., 2013). A low chloride concentration exhibited poor elution efficiency while a high chloride concentration can offer good elution but is not industrially favourable. Elution by perchlorate involves competition among loaded metallic anions on exchanger matrix and perchlorate ions, followed by the formation of metal perchlorate complexes (Iglesias et al., 2000). Platinum can be selectively recovered from other precious metals due to formation of more stable platinum perchlorate complexes (Bernardis et al., 2005; Haga et al., 2018; Iglesias et al., 2000). Similarly, metal elution with ammonia solution occurs through the formation of metal amine complexes (Gaita and Al-Bazi, 1995; Sánchez et al., 2004; Totland and Jarvis, 1997). Selective elution by ammonia is possible by controlling its concentration; a low concentration is sufficient for quantitative elution of Pd^{2+}, higher concentrations and temperatures are required for Pt^{4+} elution (Gaita and Al-Bazi, 1995; Sánchez et al., 2004; MacNevin and Crummett, 1953) but these do not elute Rh^{3+} (Bernardis et al., 2005). HCl and thiourea form highly stable metal complexes (Shillington and Tait, 1991; Warshawsky et al., 1980; Warshawsky, 1982) except for Rh^{3+} due to the inertness of Rh^{3+} chloride complexes (Cotton and Wilkinson, 1980; Livingstone, 2016; Alam et al., 1998).

ACKNOWLEDGEMENTS

This work was supported by the Brain Pool Programme through the National Research Foundation of Korea (NRF) funded by the Ministry of Science and ICT (Grant No. 2019H1D3A2A02101993) and the Basic Science Research Programme through the National Research Foundation of Korea (NRF) funded by the Ministry of Education (Project no. 2020R1I1A1A01074249).

REFERENCES

Aguilar, M., Farran, A., Marti, V. (1997). Capillary electrophoretic determination of cyanide leaching solutions from automobile catalytic converters. *Journal of Chromatography*, 778: 397–402.

Alam, M. S., Inoue, K., and Yoshizuka, K. (1998). Ion exchange/adsorption of rhodium (III) from chloride media on some anion exchangers. *Hydrometallurgy*, 49(3), 213–227. DOI: 10.1016/S0304-386X(98)00024-3.

Barbaro, P., and Liguori, F. (2009). Ion exchange exchangers: catalyst recovery and recycle. *Chemical Reviews*, 109(2), 515–529. DOI: 10.1021/cr800404.

Bernardis, F. L., Grant, R. A., and Sherrington, D. C. (2005). A review of methods of separation of the platinum-group metals through their chloro-complexes. *Reactive and Functional Polymers*, 65(3), 205–217. DOI: 10.1016/j.reactfunctpolym.2005.05.011.

Buslaeva, T. M., Umreyko, D. S., and Novitskiy, G. G. (1990). *Chemistry and spectroscopy of halides of platinum group metals*. Minsk: Izdatelstvo Universitetskoe, 241.

Butewicz, A., Gavilan, K. C., Pestov, A. V., Yatluk, Y., Trochimczuk, A. W., and Guibal, E. (2010). Palladium and platinum sorption on a thiocarbamoyl-derivative of chitosan. *Journal of applied polymer science*, 116(6), 3318–3330. DOI: 10.1002/app.31877.

Can, M., Bulut, E., Örnek, A., Özacar, M. (2013). Synthesis and characterization of valonea tannin resin and its interaction with palladium (II), rhodium (III) chloro-complexes. *Chemical Engineering Journal*, 221: 146–158.

Can, M., Bulut, E., Özacar, M. (2012). Synthesis and characterization of gallic acid resin and its interaction with palladium (II), rhodium (III) chloro-complexes. *Industrial & Engineering Chemistry Research*, 51 (17): 6052–6063.

Chassary, P., Vincent, T., Marcano, J. S., Macaskie, L. E., & Guibal, E. (2005). Palladium and platinum recovery from bicomponent mixtures using chitosan derivatives. *Hydrometallurgy*, 76(1–2), 131–147. DOI: 10.1016/j.hydromet. 2004.10.004.

Cortina, J. L., Meinhardt, E., Roijals, O., and Marti, V. (1998). Modification and preparation of polymeric adsorbents for precious-metal fextraction in hydrometallurgical processes. *Reactive and Functional Polymers*, 36(2): 149–165. DOI: 10.1016/ S1381-5148(97)00109-0.

Cotton, F. A., and Wilkinson, G. (1980). *Inorganic chemistry. A Comprehensive Text*, 4th ed., New York: Wiley, p. 943.

Dybczyński, R., and Maleszewska, H. (1974). Separation of four platinum metals by anion-exchange in hydrobromic acid medium. *Journal of Radioanalytical and Nuclear Chemistry*, 21(1): 229–245. DOI: 10.1007/BF02520865.

Els, E. R., Lorenzen, L., and Aldrich, C. (2000a). The adsorption of precious metals and base metals on a quaternary ammonium group ion exchange exchanger. *Minerals Engineering*, 13(4): 401–414. DOI: 10.1016/S0892-6875(00)00022-4.

Els, E. R., Lorenzen, L., and Aldrich, C. (2000b). The adsorption of precious and base metals on XAD7 ion exchange exchanger. In *Developments in Mineral Processing*. Elsevier. pp.6–50.

Fagan, P. (2000). Personal communication: Report on the Ballarat Gold Forum. Gold Processing in the 21st Century: An International Forum. Ballarat, Australia.

Fayemi, O. E., Ogunlaja, A. S., Kempgens, P. F., Antunes, E., Torto, N., Nyokong, T., and Tshentu, Z. R. (2013). Adsorption and separation of platinum and palladium by poly-amine functionalized polystyrene-based beads and nanofibers. *Minerals Engineering*, 53: 256–265. DOI: 10.1016/j.mineng.2013.06.006.

Fontàs, C., Hidalgo, M., and Salvadó, V. (2009). Adsorption and preconcentration of Pd (II), Pt (IV), and Rh (III) using anion-exchange solid-phase extraction cartridges (SPE). *Solvent Extraction and Ion Exchange*, 27(1): 83–96. DOI: 10.1080/07366290802544635.

Fujiwara, K., Ramesh, A., Maki, T., Hasegawa, H., and Ueda, K. (2007). Adsorption of platinum (IV), palladium (II) and gold (III) from aqueous solutions onto l-lysine modified crosslinked chitosan exchanger. *Journal of Hazardous Materials*, 146(1-2): 39–50. DOI: 10.1016/j.jhazmat.2006.11.049.

Gaita, R., and Al-Bazi, S. J. (1995). An ion-exchange method for selective separation of palladium, platinum and rhodium from solutions obtained by leaching automotive catalytic converters. *Talanta*, 42(2): 249–255. DOI: 10.1016/ 0039-9140(94)00246-O.

Gandhi, M. R., Yamada, M., Kondo, Y., Shibayama, A., and Hamada, F. (2015). p-Sulfonato-thiacalix [6] arene-impregnated exchangers for the sorption of platinum group metals and effective separation of palladium from automotive catalyst residue. *Journal of Industrial and Engineering Chemistry*, 30: 20–28. DOI: 10.1016/j.jiec.2015.04.024.

GE Healthcare. 2010. *Ion Exchange Chromatography and Chromatofocusing, Principles and Methods, Hand book, from 11-0004-21*, Bio-Sciences, Sweden.

Ginzburg, S.I., Ezerskaya, V.I., Prokofieva, I.V., Fedorenko, N.V., Shlenskaya, Y.I. and Belskiy, N.K.(1972). *Analytical Chemistry of Platinum Group Metals*. Moscow: Nauka, p. 615.

Groenewald, T. (1977) Potential applications of thiourea in the processing of gold. *Journal of the Southern African Institute of Mining and Metallurgy*, 77(11): 217–223.

Guibal, E., Vincent, T., Mendoza, R. N. (2000). Synthesis and characterization of a thiourea derivative of chitosan for platinum recovery. *Journal of Applied Polymer Science*, 75(1): 119–134.

Gulko, A., Feigenbaum, H., and Schmuckler, G. (1972). Separation of palladium (II) and platinum (II) chlorides by means of a guanidine exchanger. *Analytica Chimica Acta*, 59(3): 397–402. DOI: 10.1016/0003-2670(72)80009-6.

Haga, K., Sato, S., Gandhi, M. R., Yamada, M., and Shibayama, A. (2018). Selective Recovery of Palladium from PGM Containing Hydrochloric Acid Solution Using Thiocarbamoyl-substituted Adsorbents. *International Journal of the Society of Materials Engineering for Resources*, 23(2): 173–177. DOI: 10.5188/ijsmer.23.173.

Hidalgo, M., Uheida, A., Salvadó, V., and Fontàs, C. (2006). Study of the sorption and separation abilities of commercial solid-phase extraction (SPE) cartridge oasis MAX towards Au (III), Pd (II), Pt (IV), and Rh (III). *Solvent Extraction and Ion Exchange*, 24(6): 931–942.

Hoshi, S., Higashihara, K., Suzuki, M., Sakurada, Y., Sugawara, K., Uto, M., and Akatsuka, K. (1997). Simultaneous determination of platinum (II) and palladium (II) by reversed phase high-performance liquid chromatography with spectrophotometric detection after collection on and elution from exchanger coated with dimethylglyoxal bis (4-phenyl-3-thisomicarbazone). *Talanta*, 44(4): 571–576. DOI: 10.1016/S0039-9140(96)02064-4.

Hubicki, Z., Leszczyńska, M., Łodyga, B., and Łodyga, A. (2006). Palladium (II) removal from chloride and chloride–nitrate solutions by chelating ion-exchangers containing N-donor atoms. *Minerals engineering*, 19(13): 1341–1347. DOI: 10.1016/j.mineng.2006.01.004

Hubicki, Z., and Wójcik, G. (2006). Studies of removal of platinum (IV) ion microquantities from the model solutions of aluminium, copper, iron, nickel and zinc chloride macroquantities on the anion exchanger Duolite S 37. *Journal of Hazardous Materials*, 136(3): 770–775. DOI: 10.1016/j.jhazmat.2006.01.007.

Hubicki, Z., Wołowicz, A., and Leszczyńska, M. (2008). Studies of removal of palladium (II) ions from chloride solutions on weakly and strongly basic anion exchangers. *Journal of hazardous materials*, 159(2-3): 280–286. DOI: 10.1016/j.jhazmat.2008.02. 017.

Hussey, S.J. (1949). Application of ion-exchange resins in the cyanidation of a gold and silver ore. U.S. Dept. of the Interior, Bureau of Mines, R.I. 4374.

Iglesias, M., Antico, E., and Salvadó, V. (1999). Recovery of palladium (II) and gold (III) from diluted liquors using the exchanger duolite GT-73. *Analytica Chimica Acta*, 381(1): 61–67. DOI: 10.1016/S0003-2670(98)00707-7.

Izatt, R. M., Izatt, S. R., Izatt, N. E., Krakowiak, K. E., Bruening, R. L., and Navarro, L. (2015). Industrial applications of molecular recognition technology to separations of platinum group metals and selective removal of metal impurities from process streams. *Green Chemistry*, 17(4): 2236–2245. DOI: 10.1039/C4GC02188F.

Jermakowicz-Bartkowiak, D., and Kolarz, B. N. (2011). Poly (4-vinylpyridine) exchangers towards perrhenate sorption and desorption. *Reactive and Functional Polymers*, 71(2): 95–103. DOI: 10.1016/j.reactfunctpolym.2010.11.023.

Kakoi, T., Goto, M., and Nakashio, F. (1994). Solvent extraction of palladium with bis (2, 4, 4,-trimethylpentyl) dithiophosphinic acid and bis (2, 4, 4,-trimethylpentyl) monothiophosphinic acid. *Solvent Extraction and Ion Exchange*, 12(3): 541–555. DOI: 10.1080/07366299408918223.

Kancharla, S., and Sasaki, K. (2019). Acid tolerant covalently functionalized graphene oxide for the selective extraction of Pd from high-level radioactive liquid wastes. *Journal of Materials Chemistry A*, 7(9): 4561–4573. DOI: 10.1039/C8TA09849B.

Kononova, O. N., Kholmogorov, A. G., Kononov, Y. S., Pashkov, G. L., Kachin, S. V. and Zotova, S. V. (2001) Sorption recovery of gold from thiosulphate solutions after leaching of products of chemical preparation of hard concentrates. *Hydrometallurgy*, 59(1): 115–123.

Kononova, O. N., Melnikov, A. M., Borisova, T. V., and Krylov, A. S. (2011). Simultaneous ion exchange recovery of platinum and rhodium from chloride solutions. *Hydrometallurgy*, 105(3-4): 341–349. DOI: 10.1016/j. hydromet.2010.11.009.

Kramer, J., Driessen, W. L., Koch, K. R., and Reedijk, J. (2005). Highly selective and efficient recovery of Pd, Pt, and Rh from precious metal-containing industrial effluents with silica-based (poly) amine ion exchangers. *Separation Science and Technology*, 39(1): 63–75. DOI: 10.1081/SS-120027401.

Kumaresan, R., Sabharwal, K. N., Srinivasan, T. G., Vasudeva Rao, P. R., Dhekane, G. (2008). Studies on the sorption of palladium using cross-linked poly (4-vinylpyridine-divinylbenzene) resins in nitric acid medium. *Solvent Extraction and Ion Exchange*, 26(5): 643–671.

Lee, S. H., and Chung, H. (2003). Ion exchange characteristics of palladium and ruthenium from a simulated radioactive liquid waste. *Separation Science and Technology*,

Leung, B. K. O., and Hudson, M. J. (1992). A novel weak base anion exchange exchanger which is highly selective for the precious metals over base metals. *Solvent Extraction And Ion Exchange*, 10(1): 173–190. DOI: 10.1080/07366299208918098.

Livingstone, S. E. (2016). *The Chemistry of Ruthenium, Rhodium, Palladium, Osmium, Iridium and Platinum*. Pergamon Texts in Inorganic Chemistry (Vol. 25). Elsevier.

MacNevin, W. M., and Crummett, W. B. (1953). Bahavior of Platinum Group Metals toward Ion Exchange Exchangers. *Analytical Chemistry*, 25(11): 1628–1630. DOI: 10.1021/ac60083a014

Majavu, A., and Tshentu, Z. R. (2017). Separation of rhodium (III) and iridium (IV) chlorido species by quaternary diammonium centres hosted on silica microparticles. *South African Journal of Chemical Engineering*, 24: 82–94. DOI: 10.1016/j.sajce.2017.07.002.

Makishima, A., Nakanishi, M., and Nakamura, E. (2001). A group separation method for ruthenium, palladium, rhenium, osmium, iridium, and platinum using their bromo complexes and an anion exchange exchanger. *Analytical Chemistry*, 73(21): 5240–5246. DOI: 10.1021/ac010615u.

Marchbank, A. R., Thomas, K. G., Dreisinger, D. and Fleming, C. (1996) *U.S. Patent No. 5,536,297*. Washington, DC: U.S. Patent and Trademark Office.

Marinho, R. S., da Silva, C. N., Afonso, J. C., and da Cunha, J. W. S. D. (2011). Recovery of platinum, tin and indium from spent catalysts in chloride medium using strong basic anion exchange exchangers. *Journal of Hazardous Materials*, 192(3): 1155–1160. DOI: 10.1016/j.jhazmat.2011.06.021.

Mel'nikov, A. M., Kononova, O. N., Ozerova, T. A., and Luk'yanenko, A. S. (2012). Sorption recovery of platinum (II, IV) from chloride and sulfate-chloride solutions. *Russian Journal of Applied Chemistry*, 85(10): 1560–1566. DOI: 10.1134/ S1070427212100138.

Morcali, M. H., and Zeytuncu, B. (2015). Investigation of adsorption parameters for platinum and palladium onto a modified polyacrylonitrile-based sorbent. *International Journal of Mineral Processing*, 137: 52–58. DOI: 10.1016/j.minpro.2015.02.011.

Morcali, M. H., Zeytuncu, B., Akman, S., Yucel, O. (2016). Preparation and sorption behavior of DEAE-cellulose-thiourea-glutaraldehyde sorbent for Pt (IV) and Pd (II) from leaching solutions. *Desalination and Water Treatment*, 57(14): 6582–6593.

Moriyama, H., Aoki, T., Shinoda, S., and Saito, Y. (1981). Tin-119 Fourier-transform nuclear magnetic resonance study of rhodium–tin complexes formed in aqueous hydrochloric acid solutions of $RhCl_3$ and $SnCl_2$. *Journal of the Chemical Society, Dalton Transactions*, (2): 639–644. DOI: 10.1039/DT9810000639

Nakano, Y., Takeshita, K., Tsutsumi, T. (2001). Adsorption mechanism of hexavalent chromium by redox within condensed-tannin gel. *Water Research*, 35(2): 496–500

Navarro, R., Garcia, E., Saucedo, I., and Guibal, E. (2012a). Platinum (IV) recovery from HCl solutions using Amberlite XAD-7 impregnated with a tetraalkyl phosphonium ionic liquid. *Separation Science and Technology*, 47(14-15): 2199–2210. DOI: 10.1080/01496395.2012.697522.

Navarro, R., Lira, M. A., Saucedo, I., Alatorre, A., and Guibal, E. (2017). Amberlite XAD-1180 impregnation with Cyphos IL101 for the selective recovery of precious metals from HCl solutions. *Gold Bulletin*, 50(1): 7–23. DOI: 10.1007/s13404- 016-0190-8.

Navarro, R., Saucedo, I., Gonzalez, C., and Guibal, E. (2012b). Amberlite XAD-7 impregnated with Cyphos IL-101 (tetraalkylphosphonium ionic liquid) for Pd (II) recovery from HCl solutions. *Chemical Engineering Journal*, 185: 226–235. DOI: 10.1016/j.cej.2012.01.090.

Nguyen, V. T., Lee, J. C., Chagnes, A., Kim, M. S., Jeong, J., and Cote, G. (2016). Highly selective separation of individual platinum group metals (Pd, Pt, Rh) from acidic chloride media using phosphonium-based ionic liquid in aromatic diluent. *RSC Advances* 6(67): 62717–62728. DOI: 10.1039/C6RA09328K.

Nikoloski, A. N., and Ang, K. L. (2014). Review of the application of ion exchange exchangers for the recovery of platinum-group metals from hydrochloric acid solutions. *Mineral Processing and Extractive Metallurgy Review*, 35(6): 369–389. DOI: 10.1080/08827508.2013.764875.

Nikoloski, A. N., Ang, K. L., and Li, D. (2015). Recovery of platinum, palladium and rhodium from acidic chloride leach solution using ion exchange exchangers. *Hydrometallurgy*, 152: 20–32. DOI: 10.1016/j.hydromet.2014.12.006.

Nourmoradi, H., Nikaeen, M., and Khiadani, M. (2012). Removal of benzene, toluene, ethylbenzene and xylene (BTEX) from aqueous solutions by montmorillonite modified with nonionic surfactant: Equilibrium, kinetic and thermodynamic study. *Chemical Engineering Journal*, 191: 341–348.

O'Malley, G. P. (2001) The elution of gold from anion exchange resins. *Australian Patent, WO, 123626.*

Paiva, A.P., Ortet, O., Carvalho, G. I., Nogueira, C. A. (2017). Recovery of palladium from a spent industrial catalyst through leaching and solvent extraction. *Hydrometallurgy*, 171: 394–401.

Parajuli, D., Kawakita, H., Inoue, K., Funaoka, M. (2006). Recovery of gold (III), palladium (II), and platinum (IV) by aminated lignin derivatives. *Industrial & Engineering Chemistry*, 45(19): 6405–6412.

Park, C. I., Jeong, J. S., and Cha, G. W. (2000). Separation and preconcentration method for palladium, platinum and gold from some heavy metals using Amberlite IRC 718 chelating exchanger. *Bulletin of the Korean Chemical Society*, 21(1): 121–124.

Parodi, A., Vincent, T., Pilsniak, M., Trochimczuk, A. W., and Guibal, E. (2008). Palladium and platinum binding on an imidazol containing exchanger. *Hydrometallurgy*, 92(1-2): 1–10. DOI: 10.1016/j.hydromet.2008.02.005.

Peng, L. I. U., Liu, G. F., Chen, D. L., Cheng, S. Y., and Ning, T. A. N. G. (2009). Adsorption properties of Ag (I), Au (III), Pd (II) and Pt (IV) ions on commercial 717 anion-exchange exchanger. *Transactions of Nonferrous Metals Society of China*, 19(6): 1509–1513. DOI: 10.1016/S1003-6326(09)60061-3

Ramesh, A., Hasegawa, H., Sugimoto, W., Maki, T., Ueda, K. (2008). Adsorption of gold (III), platinum (IV) and palladium (II) onto glycine modified crosslinked chitosan resin. *Bioresource Technology*, 99(9): 3801–3809.

Rovira, M., Cortina, J. L., Amaldos, J., and Sastre, A. M. (1998). Recovery and separation of platinum group metals using impregnated exchangers containing Alamine 336. *Solvent extraction and ion exchange*, 16(5): 1279–1302. DOI: 10.1080/07360299808934580.

Rovira, M., Cortina, J. L., Amaldos, J., Sastre, A. M. (1999). Impregnated resins containing di-(2-ethylhexyl) thiophosphoric acid for the extraction of palladium. II. Selective palladium (II) recovery from hydrochloric acid solutions. *Solvent Extraction and Ion Exchange*, 17(2): 351–366.

Sánchez, J. M., Hidalgo, M., and Salvadó, V. (2004). A comparison of the separation behavior of some new coordinating exchangers and commercial quaternary ammonium exchangers with reference to their separation of gold (III) and palladium (II) in hydrochloric acid media. *Solvent extraction and ion exchange*, 22(2): 285–303. DOI: 10.1081/SEI-120030463

Sayın, M., Can, M., İmamoğlu, M., and Arslan, M. (2015). 1, 3, 5-Triazine-pentaethylenehexamine polymer for the adsorption of palladium (II) from chloride-containing solutions. *Reactive and Functional Polymers*, 88: 31–38. DOI: 10.1016/j.reactfunctpolym.2015.02.003.

Sayın, M., Can, M., İmamoğlu, M., and Arslan, M. (2017). Highly efficient adsorption of Rh (III) from chloride containing solutions by triazine polyamine polymer. *Water, Air, & Soil Pollution*, 228(3): 100.

Schoeman, E., Bradshaw, S. M., Akdogan, G., Snyders, C. A., and Eksteen, J. J. (2017). The extraction of platinum and palladium from a synthetic cyanide heap leach solution with strong base anion exchange exchangers. *International Journal of Mineral Processing*, 162 :27–35. DOI: 10.1016/j.minpro.2017.02.017.

Shillington, D. P., and Tait, B. K. (1991). Diamine Extractants in Metal Separation. An Illustration of the Potential of the Chelate Extraction Mode in the Platinum(IV)--Palladium(II)--Base Metal System. *Solvent Extraction and Ion Exchange(USA)*, 9(5): 749–758. DOI: 10.1080/07366299108918082.

Siddhanta, S., Das, H. R. (1985). Separation and concentration of some platinum metal ions with a new chelating resin containing thiosemicarbazide as functional group. *Talanta*, 32(6): 457–460.

Silva, R. A., Hawboldt, K., and Zhang, Y. (2018). Application of exchangers with functional groups in the separation of metal ions/species–a review. *Mineral Processing and Extractive Metallurgy Review*, 39(6): 395–413. DOI: 10.1080/08827508.2018.1459619.

Sinitsyn, N. M., and Buslaeva, T. M. (1992). *Chemistry of complex halides of platinum group metals*. Moscow: AO Rosvuznauka, 79.

Sivrikaya, S., Altundag, H., Zengin, M., Imamoglu, M.(2011). Separation, preconcentration, and recovery of Pd (II) ions using newly modified silica gel with bis (3-aminopropyl) amine. *Separation Science and Technology*, 46(13): 2032–2040.

Sun, P. P. and Lee, M. S. (2011). Separation of Pt from hydrochloric acid leaching solution of spent catalysts by solvent extraction and ion exchange. *Hydrometallurgy*, 110(1-4): 91–98. DOI: 10.1016/j.hydromet.2011.09.002.

Sun, P. P., Lee, J. Y., and Lee, M. S. (2012). Separation of platinum (IV) and rhodium (III) from acidic chloride solution by ion exchange with anion exchangers. *Hydrometallurgy*, 113: 200–204. DOI: 10.1016/j.hydromet.2011.12.009.

Susoyeva, A. A., Blokhin, A. A., Murashkin, Y. V., and Mikhaylenko, M. A. (2016). Sorption recovery of rhodium (III) from multicomponent chloride solutions in the presence of tin (II) chloride. *Russian Journal of Non-Ferrous Metals*, 57(7): 681–685. DOI: 10.3103/S1067821216070142.

Tanaka, S., Harada, A., Nishihama, S., and Yoshizuka, K. (2012). Selective recovery of platinum group metals from spent automobile catalyst by integrated ion exchange methods. *Separation Science and Technology*, 47(9): 1369–1373. DOI: 10.1080/01496395.2012.672526.

Tokalıoğlu, Ş., Yılmaz, V., Kartal, Ş., Delibaş, A., Soykan, C. (2009). Solid phase extraction of Pd (II) on a newly synthesized chelating resin prior to determination by flame atomic absorption spectrometry. *Microchimica Acta*, 165(3–4): 347–352.

Topp, K. D., and Grote, M. (1996). Synthesis and characterization of a 1, 2, 4, 5-tetrazine-modified ion-exchange exchanger. *Reactive and Functional Polymers*, 31(2): 117–136. DOI: 10.1016/1381-5148(96)00049-1.

Totland, M., and Jarvis, K. (1997). Assessment of Dowex 1-X8-based anion-exchange procedures for the separation and determination of ruthenium, rhodium, palladium, iridium, platinum and gold in geological samples by inductively coupled plasma mass spectrometry. *Analyst*, 122(1): 19–26. DOI: 10. 1039/A606169I.

Trautmann, M., and Holdt, H. J. (2015). Separation of platinum and ruthenium by a sulphoxide modified polystyrene exchanger in laboratory column systems. *Separation and Purification Technology*, 149: 279–287. DOI: 10.1016/j.seppur.2015.05.013.

Trinh, H. B., Lee, J. C., Srivastava, R. R., Kim, S., Ilyas, S. (2017). Eco-threat Minimization in HCl Leaching of PGMs from Spent Automobile Catalysts by Formic Acid Prereduction. *ACS Sustainable Chemistry and Engineering*, 5: 7302–7309.

Truong, H. T., and Lee, M. S. (2018). Separation of Pd (II) and Pt (IV) from hydrochloric acid solutions by solvent extraction with Cyanex 301 and LIX 63. *Minerals Engineering*, 115: 13–20. DOI: 10.1016/j.mineng.2017.10.001.

Uheida, A., Iglesias, M., Fontàs, C., Hidalgo, M., Salvadó, V., Zhang, Y., and Muhammed, M. (2006). Sorption of palladium (II), rhodium (III), and platinum (IV) on Fe3O4 nanoparticles. *Journal of Colloid and Interface Science*, 301(2): 402–408. DOI: 10.1016/j.jcis.2006.05.015.

Vincent, T., Guibal, E., and Chiarizia, R. (2007). Palladium Recovery by Reactive Precipitation using a Cyanex 301-Based Stable Emulsion. *Separation Science and Technology*, 42(16): 3517–3536. DOI: 10.1080/01496390701626735.

Virnig, M. J. and Sierakoski, J. M. (2001) *U.S. Patent No. 6,197,214*. Washington, DC: U.S. Patent and Trademark Office.

Warshawsky, A. (1982). Integrated ion exchange and liquid-liquid extraction process for the separation of platinum group metals (PGM). *Separation and Purification Methods*, 11(2): 95–130. DOI: 10.1080/03602548208068391.

Warshawsky, A., Fieberg, M. M., Mihalik, P., and Murphy, T. G. (1980). The separation of platinum group metals (PGM) in chloride media by isothiouronium exchangers. *Separation and Purification Methods*. 9(2): 209–265. DOI: 10.1080/03602548008066001.

Wołowicz, A., and Hubicki, Z. (2010). Effect of matrix and structure types of ion exchangers on palladium (II) sorption from acidic medium. *Chemical Engineering Journal*, 160(2): 660–670. DOI: 10.1016/j.cej.2010.04.009.

Wołowicz, A., and Hubicki, Z. (2012). The use of the chelating exchanger of a new generation Lewatit MonoPlus TP-220 with the bis-picolylamine functional groups in the removal of selected metal ions from acidic solutions. *Chemical Engineering Journal*, 197: 493–508. DOI: 10.1016/j.cej.2012.05.047.

Wołowicz, A., and Hubicki, Z. (2014). Adsorption characteristics of noble metals on the strongly basic anion exchanger Purolite A-400TL. *Journal of Materials Science*, 49(18): 6191–6202. DOI: 10.1007/s10853-014-8333-x.

Xiong, C., Zheng, Y., Feng, Y., Yao, C., Ma, C., Zheng, X., Jiang, J. (2014). Preparation of a novel chloromethylated polystyrene-2-amino-1, 3, 4-thiadiazole chelating resin and its adsorption properties and mechanism for separation and recovery of Pt (IV) from aqueous solutions. *Journal of Materials Chemistry A*, 2(15):5379–5386.

Xu, Z., Zhao, Y., Wang, P., Yan, X., Cai, M., and Yang, Y. (2019). Extraction of Pt (IV), Pt (II), and Pd (II) from Acidic Chloride Media Using Imidazolium-Based Task-Specific Polymeric Ionic Liquid. *Industrial & Engineering Chemistry Research*, 58(5): 1779–1786. DOI: 10.1021/acs.iecr.8b03408

Yi, Q., Fan, R., Xie, F., Zhang, Q., Luo, Z. (2016). Recovery of Palladium (II) from nitric acid medium using a natural resin prepared from persimmon dropped fruits residues. *Journal of the Taiwan Institute of Chemical Engineers*. 61: 299–305.

Yi-Yong, C., and Xing-Zhong, Y. (1994). Synthesis and properties of 1-(2-aminoethyl) piperazine exchanger used in the sorption of the platinum group and gold ions. *Reactive polymers*, 23(2-3): 165–172. DOI: 10.1016/0923-1137(94)90017-5.

Zagorodni, A. A. (2006). *Ion exchange materials: properties and applications*. Elsevier.

Zhang, C., Li, X., Pang, J. (2001). Synthesis and adsorption properties of magnetic resin microbeads with amine and mercaptan as chelating groups. *Journal of Applied Polymer Science*, 82 (7):1587–1592.

Zhang, B.W., Zhang, Y., Grote, M., Kettrup, A. (1994). Studies on macroporous cross-linked polyacrolein-styrene resin I. Synthesis of polyacrylic aldehyde-hydrazone and polyacrolein-phenylhydrazone resins and their chelating properties for gold and platinum group metals. *Reactive and Functional Polymers*, 22(2):115–125.

Zhou, L., Xu, J., Liang, X., and Liu, Z. (2010). Adsorption of platinum (IV) and palladium (II) from aqueous solution by magnetic cross-linking chitosan nanoparticles modified with ethylenediamine. *Journal of Hazardous Materials*, 182(1-3): 518–524. DOI: 10.1016/j.jhazmat.2010.06.062

9 Integrated Recovery Processes for Precious Metals from Urban Mine Sources and Case Studies

Sadia Ilyas
Mineral Resources and Energy Engineering, Jeonbuk National University, Jeonju, Jeonbuk 54896, Republic of Korea

Hyunjung Kim
Mineral Resources and Energy Engineering, Jeonbuk National University, Jeonju, Jeonbuk 54896, Republic of Korea

Department of Environment and Energy, Jeonbuk National University, Jeonju, Jeonbuk 54896, Republic of Korea

Rajiv Ranjan Srivastava
Center for Advanced Chemistry, Institute of Research and Development, Duy Tan University, Da Nang 550000, Vietnam

CONTENTS

9.1 INTEGRATED RECOVERY PROCESSES FOR PRECIOUS METALS FROM URBAN MINE SOURCES AND CASE STUDIES: AN OVERVIEW

Scientific discoveries have taken advantage of the unique chemical and physical properties of metals to enable creation of a myriad of high-tech products that have transformed twenty-first-century society. However, due to the finite primary supply of precious metals, their burgeoning consumption by consumers and industry is unsustainable without efficient recycling. Vastly improved value recovery from end-of-life metal products is needed, both by increasing the rate of metal recycling and by improving the performance of recycling technologies. Considerable efforts are therefore being made to develop an integrated approach to metallurgical processing of urban-mined resources.

9.2 WARSHAWSKY INTEGRATED REFINING PROCESS FOR PRECIOUS METALS

An integrated process proposed by Warshawsky (1980, 1982) consists of a consecutive series of dissolution, ion-exchange, distillation, and liquid-liquid extraction processes. After wet chlorination, PM-containing leach liquor is passed through a Monivex exchanger (anion exchanger) for quantitative absorption of platinum-group metals from less valuable base metals. During this step, the functional iso-thiouronium group as a weak base is subject to the following acid-base equilibrium:

$$(9.1)$$

The basic reactions taking place on the exchanger can be summarized in successive adsorption and elution steps.

$$(9.2)$$

$$\text{(P)}-CH_2-S-C \begin{array}{c} NH_2 \\ \| \\ \| \\ NH_2 \end{array} [MCl_xOH_y]^{z-} \quad \xrightarrow[\substack{\text{Ligand substitution}\\ \\ NH_2-CS-NH_2/HCl}]{} \quad \text{(P)}-CH_2-S-C \begin{array}{c} NH_2 \\ \| \\ Cl^- + \text{thiourea} \\ \text{complexes} \\ NH_2 \end{array} \qquad (9.3)$$

In the adsorption step, the anion exchanger adsorbs platinum-group metal ions of type $[MCl_xOH_y]^{z-}$ in a continuous ion-exchange process with high adsorption rates. The adsorption mechanism depends strongly on acidic strength. An anion-exchange mechanism between the anionic chloro-complexes of precious metals and the chloride counter-ion takes place at high acid concentrations. In dilute acids, chelating complexes are formed with equivalent liberation of hydrogen ions which can lead to gradual poisoning of the exchanger.

During elution, the metals are released from the exchanger only when the negatively charged chlorides in the PM anionic complex have been replaced by neutral thiourea to the degree that the complex is positively charged or neutral.

The elution rates can also vary considerably with the variation in the rates of substitution of the precious metals in solution. Platinum, palladium, and/or gold are eluted quickly, and the remaining platinum-group metal ions are much slowly eluted. An additional step prior to the PM (platinum-group metal ions) separation is required for back conversion of metal-thiourea complexes into chloride complexes. This chloride ion containing raffinate, after distillation removal of ruthenium and osmium, is passed through a conditioning step to prepare feed suitable for the solvent extraction process with tertiary amine-based extractants. This step ensures separation of platinum, palladium, and/or gold (present as extractable anionic complexes) from rhodium, ruthenium, and iridium, which exist as cationic or neutral non-extractable complexes.

After conditioning, recovery of ruthenium and osmium is ensured by distillation. At this stage, ruthenium and osmium are distilled off as RuO_4 and OsO_4 tetraoxides. This involves neutralization of the acid formed during the conversion with sodium hydroxide. Very accurate pH control is required for the removal of RuO_4 because the complex can form over a wide pH range, and can even be formed during the conversion step. At pH values of 4 to 9, a large proportion of the PMs are present as insoluble hydroxides. Adjustment of pH allows the OsO_4 and RuO_4 to be distilled with vigorous chlorine sparging. They are recovered by scrubbing with concentrated hydrochloric acid. Then raffinate is passed through tertiary amine for further recovery of metals (Figure 9.1).

The solvent extraction of PM ions in chloride solution has the following objectives:(1) separation of Pt, Pd, and Au in the organic phase; 2) concentration of Rh, Ru in the aqueous phase; and 3) selective stripping of both metals (Pd, Pt) by thiocyanate and thiourea.

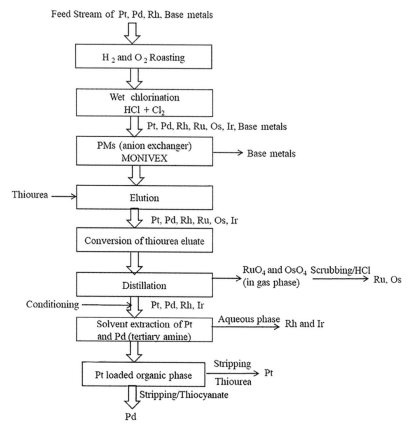

FIGURE 9.1   Warshawsky integrated refining process for precious metals.

Source: Modified from Warshawsky (1980, 1982); Cole and Ferron (2002).

9.3 TANAKA INTEGRATED RECOVERY PROCESS FOR PRECIOUS METALS

In this process, the use of a dihexyl sulphide (DHS)-impregnated exchanger and weak anion exchanger, Diaion WA-21, were proposed for selective recovery of precious metals from a feed stream of spent automotive catalysts after wet chlorination (Tanaka et al., 2012). The DHS exchanger selectively recovered Pd over other metals (Pt, Rh, Fe, Mg, Al) from hydrochloric acid solutions. Ammonia solution was chosen for elution of Pd from the loaded DHS exchanger. Raffinate was further treated with anion exchanger (Diaion WA-21) for selective separation of Pt and Rh from base metals. The separation of these metals was achieved in a two-stage elution process: elution with thiourea in HCl solution for Pt recovery and then with sulphuric acid solution for Rh recovery. An integrated flowsheet with modifications is presented in Figure 9.2.1.

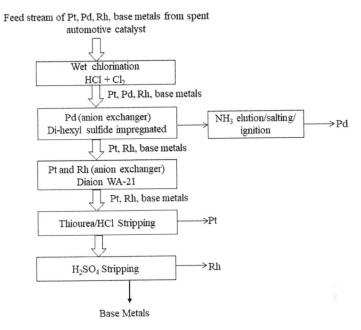

Feed stream of Pt, Pd, Rh, base metals from spent automotive catalyst

Wet chlorination
HCl + Cl₂

Pt, Pd, Rh, base metals

Pd (anion exchanger)
Di-hexyl sulfide impregnated

NH₃ elution/salting/
ignition → Pd

Pt, Rh, base metals

Pt and Rh (anion exchanger)
Diaion WA-21

Pt, Rh, base metals

Thiourea/HCl Stripping → Pt

H₂SO₄ Stripping → Rh

Base Metals

FIGURE 9.2   An integrated process flowsheet for recovery of precious metals.
Source: Modified from Tanaka et al. (2012); Cole and Ferron (2002).

9.4 IMPALA PROCESS FOR RECOVERY OF PRECIOUS METALS

The Impala Platinum Process (IPP) is commercially viable for separation of PMs from wet chlorinated converter matte (65% PMs)and can be applied to urban-mined material (Figure 9.3). After wet chlorination the residue is leached with NH_4OH and HCl is added to precipitate Ag^{1+} as AgCl. The raffinate, after silver recovery, is passed through Amberlite XAD-7 (anion exchanger) to recover gold as Au^{3+} ions, which is eluted from the XAD-7, then reductively precipitated with 99.95% purity. Palladium is recovered by SuperLig® (anion exchanger, function-alized polystyrene beads), at a specific limit of redox potential and precipitated in salt form. Base metals from the palladium-depleted raffinate are removed by cation exchange and precipitated collectively. After cation exchange the raffinate is boiled with the addition of $NaClO_3$ and $NaBrO_3$ to oxidize Ru^{3+} to its tetraox-ide (Ru^{4+}).

Ruthenium tetraoxides are then stripped to the gas phase and scrubbed with HCl in the distillation process. Ruthenium is precipitated from scrubbed solution as $(NH_4)_2RuNOCl_5$ (ruthenium nitrosyl salt) and ignited to obtain pure ruthenium metal. The remaining metal-containing raffinate consists of Pt, Ir, and Rh. An increase in pH till 6 after ruthenium and/or osmium distillation will precipitate Rh and Ir as hydrox-ides. This slurry is filtered, boiled to eliminate excess acid, re-dissolved in deminer-alized H_2O, oxidized and neutralized with alkali. Platinum is usually precipitated

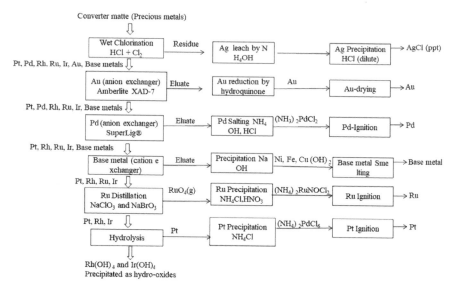

FIGURE 9.3 Impala Process.

Source: Modified from Crundwell et al. (2011).

using NH_4Cl to form ammonium hexachloroplatinate $(NH_4)_2PtCl_6$. This salt is then ignited to form pure platinum metal (Crundwell et al., 2011; Sole et al., 2018; Fleming, 2002; Mpinga et al., 2015; Milbourne et al., 2003). The process is comprehensively illustrated in Figure 9.3.

9.5 PLATSOL™ PROCESS

Platsol™ is a new single-step process to recover platinum-group metals, gold and base metals such as Cu, Ni and Co, from a variety of high- and low-grade ores, concentrates, mattes, autocatalysts and other industrial products. Platsol™ is a technically viable alternative to smelting, and could be a particularly attractive alternative for the treatment of feeds that are lower grade in precious metals and sulphides, and feeds that contain impurities that are difficult to treat in a smelter. Here hig- temperature (220°C), pressure leaching (700 kPa O_2 and 3200 kPa total pressure) is performed, in which base-metal sulphides are oxidized with oxygen to soluble sulphate complexes and sulphuric acid while PMs (gold and platinum-group metals) are solubilized as chloro-complexes by the addition of a small amount of chloride salts to an autoclave feed. Precious metals including gold, platinum, palladium, and rhodium are recovered from the acidic autoclave liquor by precipitation with NaHS. Copper is then subjected to solvent extraction and electrowinning. Copper raffinate (-75 %) is recycled to the autoclave feed, and a bleed stream is taken to another plant where nickel and cobalt are recovered by solvent extraction (Figure 9.4) (Fleming, 2002; Milbourne et al., 2003; Mpinga et al., 2015, Hoffmann and Wesstrom, 1994).

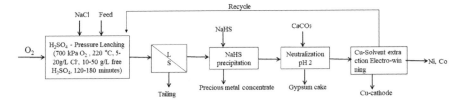

FIGURE 9.4   Conceptual flowsheet for gold, PGM and base-metal recovery from sulphide concentrates by Platsol™ process.

Source: Modified from Fleming (2002); Milbourne et al. (2003).

9.6 THE MERRILL–CROWE PROCESS

The Merrill–Crowe Process (Figure 9.5) consists of four basic steps for extracting gold by cementation from cyanide-based liquors instead of using zinc shavings (Crowe, 1918):

  i. Clarification of the gold-containing cyanide solution
 ii. De-aeration
iii. Addition of zinc powder and lead salts
 iv. Recovery of zinc-gold precipitates.

The prime advantage of this process over CIP arises where there is a high silver-to-gold ratio; a ratio above 4:1 commonly favours the Merrill–Crowe process. The most important point is to obtain a clear gold solution (leach liquor) hence, the cloudy solution after a counter-current decantation is sent to a storage tank for settling of suspended particles. Complete precipitation of gold (and silver) is achieved by the removal of dissolved oxygen in the Crowe vacuum tower. The tower's splash plates and cascade trays contribute to increasing the surface area of the solution, thus complete de-aeration is possible by applying the vacuum. The hydrogen evolution during cementation nullifies the effect of any traces of oxygen remaining in solution. Soon after clarification and de-aeration of the impregnated solution, zinc dust is continuously added through a zinc feeder, precipitating the gold without exposure to air The solution flows to the precipitation filters where pressure candle filters are used to filter the zinc-gold slime. The impregnated leach solution has to percolate through the fine zinc layers, creating an extensive surface for solid-liquid precipitation. The resulting metal precipitate is mixed and blended with flux to smelt and collected bars are then subjected to refining. The refining process usually depends on other co-existing metals such as Cu, Pt, and Ag, etc.

Alternatively, aluminium can be used with NaOH solution, which is essential for the precipitation reaction as follows:

$$Al^0 \rightarrow Al^{3+} + 3e^- \tag{9.4}$$

$$Al^{3+} + 3OH^- \rightarrow Al(OH)_3 \tag{9.5}$$

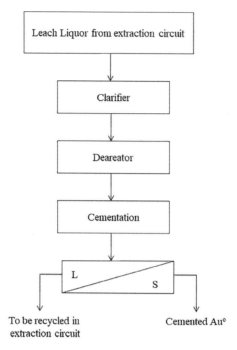

FIGURE 9.5   Integrated Merrill-Crowe Process for recovery of precious metals.
Source: Modified from Crowe (1918).

$$Al(OH)_3 + Na^+ + OH^- \rightarrow AlO_2^- + Na^+ + 2H_2O \qquad (9.6)$$

$$3Au^+ + 3e^- \rightarrow 3Au^0 \qquad (9.7)$$

Or, overall the reaction can be written as:

$$Al^0 + 4OH^- + Na^+ + 3Au^+ \rightarrow 3Au^0 + AlO_2^- + Na^+ + 2H_2O \qquad (9.8)$$

However, attempts to use aluminium have encountered difficulties in the filtration (due to formation of calcium aluminates) and smelting of the precipitate. In a sodium regime, the formation of soluble aluminate created by the surface films precedes the cementation process unhindered. The soluble reducing reagents (H_2S, SO_2, $NaSO_3$, and $FeSO_4$) used at commercial level for cementing gold from chloride solutions cannot be used for quantitative precipitation of gold from cyanide solutions.

9.7 PHELPS DODGE INTEGRATED REFINING PROCESS

The Phelps Dodge anodic slime process is described by Hoffmann (1994). A simplified and modified form of the process is presented in Figure 9.6.

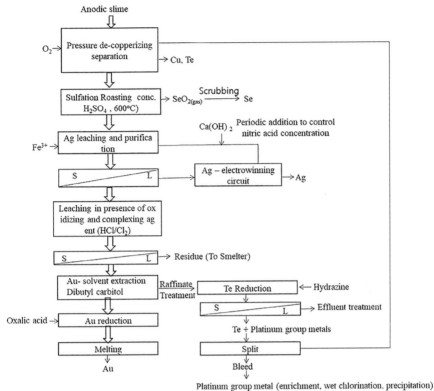

FIGURE 9.6 Phelps Dodge anodic slime treatment process.

Source: Modified from Hoffmann (1994); Cole and Ferron (2002).

Phelps Dodge processes copper refinery anodic slimes by first pressure de-copper-izing/de-tellurizing followed by de-selenizing the copper-free slimes by sulphation roasting with concentrated sulphuric acid. During sulphation roasting, intermetallic selenides and/or elemental Se are scrubbed from the gaseous phase by HCl and separated from metal sulphates of the roaster calcine. Then, after metathetical leaching, silver sulphate is converted into silver nitrate which is electrolyzed along with calcium nitrate and recovered. The overall reaction (see Equations 9.9–9.19) indicates an equivalent amount of nitric acid generation during the electrowinning of silver. If the nitric acid concentration is not controlled, the efficiency of silver electrowinning may be reduced. This can be controlled by periodic addition of calcium hydroxide to the electrolyte, which generates an equimolar amount of calcium nitrate, ensuring complete recycling of the lixiviant. Chlorine and aqueous hydrochloric acid are employed for the solubilization of gold and platinum-group metals. Chlorine requirements remain modest only due to the presence of gold, platinum, and palladium in elemental form in the silver leach residue. Gold is concentrated by solvent extraction of the filtrate from wet chlorination by an appropriate organic extractant (dibutyl carbitol) which has a distribution coefficient (*O/A*) greater than 1000 for gold. This recovers >99.9% gold in a two-stage counter-current extraction process. The gold-loaded organic phase then passes through reductive stripping with oxalic acid.

Quite small concentrations (100 ppm) of all the platinum, palladium, and rhodium dissolved during wet chlorination are recovered quantitatively from solution by solvent extraction with a reductant that reduces tellurium from solution. The reduction of tellurium causes quantitative co-precipitation of gold, platinum, palladium, and rhodium from raffinate.

The small proportion of platinum-group metals does not warrant processing to recover them; instead, the tellurium precipitate containing the platinum metals is recycled to the pressure de-copperizing step. Here, the tellurium is dissolved and removed from the circuit but the platinum-group metals are recycled to wet chlorination where they are again dissolved and their concentration increased. This process is repeated until the level of platinum metals in solution warrants their recovery using conventional precipitation chemistry. The overall chemistry of the process is described in Equations 9.9–9.19.

$$Ag_2Se + 2H_2SO_4 \rightarrow Ag_2SO_4 + SeO_2 + 2H_2O \tag{9.9}$$

$$Se + 2H_2SO_4 \rightarrow SeO_2 + 2H_2O + 2SO_2 \tag{9.10}$$

$$CuSe + 4H_2SO_4 \rightarrow CuSO_4 + SeO_2 + 3SO_2 + 4H_2O \tag{9.11}$$

$$Te + 2H_2SO_4 \rightarrow TeO_2 + 2SO_2 + 2H_2O$$

$$Anode\ H_2O \rightarrow \frac{1}{2}O_2 + 2H^+ + 2e \tag{9.12}$$

$$Cathode\ 2AgNO_3 + 2e \rightarrow 2Ag + 2NO_3^{3-} \tag{9.13}$$

$$Over\ All\ reaction\ 2AgNO_3 + H_2O \rightarrow 2Ag + 2HNO_3 + \frac{1}{2}O_2 \tag{9.14}$$

$$2HNO_3 + Ca(OH)_2 \rightarrow Ca(NO_3)_2 + 2H_2O \tag{9.15}$$

$$2Au + 3Cl_2 + 2HCl \rightarrow 2HAuCl_4 \tag{9.16}$$

$$Pt + 2Cl_2 + 2HCl \rightarrow HPtCl_6 \tag{9.17}$$

$$Pd + Cl_2 + 2HCl \rightarrow H_2PdCl_4 \tag{9.18}$$

$$2HAuCl_4 + 3(HOOC)_2 \rightarrow 2Au + 6CO_2 + 8HCl \tag{9.19}$$

9.8 USMR INTEGRATED PROCESS FOR PRECIOUS METALS

The USMR process integrates leaching, precipitation, cementation, and smelting, processing about 210,000 t/y of scrap (Figure 9.7). The process consists of copper smelting, converting, electro-refining, and anode slime production. The generated slime is

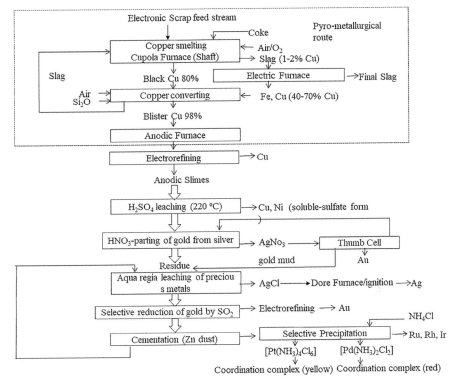

FIGURE 9.7 USMR integrated recovery process for precious metals.
Source: Modified from Hoffmann (1988).

subjected to H_2SO_4 leaching to remove Cu and Ni as soluble metal sulphate. Gold is separated from silver by nitric acid and the silver is sent for electro-refining in a Thum cell, while the gold mud is leached with aqua regia. After that, selective reduction of gold is carried out with SO_2. The raffinate passes through Zn cementation, selective precipitation with ammonium chloride, and selective precipitation of platinum and palladium into their respective Ir, Ru, and Rh coordination complexes (Hoffmann, 1988).

When the amounts of precious metals (Ir, Ru, Rh) are such that they would become insoluble in the anodes, they are cast and batch-treated in a separate circuit; the silver is recycled to the main circuit, and the sludge is boiled in aqua regia to solubilize Au, Pt, and Pd. The residue containing Ir, Ru, and Rh is melted with Pb; the Pb–Rh alloy is leached with nitric acid to dissolve the Pb and the crude rhodium purified. The (Ir+Ru)-rich nitric acid leach residue is fused with sodium peroxide to leach the Ru, while the residue is chlorinated and purified via the classical route to Ir powder.

9.9 AMAX PROCESS FOR THE TREATMENT OF PRECIOUS METALS

Amax developed a process to recover precious metals from spent catalytic converters in 1981. A comprehensive flowsheet of the process is shown in Figure 9.8. It consists of calcination at 1500°C, aqua-regia leaching of precious metals followed by

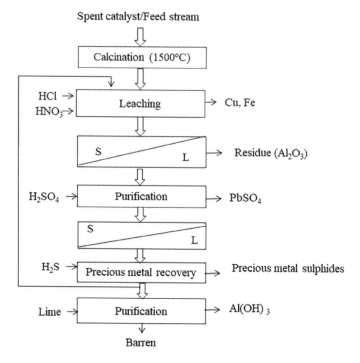

FIGURE 9.8   Amax process for the recovery of precious metals.
Source: Modified from Bonucci and Parker (1984); Cole and Ferron (2002).

filtration and washing, lead precipitation from leach solution using sulphuric acid, hydrogen sulphide (H_2S) precipitation of precious metals, recycling of the leach solution and treatment of bleeds to precipitate aluminium. Except in the monolithic case, calcination is required to transform the soluble γ-alumina into insoluble α-alumina, thereby decreasing acid consumption by recycling a large portion of the leach solution (Bonucci and Parker, 1984).

9.10 INTEGRATED DEGUSSA PROCESS FOR SEPARATION OF PRECIOUS METALS

The Degussa dmC^2 refinery in Hanau, Germany (Hagelüken, 2001) established a new process for separation of precious metals from various secondary waste streams. The process used refractories from glass industry and Al_2O_3 chemical catalyst as feed stream for the treatment of autocatalysts (Figure 9.9).The reduction furnace slag contains 10–50 g/t precious metals and is recycled to the copper smelter. The Cu metal from the furnace contains 10–15% precious metals, as well as iron and nickel.

Metal Concentrate/Various waste streams

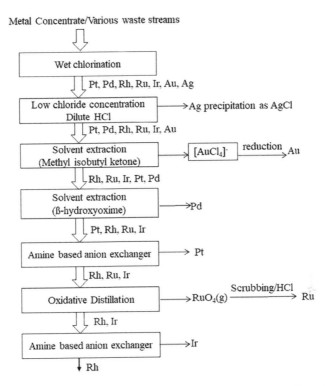

FIGURE 9.9 Flowsheet for integrated Degussa process for recovery of precious metals. *Source:* Modified from Hagelüken (2001); Cole and Ferron (2002).

9.11 INTEGRATED CETEM PROCESS FOR RECOVERY OF PRECIOUS METALS

Residues from national mints contain significant platinum group elements (PGEs). For example, Brazilian mint residue contains by assay 13.6% Cu, 2.2% Fe, 1.6% Pb, 8.3% S, 35.6% Pd, 0.9% Pt and 0.1% Au. The process, which was developed by the Centre for Mineral Technology (CETEM) and is applied industrially, (Sobral and Granato, 1992), consists of sulphuric acid leaching, nitric acid leaching, ammonium hydroxide-assisted purification, precipitation, reduction and smelting (Figure 9.10).

In the sulphuric leaching step, varying percentages of both pulp solid (10, 20, and 25%), and sulphuric acid concentration (5, 10, and 25% w/v) were used. Each test was conducted both with and without aeration. Each test was run for four hours and aliquots were taken hourly for chemical analysis. Under all the leaching conditions studied, the concentrations of palladium in solution were found to be very similar. From this result, it can be concluded that Pd is absorbed in small amounts in the residue as palladium chloride. The presence of this salt is thought to be due

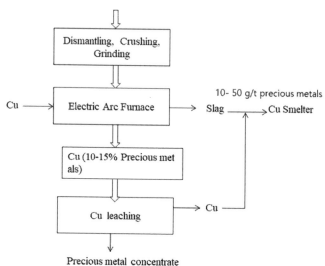

FIGURE 9.10   Integrated CETEM process for palladium recovery.

Source: Modified from Sobral and Granato (1992); Cole and Ferron (2002).

to surface contact of the residue with dilute hydrochloric acid, caused by inefficient washing of the residue. Increasing the percentage solid in the pulp gave low base-metal extraction, owing to a lower amount of acid being available for the reactions. Forced aeration did not cause a significant increase in the leaching process. Nevertheless, an increase in the sulphuric acid concentration produced enhanced iron extraction.

With regard to copper, a sulphuric acid concentration of 10% (w/v) promoted the complete dissolution of the metal. However, the use of concentrations higher than this caused a decrease in copper extraction due to the solution then being more viscous, causing a subsequent loss in acid dissolution. The results of aqueous leaching of the solid residue show that most of the copper was available as cuprous chloride. The presence of residual hydrochloric acid explains the low pH value of the aqueous solution after leaching and also the presence of cuprous chloride. The available metallic copper is mainly dissolved by the diluted sulphuric acid-aerated solutions. The purpose of this first leaching step was to extract as much copper and iron as possible, thus eliminating them from subsequent steps in the process. The next step of this study was to define the best conditions for the nitric acid leaching of palladium. The reaction in this step is shown below:

$$Pd + 8HNO_3 \rightarrow Pd(NO_3)_4 + 4NO_2 + 4H_2O \tag{9.20}$$

The tests carried out show that increasing the palladium concentration did not affect the leaching kinetics, and solutions up to 130g/l Pd were obtained, confirming the high solubility of the palladium nitrate (Granato and Sobral, 1985; Cleare et al., 1970; Furman, 1975). To obtain a suitable solid suspension in the pulp it was necessary to use at least twice the stoichiometric amount of nitric acid to dissolve all the enclosed palladium. Through experiments it was possible to verify that a further increase of nitric acid would not yield any significant increase in palladium extraction. However, temperature was found to be a decisive parameter in the kinetics of leaching, greatly speeding up the process. However, total extraction was not achieved. X-ray diffraction analysis of the nitric leaching residue showed the presence of palladium sulphide, which is only slightly soluble in nitric acid and totally soluble in aqua regia. It was therefore possible with aqua-regia leaching tests to extract up to 97% of the palladium.

Some purification tests were carried out on the palladium leaching solution, and some yellow salts were precipitated. These tests consisted of a precipitation of the metallic impurities in the solution as hydroxides, which was achieved by increasing the pH of the solution to 6 with ammonium hydroxide. The pH was then further increased, by the addition of ammonium hydroxide, to a value greater than 9, producing a soluble palladium amino compound. Finally, to precipitate the palladium yellow salt (dichlorodiamine-palladium II), hydrochloric acid was added to bring the pH down to a value of 1. The chemistry of the precipitation process is described in the following equations:

$$M^{x+} + xOH^- \rightarrow M(OH)_x \quad (M = Fe, Cu, Zn, Pb) \tag{9.21}$$

$$Pd(NO_3)_2 + 4NH_4OH \rightarrow Pd(NH_3)_4(NO_3)_2 + 4H_2O \tag{9.22}$$

$$Pd(NH_3)_4(NO_3)_2 + 4HCl \rightarrow Pd(NH_3)_2(Cl)_2 + 2NH_4NO_3 \tag{9.23}$$

Dilution of the original leaching solution (about 100g/1 in palladium) was necessary, considering the results obtained. The neutralization of the residual nitric acid, with ammonium hydroxide, caused a substantial increase in temperature and gave rise to lower palladium recovery as the yellow salt. It was decided to first cool this liquor and repeat the cycle of changing the pH, allowing 99% palladium recovery. After that the original leaching solution was dilute but the increase in temperature was still significant after the first pH cycle. The increase in the volume of the solution to be treated, with a consequent decrease in the palladium concentration, promoted a slight reduction in the extraction of this metal. The pH cycling in this case also allowed satisfactory palladium recovery. The use of ammonium carbonate for impurities precipitation eliminated the dilution problem as well as avoiding an increase in the solution temperature. With regard to the former tests, palladium extraction increased in the first pH cycling to 88%, showing that a second pH cycling step was required to enhance metal recovery.

The yellow salt produced was submitted to reduction tests, and two reduction routes were evaluated. The first involved thermal decomposition, and the second hydrometallurgical reduction using hydrazine hydrate in alkaline or ammoniacal medium (Equation 9.24-9.25).

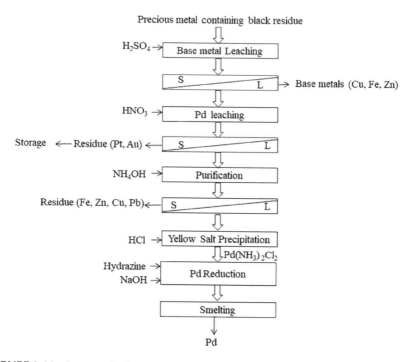

FIGURE 9.11   Integrated solvent extraction and ion-exchange process.

Source: Modified from Bernardis et al. (2005); Cleare et al. (1981); Renner (1992).

$$Pd\left(NH_3\right)_2\left(Cl\right)_2 \rightarrow 3Pd + 4NH_4Cl + N_2 + 2HCl \qquad (9.24)$$

$$Pd\left(NH_3\right)_2\left(Cl\right)_2 + N_2H_4 + 2NaOH \rightarrow Pd + 4NH_2OH + 2NH_3 + 2NaCl \quad (9.25)$$

Both the processes tested allowed recovery of metallic palladium, which was greater than 99.9% pure. However, the pyrometallurgical route presented two inconveniences: the necessity of using an inert or reducing atmosphere during the cooling of the metallic palladium produced; and the reaction by-products, one of which was hydrochloric acid gas which required special exhaust facilities, being extremely corrosive. The hydrometallurgical reduction required special care when dealing with the hydrazine hydrate, and the toxic effluents generated also required special exhaust facilities (Granato and Sobral, 1985; Cleare et al., 1970; Furman, 1975). An integrated process flowsheet is presented in Figure 9.10.

9.12 INTEGRATED MATTHEY RUSTENBURG REFINERS PROCESSES

An integrated solvent extraction ion-exchange method based on a refining method used by Matthey Rustenburg Refiners deals with complete dissolution of precious metals from various waste streams and concentrates (Bernardis et al., 2005). Feed stream is wet chlorinated and silver is precipitated at dilute acid concentration as silver chloride. Gold is extracted by methyl- isobutyl ketone (MIBK) solvent extraction. Palladium from gold-depleted raffinate is extracted by ß-hydroxyoxime, following which the raffinate is passed through an amine-based exchanger for selective recovery of platinum. Then ruthenium-, rhodium- and iridium-containing raffinate undergoes oxidative distillation. Ruthenium is scrubbed from the gas phase with HCl and rhodium and iridium are separated from each other by anion exchanger.

Similarly, the refining of PGE is mostly based on the formation of chloro-complexes, but other chemistries, such as those involving phosphates or fluorides, are also available (Patrushev, 1998; Izatt et al., 1987). It is known that iridium metal can be oxidized to form soluble fluoro-complexes, as per the following reaction (Mitkin, 2000):

$$Ir + 2BrF_3 \rightarrow IrF_5 + BrF + Br \qquad (9.26)$$

This property can be used to recover iridium from ceramic zirconium blocks to produce iridium crucibles. In the process suggested, the iridium-contaminated zirconium block (0.8–1.2% Ir) was oxidized to iridium (+5) using halogen fluoride (BrF_3); after separation of the iridium fluoride (IrF_5) formed from the zirconium block, the solution was treated with HCl to form $K_2 IrCl_6$. Using this process, iridium recovery from the zirconium block was 98–99%.

9.13 INTEGRATED RECYCLING BY UMICORE, HOBOKEN

Umicore refineries' integrated pyro-hydro-electrometallurgy process uses modern technology to recover 20 different metals (Au, Ag, Pd, Pt, Rh, Ir, Ru, Cu, Pb, Zn, Ni, Sn, Bi, In, Se, Te, Sb, As, Co, REE) from electronic waste to world-class environmental and quality standards (Mesker et al., 2009). At Umicore a total of about 350,000 tons, consisting of over 200 different types of raw materials, are processed each year in a highly flexible flowsheet (http://www.ewasteguide.info/files/UNEP_2009_eW2R.PDF). The plant is one of the world's largest and most complex precious metals recycling facilities with a yearly capacity of 50 tons of platinum-group metals (i.e., 7% of world mine production), 100 tons of Au, and 2400 tons of Ag. Industrial by-products are 86% by volume (75% by revenue), and end-of-life (EoL) recycles are 14% by volume (25% by revenue) for Umicore.

Feed material is initially subjected to smelting. The vertical Isa Smelt furnace uses submerged lance combustion technology with oxygen-enriched air (90%) and oil/natural gas injection, is equipped with extensive off-gas emission controls, and processes about 1000 tons of feed material per day. At about 1200°C, enriched air and fuel are injected through a lance in a liquid bath, and coke (4.5% by mass) is added for chemical reduction of the metals. Organic components from the circuit boards function as an additional reducing agent and fuel, and are thus classified as feedstock recycling. The furnace is fed from the top. Blowing air and fuel into the bath ensures rapid chemical reactions and good mixing as the solid feed material, the Cu metal phase, and the Pb slag phase are stirred vigorously. The precious metals dissolve in the Cu, while most other metals are concentrated in the Pb slag together with oxide compounds such as silica and alumina. Molten metal and slag are tapped from the furnace bottom. After smelting the Cu goes to the leach-electrowinning plant and the Pb slag goes to the blast furnace.

At the leach-electrowinning plant (built in 2001–2003), which combines hydro- and electrometallurgy, the granulated Cu is dissolved with sulphuric acid resulting in a copper sulphate solution, and the precious metals are concentrated in residue almost ten times higher than the feed material. The copper sulphate solution is sent to the electrowinning plant for recovery of the Cu as 99.99% pure cathodes. The remaining acid is returned to the dissolution step. The precious metal-concentrated residue is further refined at the precious metal refinery. In an integrated process, all possible variations and ratios of Ag, Au, and platinum-group metals are recovered one by one as high-purity metals (>99.9% pure). Lead oxide slag from the smelter containing Bi, Pb, Sn, In, Ni, Sb, Se, As, Cu and some precious metals is further treated in the lead blast furnace together with lead-containing raw materials. The furnace produces about 200–250 tpd of lead bullion (95% Pb) in which special metals and Ag are collected. In addition to bullion the blast furnace produces Cu matte (returned to the smelter), Ni speiss (sent to the Ni refinery), and slag, which is sold as a construction material/additive for concrete. Any precious metal is sent to the precious metal refinery. Refining of the bullion in the Pb refinery yields – in addition to Pb – Bi, Sn, As, Sb, silver and indium-tellurium residue. The silver residue is further treated in the precious metal refinery. The In-Te residue is further treated in the special metal refinery together with the Se residue from the precious metal refinery. The integrated process achieves high precious metals recoveries (above 95%) from complex electronic urban-mined waste. Individual metals with high purity are obtained from the respective processing operations, and slag is used as certified building material. Figure 9.12 presents a detailed process flowsheet.

The smelter, blast furnace, and refinery are equipped with heat recovery systems, dust is captured by an electrostatic precipitator and returned to the smelter; toxic dioxin emissions are prevented; and sulphur dioxide gases are converted to sulphuric acid for use in the plant and externally.

Smelting of spent printed circuit boards requires 1500 kJ kg^{-1} and further refining needs 6500 kJ kg^{-1}. The energy content of spent printed circuit boards is around 9600 kJ kg^{-1}. Spent printed circuit boards release the necessary energy during smelting and provide excess energy for steam generation. Furthermore, the recovery of metals from electronic waste avoids the high carbon dioxide emissions associated with primary metal production. Carbon dioxide emissions to produce precious metals from ore range between 9380 and 13,954 tons of carbon dioxide/ton for platinum-group metals compared to 3.4 tons of carbon dioxide/ton for Cu. Demand for primary production of the metal (4.7 million t y^{-1}) for electronic waste manufacturing accounts for annual carbon dioxide emissions of 23.4 million tons, almost 1/1000 of the world's carbon dioxide production. The carbon dioxide emissions of the Umicore process used in recover of 75,000 tons of metal from 300,000 tons of recyclables and smelter by-products is only 3.73 tons carbon dioxide/ton metal produced, compared to 17.1 tons carbon dioxide/ton in primary production. This single operation can thus prevent carbon dioxide emissions and substantially lower the environmental footprint of the metals (Mesker et al., 2009).

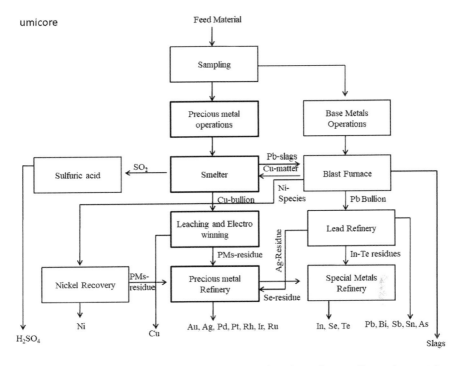

FIGURE 9.12   Umicore's integrated recycling of secondary electronic waste for precious metals.

9.14 AUSTRIAN MÜLLER-GUTTENBRUNN INTEGRATED URBAN MINING PRACTICES

MGG is one of the key recyclers of electronic waste in seven central and south-east European countries, with numerous facilities in the region located in Austria and the countries along the Danube. The process handles collection (with its own fleet of trucks, rails connections, and harbour links along the Danube), de-pollution, shredding, and ferrous metal separation followed by nonferrous separation and even plastic recycling. Mixed plastic is first separated from non-plastics and then sorted by type and grade in a fully automated process that converts the material to high-value new materials to be used for many demanding applications. The plastics produced are RoHS and REACH compliant and can be used for new electronic products. The de-pollution and shredding stages at the Müller-Guttenbrunn plant include a smasher, hand sorting, shredding, and ferrous recovery. The main differences between this plant and other recycling plants are using a 'smasher' for low-energy opening of electronic waste, and picking out pollutants and valuables before shredding. At the Metran plant, nonferrous metals are separated by sieving, eddy current separation, two-step heavy media density separation, optical separation, air-table separation for precious metal concentration, and finally smelting to generate Cu and precious metals. MBA Polymers process the recycled plastics to produce newly compounded and pelletized ABS, HIPS, and PP. These processes result in the least possible loss of precious metals. MGG processes 80 Kt of electronic waste a year. A recovery rate of

85% is achieved, which exceeded the EU-2018 target (European Parliament, 2018)). MGG recovers 850,000t of metals annually and contributes to a saving of over 1 million tons of carbon dioxide (http://www.mgg-recycling.com/).

9.15 INTEGRATED URBAN MINING BY ELDAN, ZARAGOZA, SPAIN

In Eldan Recycling of Zaragoza, Spain, plant are designed for automatic processing, i.e., staff are only required for surveillance. There are three waste electric and electronic equipment systems of different capacities at Elden. The small-capacity system has a capacity of 1.5 tons h^{-1}, the complete-capacity system 3.0 tons h^{-1}, and the large-capacity system 5–7 tons h^{-1}.

The electronic waste is fed first into a super pre-chopper and then into a ring shredder. An electromagnet overband removes ferrous metals, while a two-stage eddy current separator is used to remove nonferrous metals. Heavy granulators (FG1504) and two separating air tables (C26) separate organics and metals. Screens and shaking tables are also used to separate organics from metals. Capacity ranges from 800 to 7000 kg h^{-1}. The ring shredder has a 10,000 m^{3}h^{-1} filtering system. Cyclones and filters recover light materials and dust. The Eldan electronic waste recycling plants are capable of processing most of the items mentioned in the EU waste electric and electronic equipment Directive Annex 1B. Exceptions are refrigerators/freezers, which instead are processed in Eldan refrigerator systems. The system offered by Eldan Recycling is modular and is designed to process the following types of input: i) computer waste, consisting of mainframe computers, PCs, keyboards, monitors without glass tubes, printers, faxes, etc; ii) small home appliances, including videos, TV sets without glass tubes, record players, CD players, hairdryers, toasters, vacuum cleaners, coffee makers, irons, microwave ovens, etc; iii) handheld tools such as drilling machines, grinding machines, etc; iv) Electrical waste such as contactors, relays, main breakers, fuses, contact bars, switches, instruments, etc; iv) electronic and telecoms scrap such as electromechanical switchboards/relays, computerized switchboards, printed circuit boards, etc; and v) small electrical motors up to approximately 1–1.5 HP.

The following output fractions are retrieved From an Eldan electronic waste recycling plant: various fractions of ferrous and stainless steel; various fractions of nonferrous metals; refining material containing Cu, brass, Zn, Pb, precious metals, etc; organic fractions with plastic, rubber, wood, textiles, etc; and dust (http://eldan-recycling.com/en/electronic-waste-recyclin).

9.16 INTEGRATED URBAN MINING BY DAIMLER BENZ RECYCLING, GERMANY

The Daimler Benz plant mainly works on the mechanical treatment approach. Their process comprises the initial coarse-size reduction to 2 * 2 cm, followed by magnetic separation for ferrous materials and a low-temperature grinding stage. The embrittlement of plastic components at temperatures $< 70°C$ was found to enable enhanced separation from nonferrous metals when subjected to grinding in a hammer mill. It was claimed that this process was cheaper even for low-grade waste printed circuit boards (Kellner, 2009). Yang (2013) developed integrated mechanical separation followed by hydrometallurgical treatment with a relatively high precious metal recovery rate. This technology includes primary crushing, liquid nitrogen refrigeration, classification, electrostatic separation, and hydrometallurgical leaching.

9.17 INTEGRATED URBAN MINING BY DOWA GROUP IN JAPAN

In Japan, the DOWA group, centred on Kosaka Smelting and Refining and Akita Zinc, comprises 11 recycling-related companies which accept and receive various types of recycled materials for extraction of valuable metals, detoxification, and waste management (http://www.dowa.co.jp/en/products_service/metalmine.html). Kosaka Smelting and Refining accept mobile phones, electronic substrates and spent catalysts for recycling, as well as mineral ores, smelting residues from Akita Zinc, incineration residues from incinerators of DOWA group companies, and low-quality materials containing valuable metals from which Cu, Au, or Ag are extracted (Figure 9.13) (http://www.dowa-csr.jp/csr2010/html/english/special02.html; http://www. dowa-csr.jp/csr2010/html/english/special02.html).

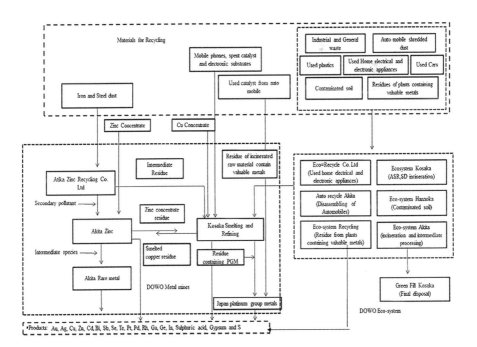

FIGURE 9.13   Integrated urban mining by DOWA in Japan.

9.18 INTEGRATED URBAN MINING PRACTICES IN ITALY

Hellatron Recycling is an Italian company with a dynamic role in the recycling of waste such as spent batteries, spent solar panels, and waste electric and electronic equipment including IT and telecoms equipment, cooling and freezing appliances, monitors, and televisions. Several processing options are utilized for efficient recycling, including manual techniques (de-pollution and material sorting), mechanical shredding, metal separation and smelting to optimize the value of the materials coming out of the plant (i.e., ferrous, Cu, Al, and others). The plant is highly automated, uses little manpower, and has low operating cost. (https://www.hellatron-weee.it/)

9.19 INTEGRATED URBAN MINING PRACTICES IN CANADA

Sepro Minerals Systems Corp. has established Sepro Urban Mining in British Columbia, Canada. Waste electric and electronic equipment is subjected to grinding, size separation, low-gravity separation, and high-gravity separation with two concentrates and a clean reject stream. One concentrate is coarse copper foil and the other is fine concentrates of Au, Ag, Pt, and Pd along with heavy metals. The reject stream is considered clean, non-hazardous, and suitable for conventional landfill disposal or subsequent reuse. Currently Sepro is working on a pyrolysis process for separation of heavy and precious metals from epoxy resin and the production of clean, natural gas from recycled plastic.

Commercial integrated pyrometallurgical and hydrometallurgical processes are carried out at the Noranda recycling facility, where about 100,000 tons of electronic waste is processed, particularly for precious metal recovery. A blend of electronic waste and copper concentrate is fed into a molten bath at 1250°C and the process temperature is maintained by injecting supercharged oxygen. The energy cost is partially reduced by combusting the plastics and other combustible materials from electronic waste. During the oxidation process, impurities including iron, lead and zinc are converted into oxides and segregated into a silica-based slag. The slag is cooled and processed for the recovery of metals before disposal. Precious metals are segregated in liquid copper, which is processed in a copper converter for higher purity. The blister copper is refined in the anode furnace and cast into anodes of 99.1% purity. The residue (0.9%) contains precious metals including gold, silver, platinum, and palladium, and some other recoverable metals such as nickel, selenium. and tellurium. Finally, precious metals are recovered by electro-refining of anodes. During mechanical separation of iron, aluminium, and plastics from electronic waste, there is a risk of losing the precious metals, which are closely tied to nonferrous metals and plastics in printed circuit boards. The acceptance of Fe, Al and plastics in the copper fraction can enhance the overall recovery of precious metals (http://seprourbanmetals.com/solutions/e-waste).

9.20 INTEGRATED URBAN MINING PRACTICES IN CHINA

At Shanghai Xin Jin Qiao Environmental Co., Ltd. and Yangzhou Ningda Precious Metal Co., 5000 tons of waste printed circuit boards are processed per year. Waste printed circuit boards are dismantled automatically and de-populated samples are

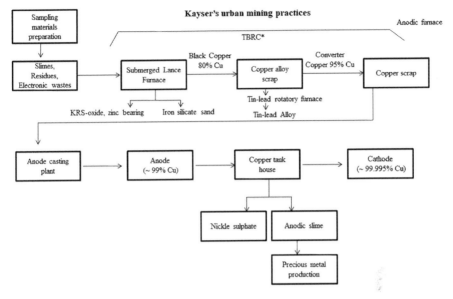

FIGURE 9.14 Flowsheet of DOWA's first e-waste hydro- and pyrometallurgical recycling plant in China.

subjected to multistage crushing and size reduction, and passed through cyclone air separation-corona electrostatic separation (CAS-CES) to separate metallic and non-metallic fractions. Metals are sequentially separated from the metallic fraction by vacuum distillation, while non-metallic fractions are used as composite material (Wang and Xu, 2015).

In 2010, DOWA Japan established the first integrated recycling model plant in China. Its three functions are home appliance recycling, hydrometallurgical processing, and pyrometallurgical processing (Figure 9.14).

9.21 INTEGRATED URBAN MINING PRACTICES IN FRANCE

Established in 2014, WEEE Metallica is a market leader in the recycling of e-waste, specializing in the treatment of spent printed circuit boards. Using their patented PCB pyrolysis process, WEEE Metallica extract valuable metals (base metals and precious metals) from spent printed circuit boards and deliver metal concentrates to smelters around the world. With an annual processing capacity of over 25,000 tons at their Isbergues facility, WEEE Metallica leads the way in the fast-growing world of e-waste recycling. To minimize environmental impact, all emissions generated during the pyrolysis process are neutralized internally before being released outside. The gases are collected directly from the furnace by extraction and go through several stages of remediation. These include post combustion – which destroys organic halogens – catalytic nitrogen oxide reduction, and sodium bicarbonate and activated carbon injection. During these treatments, the gases reach temperatures of above 1100 degrees (https://www.weeemetallica.com/our-solution).

9.22 INTEGRATED URBAN MINING PRACTICES IN TAIWAN

In Taiwan, commercial recycling processes for the spent printed circuit board/edge trim industry mainly focus on the recovery of copper and precious metals, with limited recycling of the non-metallic fraction which is mostly sent to landfill. The edge trim of printed circuit boards has a high copper (25–60%) and precious metal content (>3 ppm). Integrated recycling includes the hydrometallurgical and mechanical processing route. Precious metals from the edge trim are selectively leached and stripped by an appropriate stripping agent. After addition of suitable reductants, the precious metal ions are reduced in metallic form. After precious metal recovery, the edge trim is subjected to mechanical treatment for removal of copper from epoxy resin on the basis of density difference by a cyclone separator. In addition to the urban mining of precious metals, tin and copper are recovered from lead-tin solder, spent basic etching solution, wastewater sludge, and rack/solder stripping solutions (https://www. epa.gov/sites/production/files/2014-05/documents/handout-10circuitboards.pdf).

9.23 INTEGRATED URBAN MINING PRACTICES IN GERMANY

Aurubis makes products at several of its sites, such as Lünen and Hamburg in Germany, Olen in Belgium, and Pirdop in Bulgaria, from a variety of material including waste printed circuit boards, ashes, foundries (generating copper residues), semis-fabricators, shredders, slags, and galvanic slimes.

A number of precious metal-containing raw materials are also processed. Copper scrap is used as input in the convertors and anode furnaces of primary and secondary smelting processes, while alloy scrap and residues are used in Aurubis AG's Kayser Recycling System (KRS). The KRS is well suited to recycling materials with low copper and precious metal content and very complex materials such as waste electric and electronic equipment. The central operation is a submerged lance furnace almost 13 m high with a submerged combustion lance, which is immersed in the furnace from above and supplies heating oil, oxygen, and air with a fast reduction and short charging time. The iron silicate sand extracted in this step of the process has very low residual copper content. The copper, nickel, tin, lead and precious metals contained in the raw materials are enriched in an alloy with a copper content of about 80% (i.e., black Cu). In a top-blown rotary converter, the copper content is further enriched to 95%, and tin and lead are separated into slag. The tin–lead slag is subsequently processed into a tin–lead alloy in the directly connected tin–lead furnace. During the KRS process, zinc is enriched in the KRS oxide, a flue dust (Figure 9.15).

Un-wrought copper with an average copper content of 95% is produced, further processed in molten form in the anode furnace, and refined with additional amounts of copper scrap. The melt is initially oxidized with air and oxygen and then deoxidized with natural gas after the slag that has formed has been removed. At the end of the pyrometallurgical process, the 99% pure copper is cast into copper anodes. This is the starting product for the final refining stage of secondary copper production, the copper tank-house process, where high-grade copper cathodes identical in quality to copper cathodes from primary copper production are produced. Important

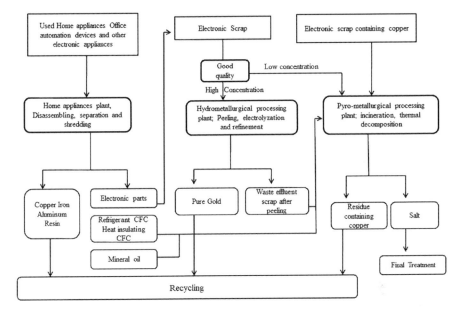

FIGURE 9.15   Kayser's urban mining practices.

by-products, in particular gold and silver, are enriched in the anode slimes. Nickel is extracted as crude nickel sulphate by electrolyte treatment.

Copper scrap, electronic waste, and residues are used at Aurubis Hamburg, Germany. The basic material for the Hamburg secondary copper production process consists of a variety of recycling materials rich in precious metals, as well as intermediate smelter products originating both from Aurubis' production plants and from external metal smelters and precious metal-separating plants. The focus of secondary copper production in this case is on enriching and recovering precious metals and separating various by-metals that result from the copper production process. In accordance with the requirements of the specific raw materials, these materials are processed in a modern electric furnace in various smelting stages. The most important target is the pyrometallurgical separation of lead and copper and the enrichment of precious metals. By-elements still existing during copper production, such as Pb, Bi, Sb, and Te, are separated in the connected Pb refinery and sold as Pb bullion, Pb–Bi alloy, Sb concentrates, and Te concentrates. The precious metals are fortified in a so-called rich Pb, which has a precious metal content of about 70%. The anode slimes from the Aurubis copper tank houses is processed together with the rich Pb from the Pb refinery in the precious metal production plant.

In Aurubis' modern, environmentally friendly precious metal production facilities, the company uses a wide range of feed materials rich in precious metals. Thus, Aurubis also processes anode slimes from other copper smelters, bullion, precious metals, and coin scrap as well as precious metal-bearing sweeps and slag. In addition to fine silver, fine gold, and precious metal concentrates, sales products from this process also include wet selenium, which is processed at the Aurubis subsidiary Retorte GmbH (https://www.aurubis.com/en/products/recycling/technology).

9.24 INTEGRATED URBAN MINING PRACTICES IN SWEDEN

The Rönnskär smelters (Boliden Ltd., Skelleftehamn, Sweden) are used for the recovery of metals from electronic waste. A variety of scrap from the nonferrous and electronics industry is introduced into the process at different stages, depending on the purity requirement of the final product. For instance, high copper-containing scrap is fed into the converting process directly, but low-grade e-waste is fed into the Kaldo furnace. More than 100,000 tons of waste (including e-waste) is recycled annually. The feed material of the Kaldo converter consists of blended lead concentrate and e-waste, which are combusted with a supply of oxygen and oil. The Kaldo furnace produces a mixed copper alloy that is treated in a copper converter for the recovery of metals including Cu, Ag, Au, Pt, Pd, Ni, Se, and Zn. Volatile metals such as Pb, Sb, In, and Cd are segregated into the vapour phase and recovered by a separate process. Off-gas emissions are treated to produce sulphuric acid and SO_2 gas (Khaliq et al., 2014, Kaya, 2018).

ACKNOWLEDGEMENTS

This work was supported by the Brain Pool Programme through the National Research Foundation of Korea (NRF) funded by the Ministry of Science and ICT (Grant No. 2019H1D3A2A02101993) and the Basic Science Research Programme through the National Research Foundation of Korea (NRF) funded by the Ministry of Education (Project no. 2020R1I1A1A01074249).

REFERENCES

Bernardis, F. L., Grant, R. A., and Sherrington, D. C. (2005). A review of methods of separation of the platinum-group metals through their chloro-complexes. *Reactive and Functional Polymers*, 65(3): 205–217. DOI: https://doi.org/10.1016/j.reactfunctpolym.2005.05.011.

Bonucci, J.A., Parker, P. D. (1984). *Recovery of PGM from automobile catalytic converters. Precious Metals: Mining, Extraction and Processing.*, Los Angeles: AIME/TMS, pp. 463–481.

Cleare, M.J., Grant, R.A., Charlesworth, P. (1981). Separation of the platinum group metals by use of selective solvent extraction techniques. *IMM Extraction Metallurgy* 1981: 34–41.

Cleare M. J. et al. (1970). Solvent Extraction in Platinum Group Metals Processing. *Journal of Chemical Technology and Biotechnology* 29: 210.

Cole, S. and Ferron, C. J. (2002). A review of the beneficiation and extractive metallurgy of the platinum-group elements, highlighting recent process innovations. *SGS Minerals Services Technical Paper*, 3: 1–43.

Crowe, J.H.V. (1918). *General smuts' campaign in East Africa.* London: John Murray.

Crundwell, F., Moats, M., Ramachandran, V., Robinson, T., and Davenport, W. G. (2011). *Extractive metallurgy of nickel, cobalt and platinum group metals.* Elsevier, UK.

European Parliament (2018). Directive 2018/851/EC of the European Parliament and of the Council of 30 May 2018 on waste electrical and electronic equipment (WEEE). *Official Journal of European Union* L150:109–140.

Fleming, C. A. (2002). Platsol[Tm] Process Provides a Viable Alternative To Smelting. *SGS mineral Services.* https://docplayer.net/55888726-Platsol-tm-process-provides-a-viable-alternative-to-smelting.html

Furman N. H. (1975). *Standard aethods of chemical analysis.* New York: R. E. Frieger Publ. Co.

Granato M. and Sobral L.G.S. (1985) Recuperacao de Palladio a partir de sucata eletronica. Encontro Nacional de tratamento de Minerios e Hidrometalurgia. v.2 Oct.

Hagelüken, C. (2001). Serving the PGM Life Cycle - the new alignment of the dmC2 refinery at Hanau, Germany. *International Precious Metal Institute (IPMI 25th annual conference,* Tucson, Arizona.

Hoffmann, J.E., (1988). Recovering platinum-group metals from auto catalysts. *JOM,* 40–44.

Hoffmann, J. E., Wesstrom, B. (1994). Hydrometallurgical processing of refinery slimes at Phelps Dodges: theory to practice. In *Hydrometallurgy 94.* London: IMM/SCI Chapman & Hall, 69–105.

Izatt, R. M., Clark, G. A., Christensen, J. J. (1987). Transport of $AgBr^{2-}$, $PdBr_4^{2-}$, and $AuBr_4^-$ in an emulsion membrane system using K+- Dicyclohexano - 18 - Crown - 6 as Carrier. *Separation Science and Technology,* 22: 691–699.

Kaya, M. (2018). Current WEEE recycling solutions. In Veglio, F., Birloaga, I. (eds). *Waste electrical and electronic equipment recycling, aqueous recovery methods.* Elsevier Science, Woodhead Publishing, England. pp. 33–93.

Kellner, D. (2009) Recycling and recovery. In: Hester, R.E., Harrison, R.M. (eds) *Electronic waste management, design, analysis and application.* Cambridge, UK: RSC Publishing, 91–110.

Khaliq, A., Rhamdhani, M. A., Brooks, G., Masood, S. (2014). Metal extraction processes for electronic waste and existing industrial routes: a review and Australian perspective. *Resources,* 3(1): 152–179.

Mesker, C. E. M., Hagelüken, C., Van Damme, G. (2009). TMS 2009 Annual Meeting & Exhibition, San Francisco, California, USA. In Howard, S.H., Anyalebechi, P., Zhang, L. (eds). *EPD Congress 2009 Proceedings,* pp. 1131–1136.

Milbourne, J., Tomlinson, M., and Gormely, L. (2003). Use of hydrometallurgy in direct processing of base metal/PGM concentrates. *Hydrometallurgy,* 625.

Mitkin, V. N. (2000). Fluorination of Iridium Metal and Its Application Possibilities in the Synthesis, Analysis and Recovery Technology for Secondary Raw Materials (Review), *Iridium: Proc. Intern. Symp.,* TMS-2000, Nashville Tennessee, 2000, 377–390.

Mpinga, C. N., Eksteen, J. J., Aldrich, C., and Dyer, L. (2015). Direct leach approaches to Platinum Group Metal (PGM) ores and concentrates: A review. *Minerals Engineering,* 78: 93–113. DOI: https://doi.org/10.1016/j.mineng.2013.09.001.

Patrushev, V. V. (1998). Reduction of platinum group metals in phosphoric acid solutions by formalin. *Hydrometallurgy.* 50: 89–101.

Renner, H. (1992). *Ulmann's Encyclopedia of Industrial Chemistry.* B. Elvers, S. Hawkins, G. Schulz (eds), 5th edition, Vol. A21. VCH Publishers. p. 114.

Sobral, L.G.S. Granato, M., (1992). Palladium: Extraction and Refining. *Minerals Engineering,* 5: 17–25.

Sole, K. C., Mooiman, M. B., and Hardwick, E. (2018). Ion exchange in hydrometallurgical processing: an overview and selected applications. *Separation & Purification Reviews:* 47(2): 159–178. DOI: https://doi.org/10.1080/15422119.2017.1354304.

Tanaka, S., Harada, A., Nishihama, S., and Yoshizuka, K. (2012). Selective recovery of platinum group metals from spent automobile catalyst by integrated ion exchange methods. *Separation Science and Technology,* 47(9): 1369–1373. DOI: https://doi.org/10.1080/01496395.2012.672526.

Wang, J. B., Xu, Z. M. (2015) Disposing and recycling waste printed circuit boards: disconnecting, resource recovery and pollution control. *Environmental Science and Technology.* 49:721–733. https://doi.org/10.1021/es504833y.

Warshawsky, A. (1982). Integrated ion exchange and liquid-liquid extraction process for the separation of platinum group metals (PGM). *Separation and Purification Methods,* *11*(2): 95–130. DOI: https://doi.org/10.1080/03602548208068391.

Warshawsky, A., Fieberg, M. M., Mihalik, P., and Murphy, T. G. (1980). The separation of platinum group metals (PGM) in chloride media by isothiouronium exchangers. *Separation and Purification methods,* 9(2): 209–265. DOI: https://doi. org/10.1080/03602548008066001.

Yang, M. (2013). *Study on the technologies and mechanism of copper and stannum extraction from waste printed circuit boards by PEG-NOx catalysis and oxidation.* PhD Dissertation, Donghua University.

Index